MICROSTRIP LINES and SLOTLINES

The Artech House Microwave Library

Introduction to Microwaves by Fred E. Gardiol
Microwaves Made Simple: Principles and Applications by W. Stephen Cheung and Frederic H. Levien
Microwave Tubes by A. S. Gilmour, Jr.
Electric Filters by Martin Hasler and Jacques Neirynck
Nonlinear Circuits by Martin Hasler and Jacques Neirynck
Microwave Technology by Erich Pehl
Receiving Systems Design by Stephen J. Erst
Microwave Mixers by Stephen A. Maas
Feedback Maximization by B.J. Lurie
Applications of GaAs MESFETs by Robert Soares, et al.
GaAs Processing Techniques by Ralph E. Williams
GaAs FET Principles and Technology by James V. DiLorenzo and Deen D. Khandelwal
Dielectric Resonators, Darko Kajfez and Pierre Guillon, eds.
Modern Spectrum Analyzer Theory and Applications by Morris Engelson
Design Tables for Discrete Time Normalized Lowpass Filters by Arild Lacroix and Karl-Heinz Witte
Microwave Materials and Fabrication Techniques by Thomas S. Laverghetta
Handbook of Microwave Testing by Thomas S. Laverghetta
Microwave Measurements and Techniques by Thomas S. Laverghetta
Principles of Electromagnetic Compatibility by Bernhard E. Keiser
Linear Active Circuits: Design and Analysis by William Rynone, Jr.
The Design of Impedance-Matching Networks for Radio-Frequency and Microwave Amplifiers by Pieter L.D. Abrie
Microwave Filters, Impedance Matching Networks, and Coupling Structures by G.L. Matthaei, Leo Young, and E.M.T. Jones
Analysis, Design, and Applications of Fin Lines by Bharathi Bhat and Shiban Koul
Microwave Engineer's Handbook, 2 vol., Theodore Saad, ed.
Handbook of Microwave Integrated Circuits by R.K. Hoffmann
Microwave Integrated Circuits, Jeffrey Frey and Kul Bhasin, eds.
Computer-Aided Design of Microwave Circuits by K.C. Gupta, Ramesh Garg, and Rakesh Chadha
Microstrip Lines and Slotlines by K.C. Gupta, R. Garg, and I.J. Bahl
Advanced Mathematics for Practicing Engineers by Kurt Arbenz and Alfred Wohlhauser
Microstrip Antennas by I.J. Bahl and P. Bhartia
Antenna Design Using Personal Computers by David M. Pozar
Microwave Circuit Design Using Programmable Calculators by J. Lamar Allen and Max Medley, Jr.
Stripline Circuit Design by Harlan Howe, Jr.
Microwave Transmission Line Filters by J.A.G. Malherbe
Electrical Characteristics of Transmission Lines by W. Hilberg
Microwave Diode Control Devices by Robert V. Garver
Tables for Active Filter Design by Mario Biey and Amedeo Premoli
Active Filter Design by Arthur B. Williams
Laser Applications by W.V. Smith
Ferrite Control Components, 2 vol., Lawrence Whicker, ed.
Microwave Remote Sensing, 3 vol., by F.T. Ulaby, R.K. Moore, and A.K. Fung

MICROSTRIP LINES and SLOTLINES

K.C. Gupta
Ramesh Garg
I.J. Bahl

ARTECH

685 Canton St.
Norwood, MA 02062

Library of Congress Catalog card number: 79-1375
Standard Book Number: 0-89006-074-6

Preface

Microwave integrated circuits use planar transmission structures like microstrip lines as the basic building block. In addition, slotlines and coplanar lines are also used. When used along with microstrip, these lines add to the flexibility of circuit design and improve the performance for some circuit functions. All these transmission lines have planar configuration, and their characteristics are controlled by dimensions in a single plane. Theory and design of these lines have been reported in numerous articles widely scattered in technical literature, but there is no comprehensive description of these lines available at one place. In particular the design information is not readily available. The present text on Microstrip Lines and Slotlines is intended for presenting a detailed account of these lines.

This book describes analyses and design of microstrip lines and slotlines, coplanar waveguides, coplanar strips and various coupled lines. The features discussed include quasi-static and fullwave analyses, design considerations and measurement procedures.

The present book is intended for graduate students, research workers and design engineers in the microwave circuits area. The book can be used as a supplementary text for a course on microwave circuits and as a source of case studies for a course on mathematical/numerical methods in electromagnetics. Sections on design considerations (2.4, 3.4, 5.3, 7.3 and 8.5) could be used directly for the design of various lines without going into details of analysis.

The preparation of *Microstrip Lines and Slotlines* started with a set of lecture notes prepared for a graduate course on 'Microwave Integrated Circuits Design' taught at the University of Waterloo (Canada) in Fall 1975. These notes were revised for a series of seminars on 'Lignes Microruban' delivered at l'Ecole Polytechnique Federale de Lausanne (Switzerland) in the summer of 1976. A revised version of the notes was used for a similar series of seminars at Technical University of Denmark, Lyngby (Denmark) in Fall 1976. This material has also been used for a graduate course on this topic at the Indian Institute of Technology Kanpur (I.I.T./K.) in Fall 1977. Work on the design of microwave integrated circuits at the Advanced Centre for Electronic Systems (I.I.T./K.) has contributed considerably to the material in the book, especially the sections on design considerations.

The text is divided into eight chapters. The first two chapters describe analysis and design of microstrip lines. There are two chapters on microstrip discontinuities. These are followed by two chapters on slotlines and a chapter on coplanar lines. The eighth chapter deals with various types of coupled lines.

For all these transmission structures and for microstrip discontinuities as well, quasi-static and fullwave analyses are discussed. There are sections on measurement of the characteristics of microstrip lines, microstrip discontinuities and coupled lines. Detailed design considerations for various lines are presented. These include design equations, effects of tolerances and enclosures, losses, etc. Special circuit functions that can be achieved by using slotlines and coplanar waveguides are discussed. A comparison of the characteristics of various lines is given in Chapter 7.

Several discussions with colleagues at the University of Waterloo, l'Ecole Polytechnique Federale de Lausanne and the Technical University of Denmark during the early stages of the book are gratefully acknowledged. Discussions with several colleagues at I.I.T. Kanpur are thankfully appreciated. Facilities extended by the Department of Electrical Engineering and the Advanced Centre for Electronic Systems at I.I.T./K. are acknowledged. The typing of manuscript has been handled efficiently by Mr. C.M. Abraham, and the artwork has been done by Mr. R.K. Bajpai.

K.C. Gupta
Ramesh Garg
I.J. Bahl

ACKNOWLEDGEMENTS

It is a pleasure to thank various authors and publishing houses who have kindly extended their permission to use illustrations from their publications. Thanks are due to:

Dr. P. Benedek, for Figure 3.16 from his paper in *IEEE Trans. on Microwave Theory and Techniques.*

Dr. D.G. Corr, for Figure 2.9(b) from his paper in *IEEE Trans. on Microwave Theory and Techniques.*

Dr. M.E. Davies, for Figures 7.5 and 7.6 from his paper in *IEEE Trans. on Microwave Theory and Techniques.*

Dr. Y. Fujiki, for Figures 7.12 and 7.13 from his paper in *Electronics and Comm. in Japan.*

Dr. W.J. Getsinger, for Figures 1.12 and 8.11 from his papers in *IEEE Trans. on Microwave Theory and Techniques.*

Dr. A. Gopinath, for Figures 3.20, 3.21, 3.33 and 3.34 from his paper in *IEEE Trans. on Microwave Theory and Techniques.*

Dr. M.A.R. Gunston, for Figures 8.4 and 8.5 from his book *Transmission Line Impedance Data.*

Dr. C. Gupta, for Figure 3.19 from his paper in *IEEE Trans. on Microwave Theory and Techniques.*

Dr. T. Hatsuda, for Figures 7.9 and 8.26 from his paper in *IEEE Trans. on Microwave Theory and Techniques.*

Dr. C. Hede, for Figure 6.19.

Dr. T. Itoh, for Figures 2.2(b) and 5.8 from his papers in *IEEE Trans. on Microwave Theory and Techniques* and *Electronics Letters.*

Dr. J.B. Knorr, for Figures 2.3, 5.9, 5.13, 5.14, 6.3, 6.6, 7.10, 7.11 and 7.14 from his papers in *IEEE Trans. on Microwave Theory and Techniques.*

Dr. G. Kompa, for Figures 1.14, 1.15, 4.3 and 4.4(b) from his papers in *Electronics Letters* and *AEU.*

Dr. G. Kowalski, for Figures 8.6 and 8.7 from his papers in *AEU.*

Dr. M. Maeda, for Figure 3.17 from his paper in *IEEE Trans. on Microwave Theory and Techniques.*

Dr. R. Mehran, for Figures 4.6 to 4.9, 4.12 and 4.13 from his papers in *AEU.*

Dr. R. Mittra, for Figures 2.6 to 2.8 from his papers in *IEEE Trans. on Microwave Theory and Techniques.*

Dr. B. Schiek, for Figures 6.13 and 6.16 from his papers in *IEEE Trans. on Microwave Theory and Techniques.*

Dr. P. Silvester, for Figures 3.14, 3.23, 3.27 and 3.32 from his papers in *IEEE Trans. on Microwave Theory and Techniques.*

Dr. B.T. Szentkuti, for Figures 2.18 and 8.22 from his paper in *Electronics Letters.*

Dr. A.F. Thomson, for Figures 3.25 and 3.28 from his paper in *IEEE Trans. on Microwave Theory and Techniques.*

Dr. J.A. Weiss, for Figure 8.16.

Dr. C.P. Wen, for Figures 7.4, 7.7 and 7.30 from his papers in *IEEE Trans. on Microwave Theory and Techniques.*

Archiv fur Elektronik und Ubertragungstechnik (AEU), Stuttgart (W. Germany) for Figures 4.3, 4.4, 4.6 to 4.9, 4.12, 4.13, 8.6 and 8.7.

Institution of Electrical Engineers (IEE), Herts (England) for Figures 1.14, 1.15, 2.18, 5.8 and 8.22.

Institute of Electrical and Electronics Engineers (IEEE), Inc. New York (USA) for Figures 1.12, 2.2, 2.3, 2.6 to 2.9, 3.14, 3.16, 3.17, 3.19 to 3.21, 3.23, 3.25, 3.27, 3.28, 3.32 to 3.34, 5.9, 5.13, 5.14, 6.3, 6.6, 6.13, 6.16, 7.4 to 7.7, 7.9 to 7.11, 7.14, 7.30, 8.11 and 8.26.

Scripta Publishing Co., Washington (USA) for Figures 7.12 and 7.13.

Contents

Chapter 1

Chapter 2

Chapter 3

Chapter 4

MICROSTRIP DISCONTINUITIES II
Fullwave Analysis and Measurements

Chapter 5

SLOTLINES I
Analyses and Design Considerations

Chapter 6

SLOTLINES II
Transitions and Applications

Chapter 7

COPLANAR LINES
Coplanar Waveguide and Coplanar Strips

Chapter 8

COUPLED LINES

Chapter 1

Microstrip Lines I : Quasi-static Analyses, Dispersion Models and Measurements

1.1 INTRODUCTION

1.1.1 Planar Transmission Structures

One of the main requirements for a transmission structure to be suitable as a circuit element in microwave integrated circuits (MICs) is that the structure should be "planar" in configuration. A planar configuration implies that the characteristics of the element can be determined by the dimensions in a single plane. As for example, the width of a microstrip line on a dielectric substrate can be adjusted to control its impedance. When the impedance can be controlled by dimensions in a single plane, the circuit fabrication can be conveniently carried out by techniques of photolithography and photoetching of thin films. Use of these techniques at microwave frequencies has led to the development of MICs. Microwave integrated circuits have been widely discussed in the literature [1-3].

There are several transmission structures that satisfy the requirement of being planar. The most common of these are: (i) microstrip, (ii) slotline, (iii) coplanar waveguide and (iv) coplanar strips. Cross-sectional views of these lines are shown in Figure 1.1. Microstrip line is the most popular of these transmission structures, mainly due to the fact that the mode of propagation on microstrip is almost TEM. This allows an easy approximate analysis and yields wide band circuits. Also simple transitions to coaxial circuits are feasible. Chapters 1 and 2 present various aspects of microstrip analysis and design. Slotline, coplanar strips and coplanar waveguide are discussed in later chapters. A comparison of characteristics of these lines (shown in Figure 1.1) is given in Section 7.5.

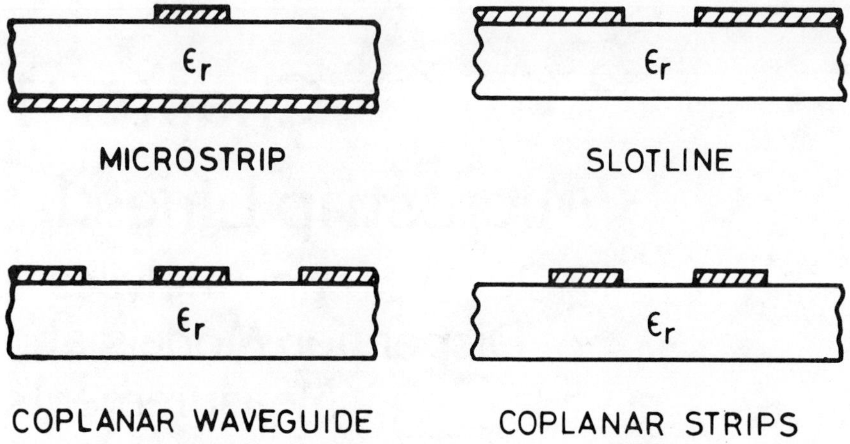

Figure 1.1 Planar Transmission Lines Used in Microwave Integrated Circuits

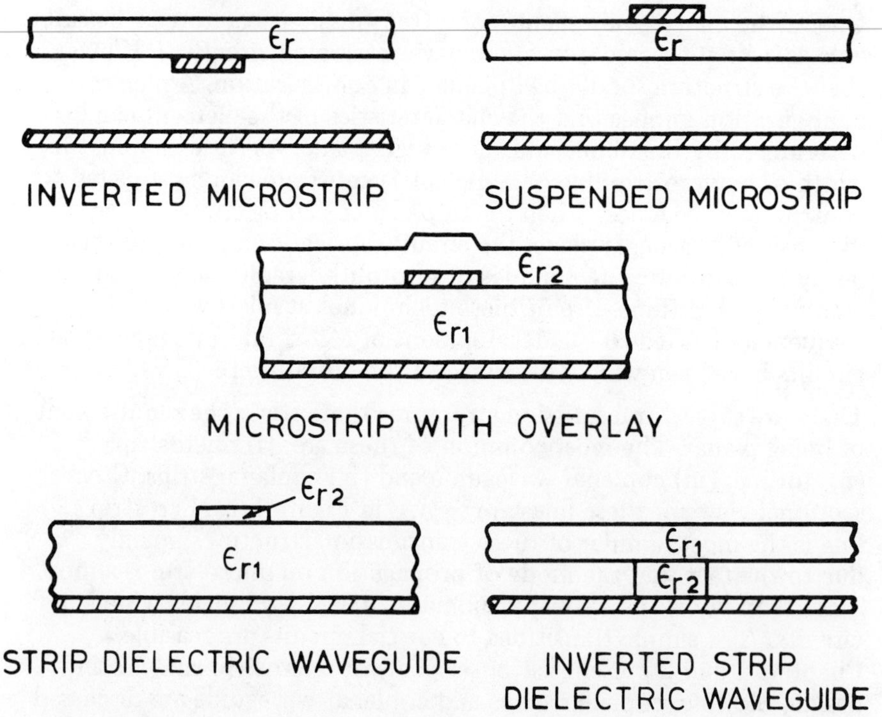

Figure 1.2 Various Transmission Lines Derived from Microstrip

There are several variations of microstrip configuration that have also been suggested for use in MICs. These include inverted microstrip, suspended microstrip, microstrip with overlay, strip dielectric waveguide and inverted strip dielectric waveguide. Cross-sectional views of these structures are given in Figure 1.2 and their analysis is available in references [4-7].

Another very commonly used transmission line that resembles microstrip line is the stripline [8, 9], shown in Figure 1.3. This is also

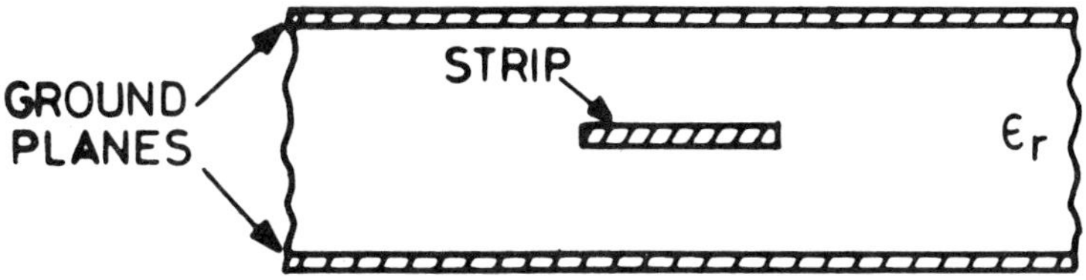

Figure 1.3 Stripline Configuration

called triplate line. Most of the basic circuit design information available for stripline is also applicable to microstrip line.

1.1.2 Microstrip Field Configuration

Microstrip is a two-conductor transmission line which can be considered to have evolved conceptually from a two-wire line as shown in Figure 1.4. Transformation from (a) to (b) is essentially a change

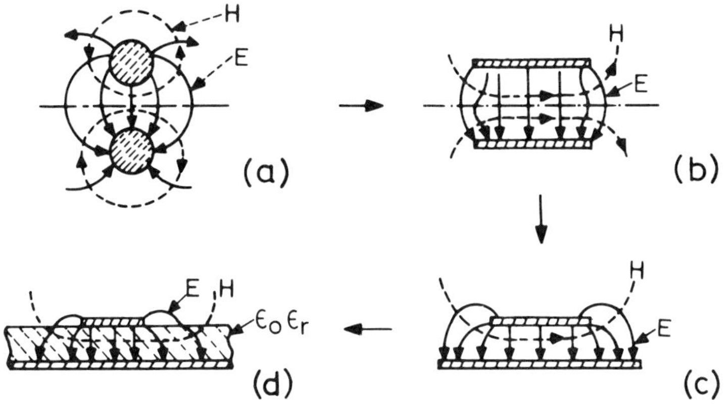

Figure 1.4 Conceptual Evolution of a Microstrip from a Two-wire Line

in the shape of the conductors, whereas that from (b) to (c) involves placing a conducting sheet at the plane of symmetry. The final configuration (d) is obtained by inserting a thin dielectric slab between the two conductors. As a consequence of the last step, the dielectric medium of the transmission line becomes inhomogeneous.

Microstrip lines differ considerably from other transmission lines. For example, comparing it with a stripline, one observes that the microstrip structure is open on the top. This open configuration makes microstrip very convenient for use in MICs where discrete lumped devices (active or passive) are to be mounted in the circuit. Also, a slight adjustment or tuning can possibly be incorporated after the circuit has been fabricated. However, along with these advantages, the open structure of microstrip brings in some complications in microstrip analysis and design. This is due to the fact that the presence of dielectric-air interface modifies the mode of propagation in microstrip to a non-TEM hybrid mode (as compared with a pure TEM-mode in stripline).

Simple arguments based on the known quasi-static field distribution of the microstrip and Maxwell's equations can be put forward to show that microstrip structure cannot support a pure TEM wave. Continuity of the tangential component of the electric field along a dielectric-air interface (see Figure 1.5) yields

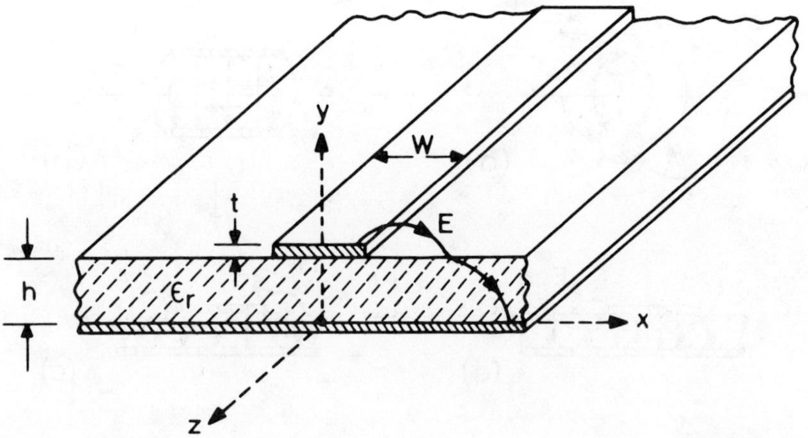

Figure 1.5 Microstrip Configuration

$$E_x|_d = E_x|_a \tag{1.1}$$

where subscripts d and a refer to the dielectric and the air side of the interface, respectively. Using Maxwell's equation, one may thus write

$$(\nabla \times H)_x|_d = \epsilon_r (\nabla \times H)_x|_a \tag{1.2}$$

Expanding Equation (1.2) and using the continuity of normal component of magnetic flux, we obtain

$$\epsilon_r \, \partial H_z/\partial y|_a - \partial H_z/\partial y|_d = (\epsilon_r - 1)\, \partial H_y/\partial z \tag{1.3}$$

As ϵ_r is not equal to unity and $H_y \neq 0$, Equation (1.3) implies that the expression on its left hand side should be a non-zero quantity, which can be true only if H_z is non-zero. Thus we note that for Maxwell's equations to hold good for the configuration of Figure 1.5, the longitudinal component of H should exist.

Similar arguments can be advanced to show that E_z, the longitudinal component of electric field, is also a non-zero quantity. It may be pointed out that it is only the fringing components E_x and H_x at the dielectric-air interface that lead to the non-TEM nature of the microstrip mode. Since these fringing field components are much smaller than the main field (within the substrate below the strip), the departure from the TEM behavior should be small. This explanation is supported by the results based on a rigorous fullwave analysis of the microstrip which will be discussed later on.

1.1.3 Methods of Microstrip Analysis

Various methods of microstrip analysis may be divided into three groups as shown in Figure 1.6. In the first group which comprises quasi-static methods, the nature of the mode of propagation is considered to be pure TEM, and microstrip characteristics are calculated from the electrostatic capacitance of the structure. It is found that this analysis is adequate for designing circuits at lower frequencies (below X-band) where the strip width and the substrate thickness are much smaller than the wavelength in the dielectric material. In the second group, called dispersion models, the deviation from the TEM nature is accounted for quasi-empirically. Some parameters of the model are determined such that the final expression agrees with the known experimental (or exact theoretical) dispersion behavior of the microstrip. The methods in the third group take into

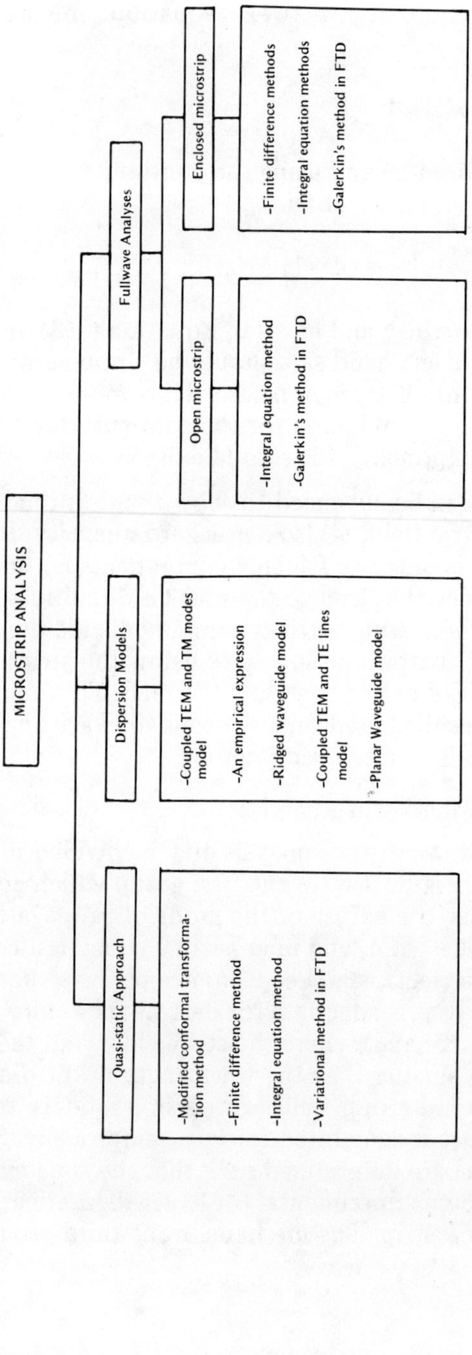

Figure 1.6 Various Methods of Microstrip Analysis

account the hybrid nature of mode of propagation. The approaches followed in these three groups are in increasing order of both rigor and analytical complexity.

The methods of analysis included in the first two groups — quasi-static and dispersion models — are discussed in this chapter. Techniques of fullwave analysis will be described in the next chapter.

1.2 QUASI-STATIC ANALYSES OF MICROSTRIP

In quasi-static analyses, the mode of wave propagation in microstrip is assumed to be pure TEM. Transmission characteristics are then calculated from the values of two capacitances, one (C_a) for a unit length of the microstrip configuration with the dielectric substrate replaced by air, and the other (C) for a unit length of the microstrip with the dielectric substrate present. Values of characteristic impedance Z_{om} and the phase constant β can be written in terms of these capacitances as follows:

$$Z_{om} = Z^a_{om}\,(C_a/C)^{1/2} \tag{1.4}$$

and

$$\beta = \beta_o\,(C/C_a)^{1/2} \tag{1.5}$$

where $Z^a_{om} = 1/(cC_a)$ and $\beta_o = \omega/c$; c being the velocity of electromagnetic waves in free space. There are various methods available for calculation of electrostatic capacitances C_a and C. Four of these are listed in Figure 1.6 and will be discussed in the following sub-sections.

1.2.1 Modified Conformal Transformation Method

An exact conformal transformation for the impedance of a zero thickness, homogeneous dielectric microstrip has been given by Schneider [6]. The transformation from the microstrip (z-plane) to a parallel plate capacitor (z′-plane) is expressed in terms of the logarithmic derivative of the theta function θ_4 and its parameter $\kappa = K'/K$ as follows:

$$z = -\frac{2hK}{\pi}\,\frac{\partial}{\partial z'}\,\ell n\,[\theta_4\,(z', \kappa)] \tag{1.6}$$

where K = K(m) and K′ = K′(m) are complete elliptic integrals of first kind with modulus m. The characteristic impedance Z_{om} of the microstrip of width W and height h (and t = 0) is obtained by solving the following equations

$$\frac{W}{h} = \frac{2}{\pi} \frac{\partial}{\partial \zeta} \ell n \; [\theta_4 \; (\zeta, \kappa)] \tag{1.7}$$

$$dn^2 \; (2K\zeta) = E/K \tag{1.8}$$

$$Z^a_{om} = \tfrac{1}{2}(\mu_o/\epsilon_o)^{1/2} \; K'/K \tag{1.9}$$

where μ_o and ϵ_o are the free space permeability and permittivity constants respectively, and Z^a_{om} is the characteristic impedance of microstrip with dielectric substrate replaced by air. E = E(m) is the complete elliptic integral of second kind and dn is the Jacobian elliptic function. The logarithmic derivative of theta function is given by the following (rapidly converging) series expansion

$$\frac{\partial}{\partial \zeta} \ell n \, [\theta_4 \; (\zeta, \kappa)] = 4\pi \sum_{n=1}^{\infty} \frac{\sin (2n\pi\zeta)}{\exp (n\pi\kappa) - \exp (-n\pi\kappa)} \tag{1.10}$$

Equations (1.7) to (1.9) can be used for the design of microstrip lines as follows. For a given characteristic impedance Z^a_{om}, K′/K is calculated from Equation (1.9). Modulus m for elliptic functions is found by looking up tables for K′/K. Also E and K are found using this value of m. The solution of Equation (1.8) now gives the value of ζ. For known ζ and κ (= K′/K), W/h for the microstrip is calculated from Equations (1.7) and (1.10).

The practical solution to this set of equations must be done with the help of a computer or with numerical tables. It is perhaps because of this limitation that the above method is not used very frequently.

The most widely used technique for microstrip analysis was introduced by Wheeler [10, 11] in 1964-65. The method involves use of a conformal transformation for evaluation of C_a and introduces a concept of effective dielectric constant for evaluation of C. The conformal transformation selected is such that the resulting expressions are explicit and can be written in terms of simple functions. The transformation used for the wide strip (W/h > 2) is

$$z = j\pi + d \tanh (z'/2) - z' \; . \tag{1.11}$$

The variable z refers to the microstrip plane (see Figure 1.7) and z′

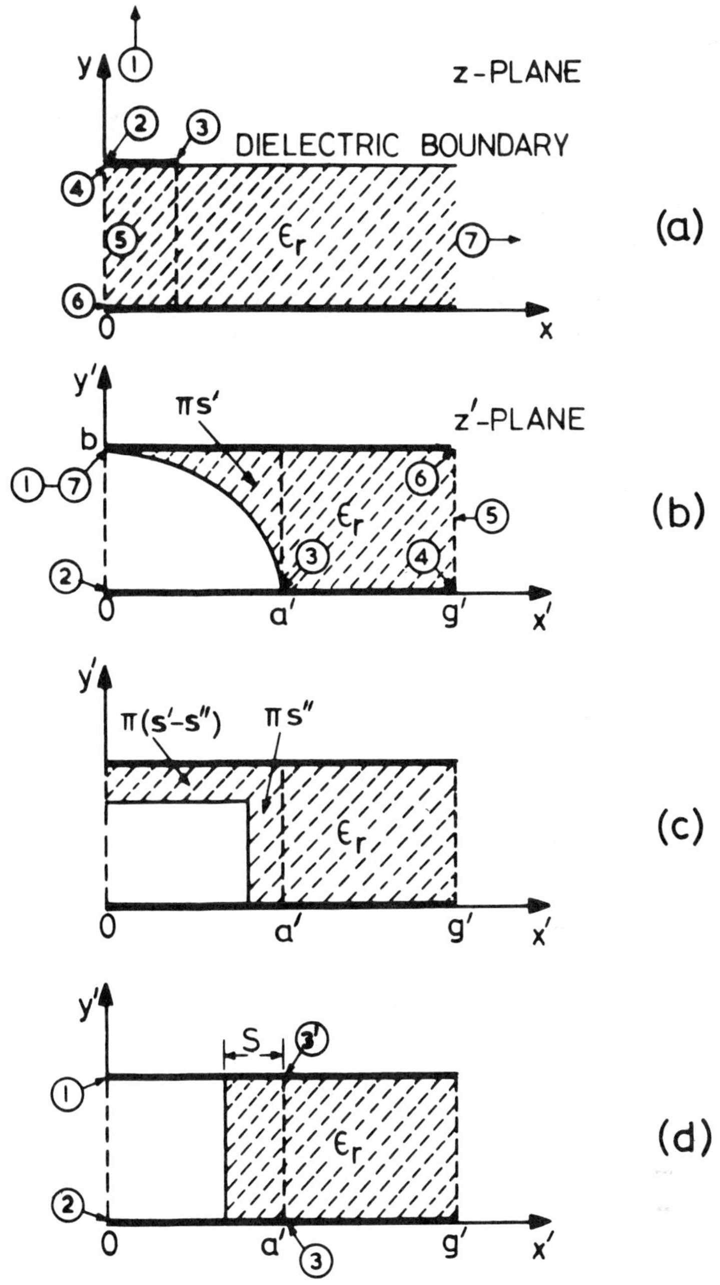

Figure 1.7 Conformal Transformation and Evaluation of Effective Dielectric Constant (from [11])

is the plane wherein the microstrip configuration transforms into a parallel plate capacitor configuration. The parameter d is approximately equal to g' of Figure 1.7(b). The dielectric-air boundary of the microstrip substrate gets transformed into an elliptical-looking curve ba' as shown in Figure 1.7(b). For evaluating the capacitance C, it is necessary to introduce approximations to modify the dielectric-air boundary. The curved dielectric-air boundary of Figure 1.7(b) is approximated by a rectangular boundary as shown in Figure 1.7(c). The area ($\pi s'$) over the curve is written in terms of a "parallel area" $\pi s''$ and a "series area" $\pi(s' - s'')$. These series and parallel areas can be written in terms of an equivalent parallel area s given by (Figure 1.7(d))

$$s = s'' + (s' - s'')/\epsilon_r \quad . \tag{1.12}$$

The effective filling fraction can then be written as

$$q = (g' - a' + s)/g' \quad . \tag{1.13}$$

The effective dielectric constant is related to effective filling fraction as

$$\epsilon_{re} = (1 - q) + q\,\epsilon_r \tag{1.14}$$

Different expressions for ϵ_{re} are derived for wide microstrip ($W/h > 2$) and for narrow microstrip ($W/h < 2$) because of the different approximations used in two cases. For wide strips [12]

$$q = 1 - \frac{1}{d}\,\ell n\,\frac{d+c}{d-c} + \frac{0.732}{d\,\epsilon_r}\left[\ell n\,\frac{d+c}{d-c} - \cosh^{-1}(0.358\,d + 0.595)\right] + \frac{\epsilon_r - 1}{d\,\epsilon_r}\left[0.386 - \frac{1}{2\,(d-1)}\right] \tag{1.15}$$

where $d = 1 + \sqrt{1 + c^2}$, and c is found implicitly from

$$\frac{\pi}{2}\,\frac{W}{h} = c - \sinh^{-1} c \tag{1.16}$$

and for narrow strips

$$\epsilon_{re} = \frac{\epsilon_r+1}{2} + \frac{\epsilon_r-1}{2} \frac{\ell n \frac{\pi}{2} + \frac{1}{\epsilon_r} \ell n \frac{4}{\pi}}{\ell n \frac{8h}{W}} \tag{1.17}$$

Formulas for the impedance of microstrip lines can be derived from these results. It is an advantage of the transformation selected by Wheeler that the impedance formulas can be written explicitly both for analysis (Z_{om} in terms of W/h and ϵ_r) and for synthesis (W/h in terms of Z_{om} and ϵ_r). These relations are listed below. For wide strips (W/h > 2)

$$Z_{om} = \frac{377}{(\epsilon_r)^{1/2}} \left[\frac{W}{h} + 0.883 + \frac{\epsilon_r+1}{\pi\epsilon_r} \left\{ \ell n \left(\frac{W}{2h} + 0.94 \right) + 1.451 \right\} + 0.165 \frac{\epsilon_r-1}{\epsilon_r^{\,2}} \right]^{-1} \tag{1.18}$$

and for narrow strip (W/h < 2)

$$Z_{om} = \frac{377}{2\pi \left(\frac{\epsilon_r+1}{2} \right)^{1/2}} \left[\ell n \left(\frac{8h}{W} \right) + \frac{1}{8} \left(\frac{W}{2h} \right)^2 - \frac{1}{2} \frac{\epsilon_r-1}{\epsilon_r+1} \left\{ \ell n \frac{\pi}{2} + \frac{1}{\epsilon_r} \ell n \frac{4}{\pi} \right\} \right] \tag{1.19}$$

where W is the strip width and h is the thickness of the substrate.

Expressions giving strip width for a desired impedance may be written as [2]:

For wide strips (W/h > 2)

$$\frac{W}{2h}\pi = \frac{377\pi}{2(\epsilon_r)^{1/2} Z_{om}} - 1 - \ell n \left\{ \frac{377\pi}{(\epsilon_r)^{1/2} Z_{om}} - 1 \right\} + \frac{\epsilon_r-1}{2\epsilon_r} \left[\ell n \left\{ \frac{377\pi}{2(\epsilon_r)^{1/2} Z_{om}} - 1 \right\} + 0.293 - \frac{0.517}{\epsilon_r} \right] \tag{1.20}$$

and for narrow strips (W/h < 2)

$$2h/W = \frac{1}{4}\,e^{h'} - \frac{1}{2}\,e^{-h'}$$

where

$$h' = \left(\frac{\epsilon_r + 1}{2}\right)^{1/2} \frac{Z_{om}}{60} + \frac{\epsilon_r - 1}{\epsilon_r + 1}\left(0.226 + \frac{0.120}{\epsilon_r}\right) \tag{1.21}$$

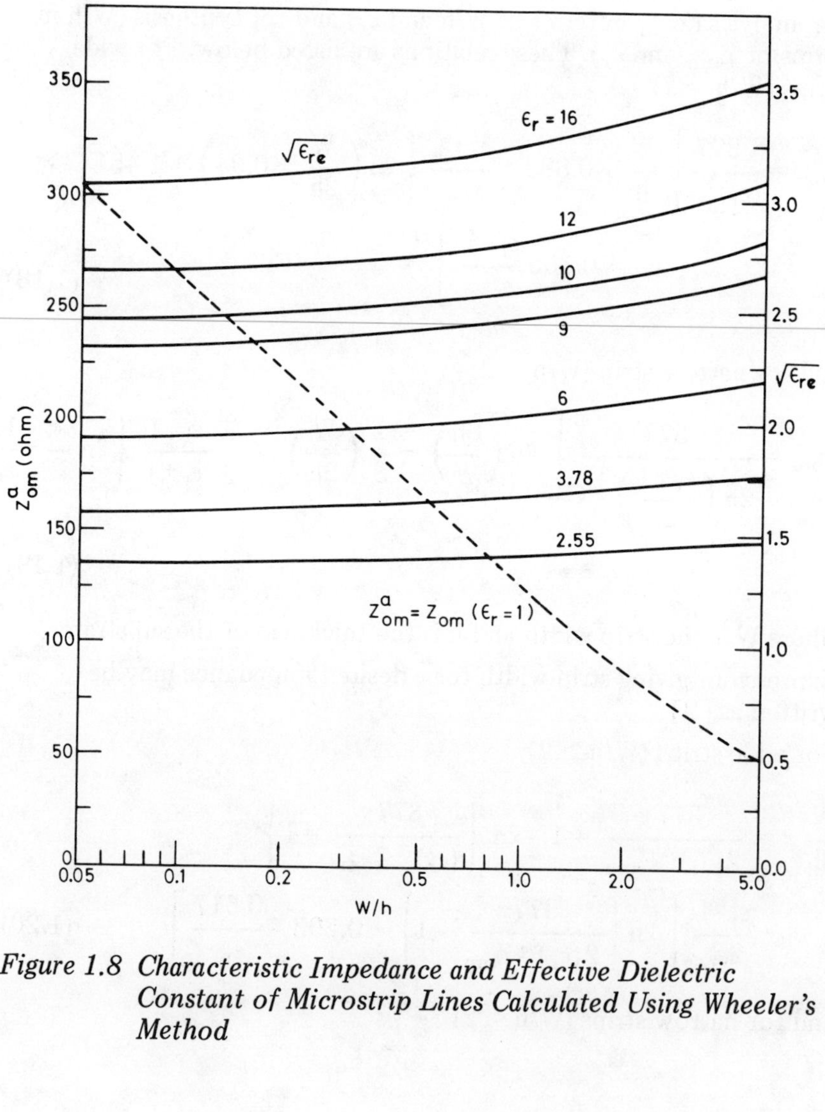

Figure 1.8 Characteristic Impedance and Effective Dielectric Constant of Microstrip Lines Calculated Using Wheeler's Method

However, Wheeler's analysis does not lead to closed form expressions for the effective dielectric constant when $W/h \geqslant 2$. Such expressions have been derived empirically by curve fitting of the numerical data and will be discussed in Section 2.4.

Values of the characteristic impedance and effective dielectric constant of microstrip, based on the method discussed above, may be obtained from Figure 1.8. In this figure the value of $\sqrt{\epsilon_{re}}$ is plotted as a function of W/h for various values of the substrate dielectric constant ϵ_r. The variation of characteristic impedance for air microstrip (Z_{om}^a for $\epsilon_r = 1$) is also shown by the dotted curve. Impedance for any value of ϵ_r can be obtained by dividing Z_{om}^a by the corresponding value of $\sqrt{\epsilon_{re}}$. It may be seen from Figure 1.8 that the impedance value decreases when the strip width to substrate height ratio (W/h) is increased because an increase in W (or decrease in h) increases the line capacitance.

Since the wavelength in microstrip λ_m is related to ϵ_{re} by the expression

$$\lambda_m = \frac{\lambda_o}{\sqrt{\epsilon_{re}}} \tag{1.22}$$

we notice from Figure 1.8 that λ_m is a function of W/h and hence that of Z_{om}. This implies that, for example, the length for a quarter wave section of 25 ohm impedance would be different from that of a section of 100 ohm impedance (at the same frequency). This factor has to be kept in mind while designing microstrip circuits.

It may be pointed out that in the modified conformal transformation method discussed above, the thickness of the microstrip conductor is ignored and the analysis is restricted to an open microstrip without any enclosure.

1.2.2 Finite Difference Method

Another method for quasi-static analysis of microstrip lines is based on the numerical solution of Laplace's equation in finite difference form [13]. This method is more suitable for enclosed microstrip, and the finite thickness of the microstrip conductor can easily be incorporated into the analysis. Laplace's equation may be written in finite difference form by considering the configuration shown in Figure 1.9. Potentials at the points A, B, C, D in the immediate vicinity of a point P may be written as

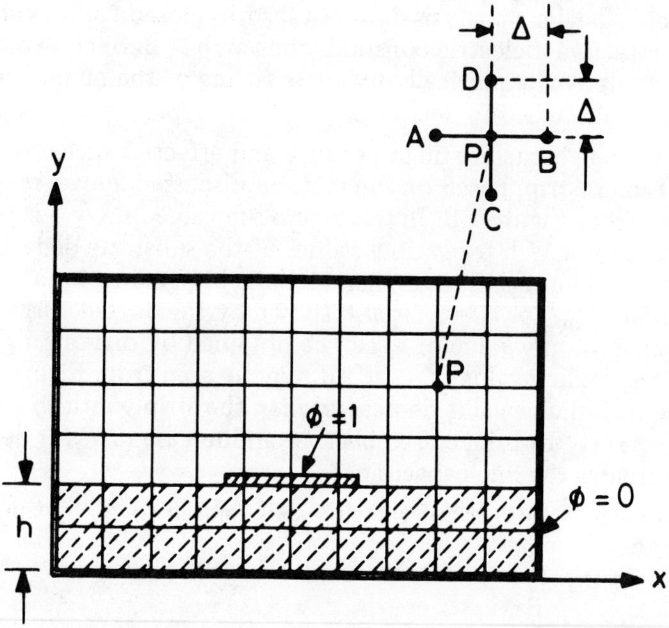

Figure 1.9 Enclosed Microstrip Configuration for Analysis by Finite Difference Method

$$\phi_A = \phi_P - \frac{\Delta\partial\phi}{\partial x} + \frac{\Delta^2}{2!}\frac{\partial^2\phi}{\partial x^2} - \frac{\Delta^3}{3!}\frac{\partial^3\phi}{\partial x^3} + \ldots \quad \ldots \tag{1.23}$$

$$\phi_B = \phi_P + \frac{\Delta\partial\phi}{\partial x} + \frac{\Delta^2}{2!}\frac{\partial^2\phi}{\partial x^2} + \frac{\Delta^3}{3!}\frac{\partial^3\phi}{\partial x^3} + \ldots \quad \ldots \tag{1.24}$$

$$\phi_C = \phi_P - \frac{\Delta\partial\phi}{\partial y} + \frac{\Delta^2}{2!}\frac{\partial^2\phi}{\partial y^2} - \frac{\Delta^3}{3!}\frac{\partial^3\phi}{\partial y^3} + \ldots \quad \ldots \tag{1.25}$$

$$\phi_D = \phi_P + \frac{\Delta\partial\phi}{\partial y} + \frac{\Delta^2}{2!}\frac{\partial^2\phi}{\partial y^2} + \frac{\Delta^3}{3!}\frac{\partial^3\phi}{\partial y^3} + \ldots \quad \ldots \tag{1.26}$$

When we ignore fourth order and higher terms and use $(\partial^2\phi/\partial x^2 + \partial^2\phi/\partial y^2) = 0$, the above relations yield

$$\phi_A + \phi_B + \phi_C + \phi_D \simeq 4\,\phi_P \ . \tag{1.27}$$

The most common method of solving finite difference Equation (1.27) is the "relaxation method." In this method one starts with assumed values of ϕ at all the grid points. These values are modified successively as follows:

$$\text{New } \phi_P = \text{old } \phi_P - \alpha R_P \tag{1.28}$$

where the "residuals" R_P are given by

$$R_P = \phi_P - (\phi_A + \phi_B + \phi_C + \phi_D)/4 \quad . \tag{1.29}$$

This successive "relaxation" is carried out until the differences between the old and new values become less than the allowed error. The speed of convergence of the "relaxation" process is determined by the constant α. Relation (1.29) needs to be modified for points near dielectric-air boundary and corners. A detailed discussion of the method is given by Green [14]. The solution of Laplace's equation by the method discussed above yields information about the potential distribution in the microstrip cross-section. Field distribution and the charge on the strip can be calculated therefrom. We have

$$Q = \epsilon_o \epsilon_r \oint E_n \cdot ds \tag{1.30}$$

where the integral is taken over a surface enclosing the strip conductor. Capacitance is obtained as the ratio of charge to voltage. Again two capacitances C and C_a are evaluated and the microstrip parameters Z_{om} and β calculated using Equations (1.4) and (1.5), respectively.

1.2.3 Integral Equation Method

The quasi-static analysis of microstrip may also be formulated in the form of an integral equation rather than a differential equation. We consider the Poisson equation in terms of line charge distribution and define a Green's function G as

$$\nabla_t^2 G(x, y; x_o, y_o) = -\frac{1}{\epsilon_o \epsilon_r} \delta(y-y_o)\, \delta(x-x_o) \tag{1.31}$$

Subscript t refers to transverse coordinates (x, y plane). Coordinates x_o, y_o refer to source location and x, y to the field point. Thus $G(x, y; x_o, y_o)$ is the potential at (x, y) produced by a line charge of unit magnitude located at (x_o, y_o). The function G satisfies the boundary and the interface conditions of the microstrip configuration but not the source condition. Using Green's function, an integral equation of the following form can be formulated and solved for the calculation of the charge distribution

$$\phi(x, y) = \int G(x, y; x_o, y_o)\ \rho(x_o, y_o)\, dx_o \tag{1.32}$$

where ϕ and ρ are the potential and the charge distributions, respectively, and the integration is carried out over the surface of the microstrip conductor at $y_o = h$. The analysis can be divided into two parts. First, the formulation of a suitable Green's function G and second, the solution of the integral Equation (1.32) by writing it in form of a matrix equation and carrying out the matrix inversion numerically. The matrix equation corresponding to Equation (1.32) may be written as

$$[v] = [p] \cdot [q] \tag{1.33}$$

where [v] and [q] are column matrices representing the potential ϕ and the charge q, respectively, and the matrix [p] can be recognized as the matrix of Maxwell's potential coefficients. Since the conductors may be presumed to be at known potentials, the matrix [v] is known and Equation (1.33) may be solved for [q] by inversion of the matrix [p]. Total charge Q and capacitance C for the microstrip can then be calculated as

$$C = Q/v = \sum_j \sum_k (p^{-1})_{jk} \tag{1.34}$$

where $(p^{-1})_{jk}$ is the jkth term of the inverse of the [p] matrix. Green's function G for the microstrip configuration is obtained from the theory of images for a charge placed in front of a dielectric-air interface and has been described by Silvester [15]. The method of images is illustrated in Figure 1.10. In this figure the partial image coefficient K is given by

$$K = (1 - \epsilon_r)/(1 + \epsilon_r)\ . \tag{1.35}$$

The Green's function G for the configuration as shown in Figure 1.10 may be written as [15]

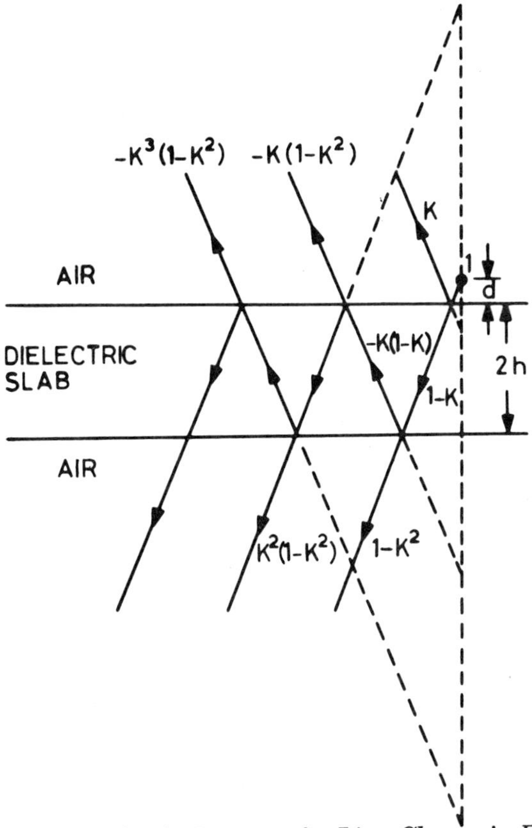

Figure 1.10(a) Multiple Images of a Line Charge in Front of a Dielectric Slab

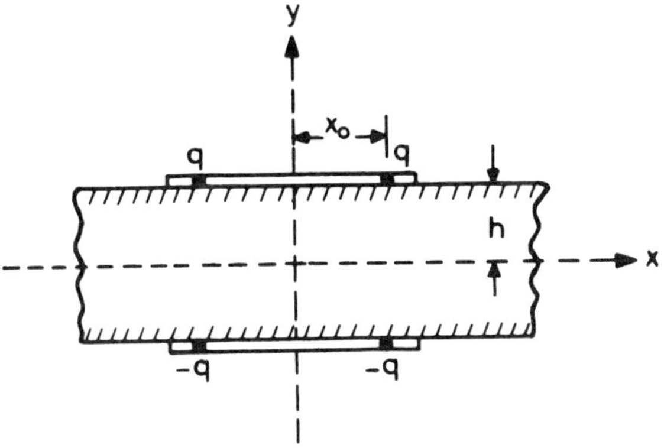

Figure 1-10(b) Microstrip Configuration Used in Integral Equation Method

$$G(h,x) = \frac{1}{2\pi(\epsilon_r+1)\epsilon_o} \left\{ \sum_{n=1}^{\infty} K^{n-1} \ell n \frac{\left[4n^2 + \left(\frac{x-x_o}{h}\right)^2\right]\left[4n^2 + \left(\frac{x+x_o}{h}\right)^2\right]}{\left[4(n-1)^2 + \left(\frac{x-x_o}{h}\right)^2\right]\left[4(n-1)^2 + \left(\frac{x+x_o}{h}\right)^2\right]} \right\} \tag{1.36}$$

Since K is negative, Equation (1.36) becomes an alternating series which is convergent and lends itself to simple estimation of truncation error. It has been found that for values of ϵ_r between 2 and 20, the number of terms of (1.36) sufficient to ensure convergence to seven significant figures lies between 15 to 150. Green's function for thick microstrip has also been reported [15].

1.2.4 Variational Method in Fourier Transform Domain

The search for microstrip analysis techniques which are computationally more efficient has led to the "variational method in Fourier transform domain (FTD)." There are two significant features of this method [16]. First, a variational method for calculating the capacitance C from the charge density ρ is used. This avoids the need for knowing the charge density distribution accurately. Secondly, the major portion of analysis is carried out in FTD with the result that the integral equation for the potential gets replaced by an ordinary product of an approximate $\tilde{\rho}$ and a factor $\tilde{g}$ derived in FTD (see Equation 1.41).

The variational expression for capacitance (upper bound) may be written as [16]

$$\frac{1}{C} = \frac{1}{Q^2} \int_s \rho(x,y)\ \phi(x,y)\, dx \tag{1.37}$$

where

$$Q = \int_s \rho(x,y)\, dx \quad (1.38$$

Here s indicates that the integral is over the strip conductor. Taking the Fourier transform of Equation (1.37) along the x-axis and using

Parseval's formula one gets

$$\frac{1}{C} = \frac{1}{2\pi Q^2} \int_{-\infty}^{\infty} \tilde{\rho}\ (\alpha)\ \tilde{\phi}\ (\alpha, h)\ d\alpha \tag{1.39}$$

where superscript ~ indicates a transformed function and is obtained from

$$\tilde{f}\ (\alpha) = \int_{-\infty}^{\infty} f\,(x)\ e^{j\alpha x}\, dx \tag{1.40}$$

It may be pointed out that it is simpler to evaluate $\tilde{\phi}\ (\alpha, h)$ than to evaluate $\phi(x, h)$ since

$$\tilde{\phi}\ (\alpha, h) = \frac{1}{\epsilon_o}\ \tilde{\rho}\ (\alpha)\ \tilde{g}\ (\alpha) \tag{1.41}$$

whereas $\phi(x, h)$ is an integral given by

$$\phi(x, h) = \frac{1}{\epsilon_o} \int_{-W/2}^{W/2} \rho(x')\, g(x, h; x', h)\, dx' \tag{1.42}$$

The potential function in the transform domain, $\tilde{\phi}\ (\alpha)$ is evaluated as follows. Except for y = h, the transform of potential $\tilde{\phi}\ (\alpha, y)$ satisfies the Laplace equation in the (α, y) plane, namely;

$$(-\alpha^2 + \frac{d^2}{dy^2})\ \tilde{\phi}\ (\alpha, y) = 0 \tag{1.43}$$

Boundary conditions to be satisfied by $\tilde{\phi}\ (\alpha, y)$ may be listed as:

$$\text{at } y = 0 \quad \tilde{\phi}\ (\alpha, 0) = 0 \tag{1.44a)}$$

$$\text{at } y = h \quad \tilde{\phi}\ (\alpha, h+0) = \tilde{\phi}\ (\alpha, h-0), \tag{1.44b)}$$

$$\text{at } y = \infty \quad \tilde{\phi}\ (\alpha, \infty) = 0 \tag{1.44c)}$$

and for $\frac{d}{dy}\tilde{\phi}$ at y = h, we have

$$\frac{d}{dy}\ \tilde{\phi}\ (\alpha, h+0) = \epsilon_r\ \frac{d}{dy}\ \tilde{\phi}\ (\alpha, h-0) - \frac{1}{\epsilon_0}\ \tilde{\rho}\ (\alpha) \tag{1.44d)}$$

In the region $0 \leqslant y \leqslant h$, the general solution of Equation (1.44) is a linear combination of $\exp(-\alpha y)$ and $\exp(\alpha y)$; whereas for $y \geqslant h$, the solution is of the form $\exp(-|\alpha| y)$ alone. Using the boundary conditions given in Equation (1.44), the solution for $\tilde{\phi}(\alpha, y)$ at y=h is given by

$$\tilde{\phi}(\alpha, h) = \frac{1}{\epsilon_o} \tilde{\rho}(\alpha)\, \tilde{g}(\alpha) = \frac{\tilde{\rho}(\alpha)}{\epsilon_o |\alpha| [1 + \epsilon_r \coth(|\alpha| h)]} \tag{1.45}$$

$\tilde{\phi}(\alpha, h)$ given by Equation (1.45) is used in Equation (1.39) for evaluating the capacitance C.

We still have to find $\tilde{\rho}(\alpha)$ before C can be computed. However, since Equation (1.37) is variational, one may use an approximate trial function for $\rho(x)$ and incur only a second order error in the value of capacitance. A trial function that maximizes the value of C gives the closest value to the exact result for the capacitance. Variation of the charge proportional to $|x|$ yields the following expression for $\tilde{\rho}(\alpha)$ [16]

$$\frac{\tilde{\rho}(\alpha)}{Q} = \frac{2 \sin(\alpha W/2)}{\alpha W/2} - \left\{ \frac{\sin(\alpha W/4)}{\alpha W/4} \right\}^2 \tag{1.46}$$

Results obtained by this method agree well with those of the modified conformal transformation method discussed earlier. This method can also be used to take into account the effect of finite strip thickness and enclosure. It can be easily extended for microstrip on composite substrates or where a dielectric overlay exists over the microstrip [17]. In these situations one simply has to find an appropriate expression for $\tilde{g}(\alpha)$ and use the above procedure. For a microstrip with a composite substrate and shielded by a top metallic wall as shown in Figure 1.11, the value of $\tilde{g}(\alpha)$ is given as

$$\tilde{g}(\alpha) = \frac{\epsilon_{r1} \coth(|\alpha| h) + \epsilon_{r2} \coth(|\alpha| s)}{|\alpha| \left\{ \epsilon_{r1} \coth(|\alpha| h) [\epsilon_{r3} \coth(|\alpha| d) + \epsilon_{r2} \coth(|\alpha| s)] + \epsilon_{r2} [\epsilon_{r2} + \epsilon_{r3} \coth(|\alpha| d) \coth(|\alpha| s)] \right\}} \tag{1.47}$$

1.3 MICROSTRIP DISPERSION MODELS

The quasi-static methods of microstrip analysis discussed above do not take into account the non-TEM nature of the microstrip mode.

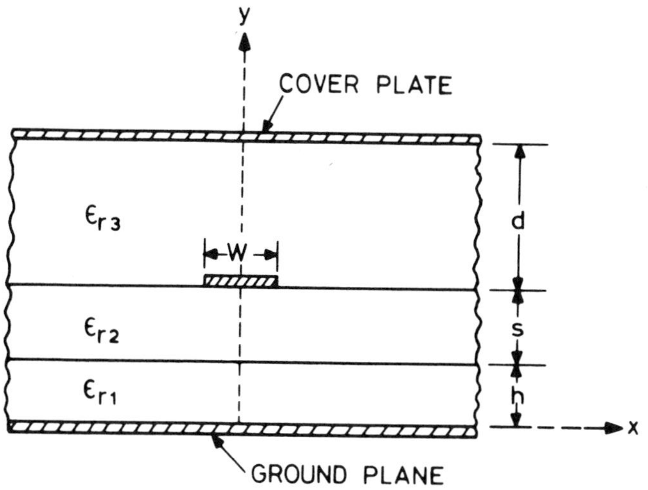

Figure 1.11 Microstrip with a Composite Dielectric Substrate and a Cover Plate

The non-TEM behavior causes the effective dielectric constant (ϵ_{re}) and impedance Z_{om} of the microstrip to be functions of frequency. Of these two, the variation of the effective dielectric constant is more significant. An exact evaluation of these variations involves a fullwave analysis of the microstrip configuration, which will be discussed in Chapter 2. However, there are several semi-empirical techniques available that lead to a closed form solution for the dependence of ϵ_{re} and Z_{om} on frequency. These dispersion models may be listed as follows:

- Model based on coupling between TEM and TM_o surface wave mode (Jain *et. al.* 1971)[18]
- An empirical relation for frequency dependent phase velocity (Schneider 1972)[19]
- LSE mode using a dielectric loaded ridged waveguide (Getsinger 1973)[20]
- Model based on coupling between a TEM and a TE mode transmission lines (Carlin 1973)[21]
- Planar waveguide model (Kompa and Mehran 1975)[22]
- Modification of Getsinger's formula (Edwards and Owens, 1976) [23]

These dispersion models are discussed briefly in the following section.

1.3.1 Coupled TEM and TM Modes Model

In this model [18] the deviation from the TEM behavior or the dispersion is considered to be caused by the coupling between the fundamental TEM mode and the lowest order surface wave TM_o mode. Using the theory of coupled modes, the frequency dependent effective dielectric constant may be written as:

$$\epsilon_{re}(f) = \left[0.5\left(\sqrt{\epsilon_{re}(0)}+\sqrt{\epsilon_{eTM}}\right) + \left\{\epsilon_{12}^2 + 0.25\left(\sqrt{\epsilon_{re}(0)} - \sqrt{\epsilon_{eTM}}\right)^2\right\}^{1/2}\right]^2 \tag{1.48}$$

where $\epsilon_{re}(0)$ is the quasi-static value of the effective dielectric constant and ϵ_{eTM} is the effective dielectric constant for the TM_o mode. An expression for the coupling parameter ϵ_{12}, obtained by a series of qualitative arguments, may be written as

$$\epsilon_{12}^2 = k(\sqrt{\epsilon_r}-1)^2 \; (W/h)^{n_3} \; (f/f_e)^{n_2} \tag{1.49}$$

where f_e is the frequency at which the phase velocity of the TEM mode equals the phase velocity of the TM_o mode, and k, n_2, n_3 are three constants found empirically for the best fit between the behavior of the coupled line model and the experimental results. The values of n_2, n_3 and k are 4/3, 3/4, and 0.22, respectively, and the range of validity for the model is stated as $2 \leqslant \epsilon_r \leqslant 104$, 0.025 in $\leqslant h \leqslant$ 0.125 in, $0.9 \leqslant W/h \leqslant 6$, and $f < 0.5\, f_e$.

1.3.2 An Empirical Relation [19]

Based on the results of various theoretical and experimental studies of dispersion, it may be noted that

a) The normalized phase velocity v_p is a monotonically decreasing function of frequency f.

b) v_p and its first order derivative at f = 0 are given by

$$v_p \Big|_{f=0} = 1/\sqrt{\epsilon_{re}(0)} \qquad \text{and} \qquad \frac{\partial v_p}{\partial f}\Big|_{f=0} = 0 \tag{1.50}$$

c) v_p and its derivative at $f \to \infty$ are given by

$$v_p \Big|_{f\to\infty} = 1/\sqrt{\epsilon_r} \qquad \text{and} \qquad \frac{\partial v_p}{\partial f}\Big|_{f\to\infty} = 0 \tag{1.51}$$

d) The second derivative of v_p is zero in the vicinity of the cut-off frequency (f_c) of the lowest order transverse electric surface wave mode; i.e.,

$$\left.\frac{\partial^2 v_p}{\partial f^2}\right|_{f=f_c} = 0 \tag{1.52}$$

The above conditions are fulfilled by the relation [19]

$$v_p = \frac{1}{\sqrt{\epsilon_r \, \epsilon_{re}(0)}} \; \frac{\sqrt{\epsilon_{re}(0)}\, f_n^{\,2} + \sqrt{\epsilon_r}}{f_n^{\,2} + 1} \tag{1.53}$$

where $\epsilon_{re}(0)$ is the quasi-static value of ϵ_{re} and f_n is defined by

$$f_n = \frac{f}{f_c} = \frac{4h\sqrt{\epsilon_r - 1}}{\lambda_o} \tag{1.54}$$

with h as the substrate thickness.

Comparison with experimental results shows that the error in Equation (1.53) is less than 3 percent.

1.3.3 Dielectric-loaded Ridged Waveguide Model [20]

This model for microstrip dispersion is based on the study of another structure which resembles microstrip as far as inhomogeneity of dielectric medium is concerned, but has a shape that can be analysed mathematically. This structure is shown in Figure 1.12. The configuration shown in Figure 1.12(b) corresponds to the microstrip cross-section shown in Figure 1.12(a). The dimensions of the structure are chosen such that it has the same electrical characteristics at zero frequency as the microstrip. The structure is analysed for dispersion and the results are compared with the measured microstrip dispersion values to determine unknown parameter [illegible]. The comparison shows that H'/h and related parameters are nearly constant or vary linearly with characteristic impedance. This feature is used to derive a simple formula that can be used to predict the dispersion of a microstrip transmission line. The resulting dispersion formula may be written as

$$\epsilon_{re}(f) = \epsilon_r - \frac{\epsilon_r - \epsilon_{re}(0)}{1 + (f^2/f_p^{\,2})G} \tag{1.55}$$

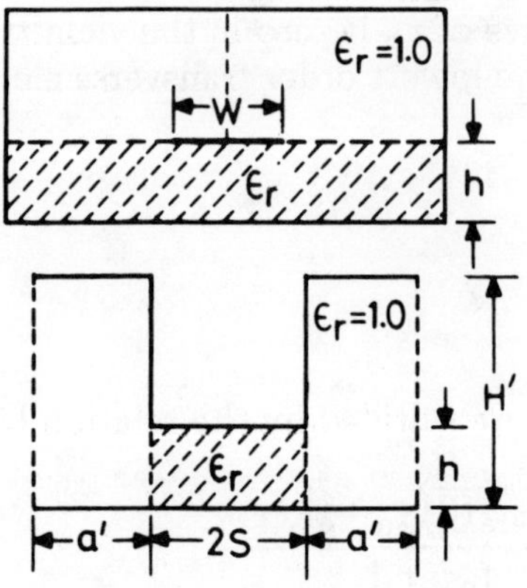

Figure 1.12 Ridged Waveguide Model for Microstrip Line (from [20])

where

$$f_p = Z_{om}/(2\mu_o h) \tag{1.56}$$

or

$$f_p\,(\text{GHz}) = 0.398\, Z_{om}/h\,(\text{mm})$$

and

$$G = 0.6 + 0.009\, Z_{om} \qquad (Z_{om} \text{ in ohms}) \tag{1.57}$$

In Equation (1.55), ϵ_{re} is the frequency dependent effective dielectric constant and $\epsilon_{re}(0)$ is the zero frequency value of ϵ_{re}.

Modification of Getsinger's formula

Edwards and Owens [23] have reported extensive measurement results on dispersion in microstrip lines of characteristic impedance ranging from 10 to 100 ohms over the frequency range of 2 to 18 GHz. They have pointed out that measured results show better agreement with Getsinger's formula when G of Equation (1.57) is modified as

$$G = \left\{ \frac{Z_{om} - 5}{60} \right\}^{1/2} + 0.004\, Z_{om} \tag{1.58}$$

Experiments of Edwards and Owens [23] have been carried out on sapphire substrates (ϵ_r = 10.73 to 11.50), and their results have been found to be in good agreement with fullwave analysis using Galerkin's method in the spectral domain (discussed later in Section 2.3.2). Modification of Equation (1.55) which results in a more accurate formula has also been suggested. This may be written as

$$\epsilon_{re}(f) = \epsilon_r - \frac{\epsilon_r - \epsilon_{re}(0)}{1 + P} \tag{1.59}$$

where

$$P = (h/Z_{om})^{1.33} \left[0.43 f^2 - 0.009 f^3\right] \tag{1.60}$$

where h is in millimeters and f in gigahertz.

1.3.4 Coupled Transmission Lines Model

This model is based on the observation that hybrid modes in a wave-guide partially filled with dielectric material may be expressed as coupled TE and TM modes [24]. These modes can be represented by equivalent transmission lines. In the present case [21] the two coupled lines shown in Figure 1.13 represent the TEM mode (the

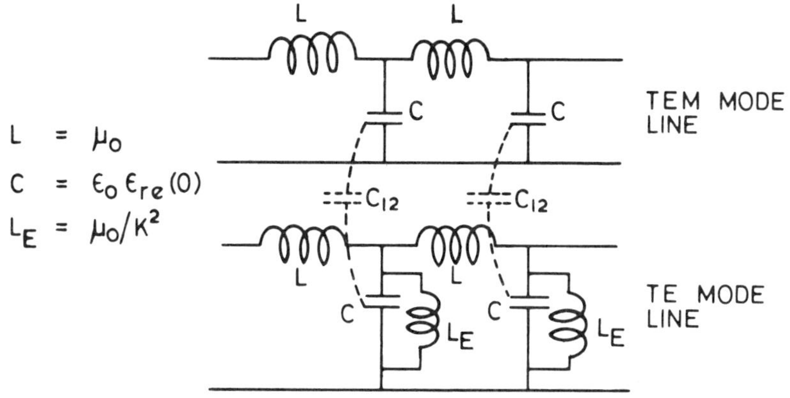

Figure 1.13 Coupled Lines Model for Dispersion in Microstrip (from [21])

fundamental microstrip mode) and a TE mode (a fictitious mode whose cut-off frequency is found empirically). Using coupled line analysis [21] an expression for frequency dependent effective dielectric constant is derived as

$$\epsilon_{re}(f) = \epsilon_{re}(0) - \frac{K^2 c^2}{2\omega^2} + \sqrt{[k\epsilon_{re}(0)]^2 + \left(\frac{K^2 c^2}{2\omega^2}\right)^2} \tag{1.61}$$

where $\epsilon_{re}(0)$ is the static effective dielectric constant. The coupling factor k is obtained by putting the high frequency limit of Equation (1.61) equal to ϵ_r

$$k = \frac{\epsilon_r - \epsilon_{re}(0)}{\epsilon_{re}(0)}, \tag{1.62}$$

and K is the cut-off wavenumber for the TE mode. This parameter is found empirically by comparing the results with Equation (1.55) at the point of inflexion of the ϵ_{re} - frequency curve and is given by

$$K^2 = \frac{k}{R} \frac{(2\pi)^2}{12h^2 G} \epsilon_{re}(0) \left(\frac{Z_{om}}{120\pi}\right)^2 \tag{1.63}$$

where

$$R = 0.2138$$

$$G = 0.5 + 0.001\, Z_{om}^{3/2}$$

The factor G is a modified version of G in Equation (1.57) and improves the accuracy.

1.3.5 Planar Waveguide Model

It has been shown [22] that the dynamic properties of microstrip (including higher order modes) can be approximated by a planar waveguide model. In this model, microstrip is represented by a parallel plate waveguide of width W_e and height h as shown in Figure 1.14. The top and bottom plates are of infinite conductivity, and there are magnetic walls at the sides. It is filled with a medium of dielectric constant ϵ_{re}. The value of ϵ_{re} at zero frequency is determined from quasi-static analysis. The effective width W_e and the effective dielectric constant ϵ_{re} are frequency dependent. The frequency

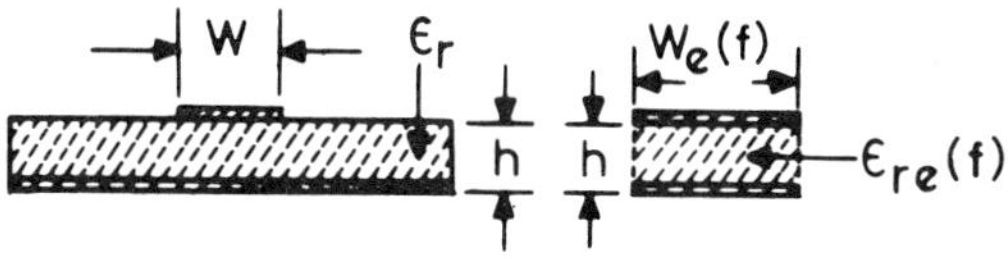

Figure 1.14(a) Planar Waveguide Model for Microstrip Line

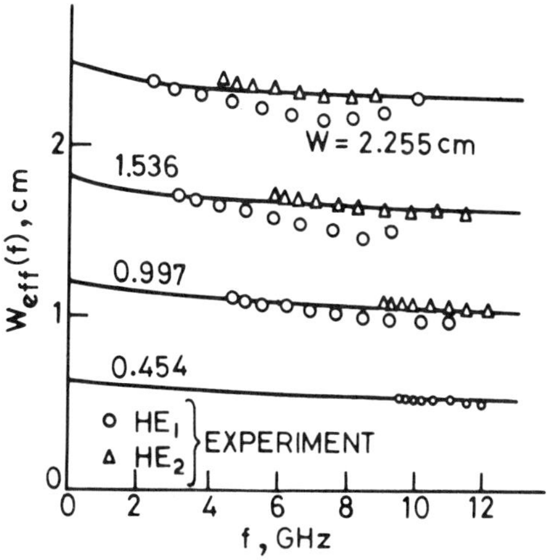

Figure 1.14(b) Variation of Effective Width with Frequency. $\epsilon_r = 9.7$, $h = 0.0635$ cm (from [22])

dependence of the dielectric constant describes the influence of the dispersion on the phase velocity, whereas the frequency dependence of the effective width describes the influence of the dispersion on the characteristic impedance. It is found, from the results of the fullwave analysis discussed later in Chapter 2, that the phase velocity of the waves in microstrip decreases with increasing frequency. Thus the value of ϵ_{re} increases with frequency. Also, the characteristic impedance of a microstrip increases with frequency (Section 2.4). This increase in impedance can be explained only by a hypothetical decrease in the effective strip width caused by the concentration of electric field lines below the strip at higher frequency. The decrease of the effective strip width with frequency is described by the following empirical relation [22]

$$W_e(f) = W + \frac{W_e(0) - W}{1 + f/f_g} \tag{1.64a}$$

where

$f_g = c/(2W\sqrt{\epsilon_r})$

$W_e(0)$ = effective width calculated from quasi-static analysis

$= 120\pi h/(Z_{om}\sqrt{\epsilon_{re}(0)})$

Frequency dependent impedance is given by

$$Z_{om}(f) = 120\,\pi h/(W_e(f)\sqrt{\epsilon_{re}(f)}) \tag{1.64b}$$

A comparison of the experimental results with the values calculated using Equation (1.64) is shown in Figure 1.14(b). Further, by knowing $W_e(f)$ one can calculate cut-off frequencies for higher order modes from the following relation [22]

$$f_c(m,0) = \frac{mc}{2\sqrt{\epsilon_{re}(f)}\,W_e(f)} \tag{1.65}$$

The guide wavelength for hybrid modes in terms of $f_c(m, 0)$ is given by

$$\lambda_{HE_m} = \frac{\lambda_o}{\sqrt{\epsilon_{re}(f)}\,\sqrt{1 - [f_c(m,0)/f]^2}} \tag{1.66}$$

Measured and calculated cut-off frequencies of the first two higher order modes are shown in Figure 1.15 [22]. The two modes indicated as m = 1 and m = 2 in this figure are HE_1 and HE_2 modes, respectively. There is a fairly good agreement between the measured results and theoretical values.

1.4 MICROSTRIP MEASUREMENTS

Just as in case of any other transmission structure the important characteristics that need be measured for a microstrip are: (i) characteristic impedance, (ii) phase velocity and (iii) attenuation constant. Also, in several cases, the dielectric constant of the substrate material is not known accurately. Since this information is required for microstrip circuit design, methods have been devised for quick determination of the dielectric constant of metallized substrates [25-27].

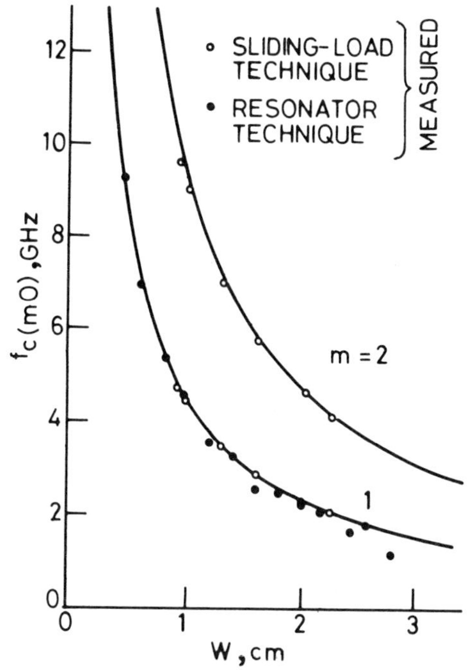

Figure 1.15 Cut-off Frequencies for Higher Order Modes in Microstrip Computed from the Planar Waveguide model. $\epsilon_r = 9.7$, *h = 0.0635 cm (from [22])*

In this section we will briefly outline the methods for the measurement of substrate dielectric constant and for microstrip characteristics.

1.4.1 Substrate Dielectric Constant

In the normal course of fabricating dielectric substrates for MICs, a dielectric filled resonator cavity is automatically constructed. The rectangular substrate with its top-and bottom-surface metallization (sides not metallized) becomes a parallel plate dielectric-loaded-waveguide resonator. This structure is shown in Figure 1.16(a). For high dielectric constant substrates the fringing field is very small, and the sides of the resonator are good approximations to open circuits. The resonant frequency f_{mn} for this type of resonator is given by

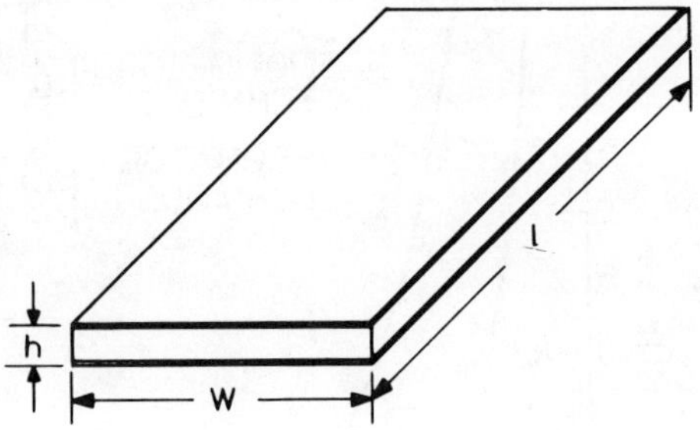

Figure 1.16(a) Metallized substrate as a Parallel Plate Resonator

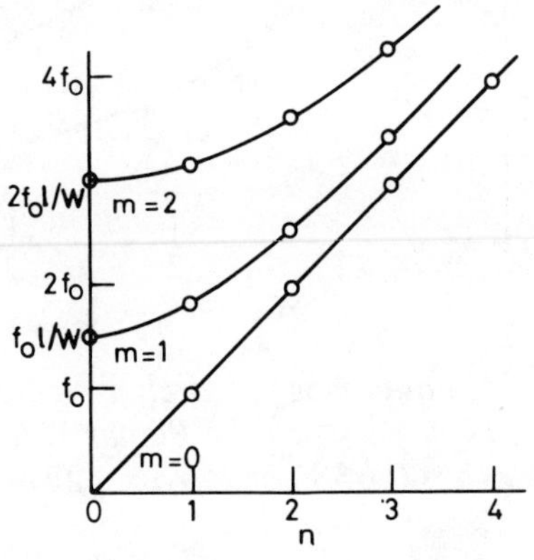

Figure 1.16(b) Resonance Frequencies for Various Modes of a Metallized Substrate Resonator (from [25])

$$f_{mn}^{2} = \frac{c^2}{\epsilon_r} \left\{ \left(\frac{m}{2W}\right)^2 + \left(\frac{n}{2\ell}\right)^2 \right\} \qquad (1.67)$$

where m and n represent the mode of resonance and correspond to the number of half cycle variations along W and ℓ, respectively. Values of f_{mn} are shown in Figure 1.16(b) as dots superimposed on the dispersion curves.

For measuring the substrate dielectric constant the parallel plate resonator is coupled to the measurement system by placing it between two APC-7 type coaxial connectors [25] as shown in Figure

1.17(a). Details of the coupling are shown in Figure 1.17(b). Transmission measurements may be carried out by using a network analyser or any other suitable system. The modes are identified by referring to Figure 1.16(b).

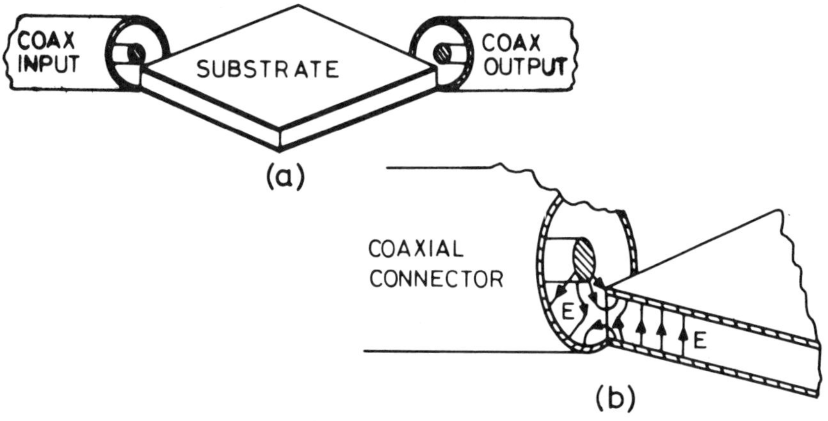

Figure 1.17 Coupling to Metallized Substrate Resonators through Coaxial Connectors

The accuracy of the above method is limited because of the fringing field and radiation due to the open sides of the resonator. A modification has been suggested [26] wherein the substrate is metallized on all the sides so that a small microwave cavity is formed. Equation (1.67) for various resonant frequencies is still valid. Resonant frequencies are measured by clearing metallization from the corners of the cavity and positioning the center conductor in APC-7 connectors as shown in Figure 1.17.

Coupling errors in cavity resonance measurements on MIC dielectric substrates are discussed by Ladbrooke *et. al.* [27]. An alternative coupling scheme wherein a coupling aperture is photolithographically cut in the top plane has been suggested. Details of this scheme are shown in Figure 1.18. The broadwall hole with an overlaid strip provides the required coupling, and the energy transfer into and out of the cavity is adequate without having to make the aperture unacceptably large. This type of coupling scheme has been used with substrates which are metallized on the sides also.

Errors because of coupling are analysed by considering the perturbation of fields. It has been pointed out [27] that the two methods of

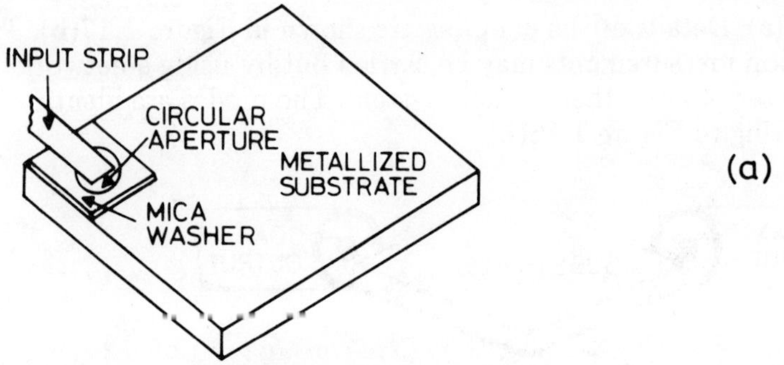

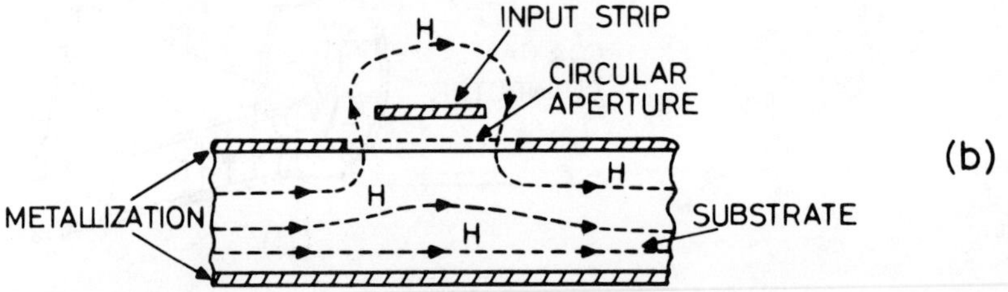

Figure 1.18 Aperture Coupling to a Substrate Resonator Metallized on all the Sides (from [27])

coupling, namely, corner coupling for resonators with open sides and aperture coupling for resonators with metallized sides, are complementary. As shown in Figures 1.17(b) and 1.18(b), respectively, corner coupling involves the perturbation of electric field lines whereas in the aperture coupling the magnetic field of the resonator is distributed. Errors in the two cases are of opposite nature, and an improved accuracy ($\simeq$ 0.5 percent) can be obtained by averaging the results obtained by the two methods.

1.4.2 Characteristic Impedance

Since fairly good coaxial to microstrip transitions are available, impedance measurement methods are identical to those for other transmission lines.

The characteristic impedance can be measured by terminating the microstrip in a matched load and measuring maximum and minimum VSWR as a function of frequency. If the impedance to be measured is Z_{om} ohm using a 50 ohm reference line, then

$$\left(\frac{Z_{om}}{50}\right)^{\pm 1} = \sqrt{VSWR_{max} \cdot VSWR_{min}} \quad (1.68)$$

where the exponent +1 is associated with high impedance lines and -1 with low impedance lines. An approximate value of Z_{om} can be obtained from time domain reflectometry (TDR) and thus the ambiguity between the exponents +1 and -1 can be resolved very easily. It may be noted that this method assumes the frequency insensivity of Z_{om} which is a good approximation for the frequency range of interest.

The above method of measurement has been described by Caulton *et. al.* [28] and by Seckelmann [29].

1.4.3 Phase Velocity or Effective Dielectric Constant

The effective dielectric constant of microstrip can be measured quite accurately by using resonance techniques. Both the linear and the ring type resonators have been used.

Use of Ring Resonators

A microstrip ring resonator is a microstrip line bent in a circular shape to close in upon itself (Figure 1.19a). The main advantage of

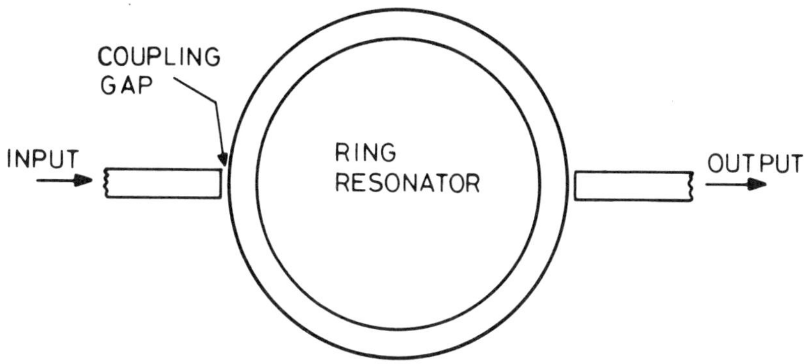

Figure 1.19(a) A Ring Resonator Set-Up for Microstrip Dispersion Measurements

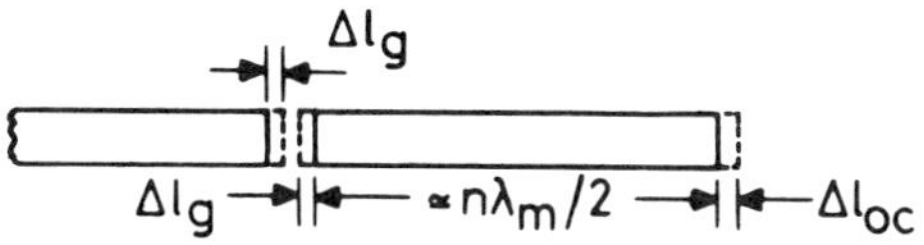

Figure 1.19 (b) A Linear Microstrip Resonator

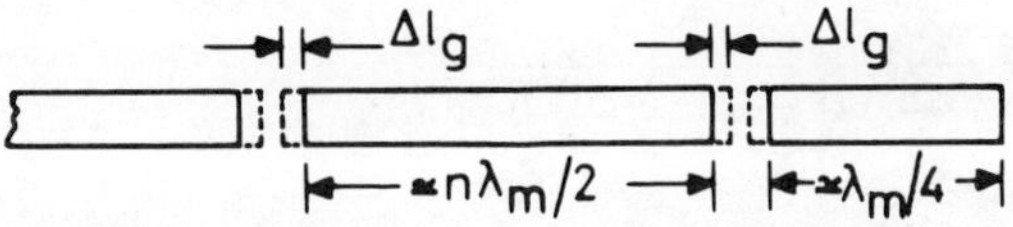

Figure 1.19 (c) Modified Linear Resonator Configuration

using ring resonators for dispersion measurements [30] is that, in contrast with the linear resonators, no end effects need to be considered. The resonant frequencies of this type of resonator could be calculated assuming that the mean length of the strip forming the resonator is a multiple of the guide wavelength on the microstrip.

For ring resonators, the curvature of the ring influences the resonance frequencies, so that only large resonators can be used. The influence of the curvature becomes large if substrate materials with small relative permittivities and lines with small impedances are used. Under these conditions the width of the lines becomes large and a mean radius cannot be well defined. When short resonators are used, an accurate analysis of ring resonators is needed. A magnetic wall model of microstrip ring resonators has been discussed by Wolff and Knoppik [31].

The eigenvalue equation resulting from the boundary conditions of a magnetic wall ring resonator model may be written as

$$\frac{J_n'(kr_a)}{J_n'(kr_i)} - \frac{N_n'(kr_a)}{N_n'(kr_i)} = 0 \tag{1.69}$$

where k is the wave number in unbounded dielectric and r_a and r_i represent outer and inner radii, respectively. $J_n'(x)$ and $N_n'(x)$ represent derivatives of Bessel functions of the first and the second kind, respectively. Some results based on the solution of Equation (1.69) are described in Reference [31]. It is shown that curvature effects are more pronounced for wider lines (impedances smaller than 50 ohms).

More accurate calculations for curvature effect in microstrip ring resonators is presented by Owens [32]. In this method a planar waveguide model is used for microstrip. Equation (1.69) still holds provided the width of the strip is replaced by the effective width given by this model. Since the effective width is frequency dependent, the frequency variation of the fringing field at the edges of the microstrip is also accounted for.

Linear Resonator Method

The main difficulty with the use of a linear resonator is caused by end effects. When a linear resonator is coupled to the measurement system at one end, as shown in Figure 1.19(b), the reactance at the two ends are different. The open end can be represented either by a shunt capacitance or by an incremental line length $\Delta\ell_{oc}$. On the other hand, the gap between the input line and the resonator is represented by a pi-network of capacitances and the incremental length $\Delta\ell_g$ shown in the figure is different from $\Delta\ell_{oc}$. Measurement of discontinuity reactances will be discussed in detail in Chapter 4. For the purposes of the present discussion, we are looking for methods to incorporate the effect of these reactances for the accurate measurement of resonant frequencies. A method suitable for this purpose has been described by Richings [33] and by Easter [34]. This method suggests the use of a modified resonator set up as shown in Figure 1.19(c). A $\lambda_m/4$ section at the other end of the resonator ensures that the reactances at two ends of the resonator are identical. Thus there are two unknowns now, and these can be evaluated if measurements are carried out for two different lengths of the resonator.

1.4.4 Attenuation Constant

The most satisfactory method of measuring the attenuation constant for low-loss substrates is from the Q-factor of a resonant section of line. The attenuation constant and the unloaded quality factor Q_o are related by the following expression

$$\alpha = \frac{27.3}{Q_o \lambda_m} \text{ (dB/cm)} \tag{1.70}$$

It has been pointed out that the ring resonator technique is less suitable for accurate measurement of microstrip losses because of increased surface wave radiation loss [35]. On the other hand, the shielded open-ended linear resonator in a waveguide below cut-off gives a reliable value of the attenuation constant.

An approximate but very simple method to measure the attenuation constant is based on the comparison technique. In this method two microstrip lines with identical electrical characteristics but different lengths are taken. Their insertion losses are measured. The difference between the two values of insertion loss is used for evaluating the attenuation constant. This procedure avoids the systematic errors caused by radiation, coaxial to microstrip transition, and so forth.

REFERENCES

[1] Gupta, K.C. and A. Singh, (eds.), *Microwave Integrated Circuits,* Halsted Press (John Wiley and Sons, New York), 1974.

[2] Young, L. and H. Sobol, (eds.), *Advances in Microwaves,* Academic Press, (New York), Vol. 8, 1974.

[3] Frey, J., (ed.), *Microwave Integrated Circuits,* Artech House, (Dedham, Mass.), 1975. (A reprint volume).

[4] Buntschuh, C., "A Study of the Transmission Line Properties of Trapped Inverted Microstrip Line," *RADC-TR-74-311, AD# A-003633,* Dec. 1974.

[5] Yamashita, E., and K. Atsuki, "Analysis of Microstrip-like Transmission Lines by Non-Uniform Discretization of Integral Equations," *IEEE Trans., Vol. MTT-24,* 1976, pp. 195-200.

[6] Schneider, M.V., "Microstrip Lines for Microwave Integrated Circuits," *B.S.T.J., Vol. 48,* 1969, pp. 1421-1444.

[7] McLevige, W.V., *et. al.,* "New Waveguide Structures for Millimeter Wave and Optical Integrated Circuits," *IEEE Trans., Vol. MTT-23,* 1975, pp. 788-794.

[8] Howe, H., *Stripline Circuit Design,* Artech House (Dedham, Mass.), 1974.

[9] Bahl, I.J., and Ramesh Garg, "A Designer's Guide to Stripline Circuits," *Microwaves, Vol. 17,* 1978, pp. 90-96.

[10] Wheeler, H.A., "Transmission Line Properties of Parallel Wide Strips by Conformal Mapping Approximation," *IEEE Trans., Vol. MTT-12,* 1964, pp. 280-289.

[11] Wheeler, H.A., "Transmission Line Properties of Parallel Strips Separated by a Dielectric Sheet," *IEEE Trans., Vol. MTT-13,* 1965, pp. 172-185.

[12] Sobol, H., "Application of Integrated Circuit Technology to Microwave Frequencies," *Proc. IEEE, Vol. 59,* 1971, pp. 1200-1211.

[13] Stinehelfer, H.E., "An Accurate Calculation of Uniform Microstrip Transmission Lines," *IEEE Trans., Vol. 16,* 1968, pp. 439-444.

[14] Green, H.E., "The Numerical Solution of Some Important Transmission Line Problems," *IEEE Trans., Vol. MTT-13,* 1965, pp. 676-692.

[15] Silvester, P., "TEM Properties of Microstrip Transmission Lines," *Proc. IEE, Vol. 115*, 1968, pp. 42-49.

[16] Yamashita, E. and R. Mittra, "Variational Method for the Analysis of Microstrip Lines," *IEEE Trans., Vol. MTT-16*, 1968, pp. 251-256.

[17] Yamashita, E., "Variational Method for the Analysis of Microstrip-like Transmission Lines," *IEEE Trans., Vol. MTT-16*, 1968, pp. 529-535.

[18] Jain, O.P. *et. al.*, "Coupled Mode Model of Dispersion in Microstrip," *Electron. Lett., Vol. 7*, 1971, pp. 405-407.

[19] Schneider, M.V., "Microstrip Dispersion," *Proc. IEEE, Vol. 60*, 1972, pp. 144-146.

[20] Getsinger, W.J., "Microstrip Dispersion Model," *IEEE Trans., Vol. MTT-21*, 1973, pp. 34-39.

[21] Carlin, H.J., "A Simplified Circuit Model for Microstrip," *IEEE Trans., Vol. MTT-21*, 1973, pp. 589-591.

[22] Kompa, G. and R. Mehran, "Planar Waveguide Model for Calculating Microstrip Components," *Electron. Lett., Vol. 11*, 1975, pp. 459-460.

[23] Edwards, T.C. and R.R. Owens, "2-18 GHz Dispersion Measurements on 10-100 ohm Microstrip Lines on Sapphire," *IEEE Trans., Vol. MTT-24*, 1976, pp. 506-513.

[24] Noble, D.F. and H.J. Carlin, "Circuit Properties of Coupled Dispersive Transmission Lines," *IEEE Trans. on Circuit Theory, Vol. CT-20*, 1973, pp. 56-65.

[25] Napoli, L.S. and J.J. Hughes, "A Simple Technique for the Accurate Determination of the Microwave Dielectric Constant for Microwave Integrated Circuits," *IEEE Trans., Vol. MTT-19*, 1971, pp. 664-665.

[26] Howell, J.Q., "A Quick, Accurate Method to Measure the Dielectric Constant of Microwave Integrated Circuit Substrates," *IEEE Trans., Vol. MTT-21*, 1973, pp. 142-143.

[27] Ladbrooke, P.H. *et. al.*, "Coupling Errors in Cavity Resonance Measurements on MIC Dielectrics," *IEEE Trans., Vol. MTT-21*, 1973, pp. 560-562.

[28] Caulton, M., *et. al.*, "Measurements on the Properties of Microstrip Transmission Lines for Microwave Integrated Circuits," *RCA Review, Vol. 27*, 1966, pp. 377-391.

[29] Seckelmann, R., "On the Measurement of Microstrip Properties," *Microwave J., Vol. 11*, Jan. 1968, pp. 61-64.

[30] Troughton, P., "Measurement Technique in Microstrip," *Electron. Lett., Vol. 5*, 1969, pp. 25-26.

[31] Wolff, I., and N. Knoppik, "Microstrip Ring Resonator and Dispersion Measurement on Microstrip Lines," *Electron. Lett., Vol. 7*, 1971, pp. 779-781.

[32] Owens, R.P., "Curvature Effect in Microstrip Ring Resonators," *Electron. Lett., Vol. 12*, 1976, pp. 356-357.

[33] Richings, J.G., "An Accurate Experimental Method for Determining the Important Properties of Microstrip Transmission Lines," *Marconi Review, 1974 (Fourth Quarter)*, pp. 210-216.

[34] Easter, B., "The Equivalent Circuit of Some Microstrip Discontinuities," *IEEE Trans., Vol. MTT-23*, 1975, pp. 655-660.

[35] Van Heuven, J.H.C., "Conduction and Radiation Losses in Microstrip," *IEEE Trans., Vol. MTT-22*, 1974, pp. 841-844.

Chapter 2
Microstrip Lines II :
Fullwave Analyses and Design Considerations

2.1 METHODS OF FULLWAVE ANALYSIS

As pointed out in Chapter 1, the microstrip configuration is not capable of supporting a pure TEM mode, and longitudinal components of both the electric and magnetic fields are present. The hybrid modes supported by the microstrip cannot be fully described in terms of static capacitances and inductances. Therefore, one has to introduce time varying electric and magnetic fields and solve the wave equation. Moreover, the charge density used in the electrostatic analyses becomes time varying and is replaced by the electric current density for fullwave analysis. Fullwave analysis is carried out for determining the propagation constant instead of the capacitance evaluated in quasi-static analysis.

Methods of studying wave propagation on microstrip without making any quasi-static assumption will now be discussed. These methods may be divided into two groups. In one group, the microstrip is considered with a rectangular enclosure, and the other group deals with open microstrip lines. This grouping becomes convenient since different types of mathematical tools are needed for handling closed and open geometries. For example, a Fourier series representation can be used to express the fields in a closed rectangular structure whereas a Fourier integral representation is suited for an open structure.

From the arguments given in Section 1.1.2, it can be seen that the microstrip modes cannot be pure TM or TE waves either. Longitudinal components of both the electric and the magnetic field are needed. These hybrid modes may be considered as superposition of TE and TM fields which may, in turn, be expressed in terms of two

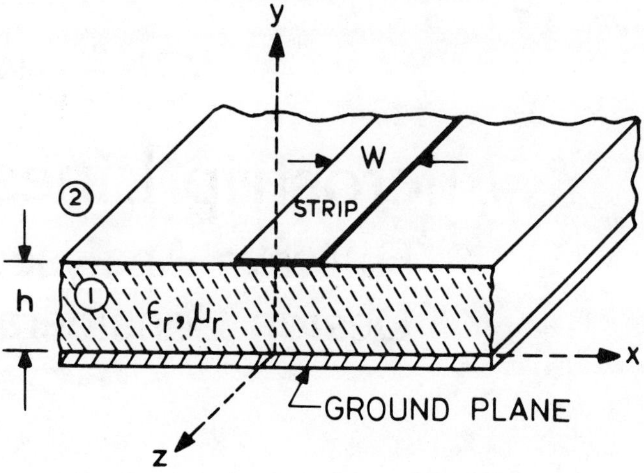

Figure 2.1 Open Microstrip Configuration

scalar potentials ψ^h and ψ^e, respectively. Referring to the microstrip configuration of Figure 2.1, the longitudinal and transverse components of the electric and magnetic fields may be written as

$$E_z = j\,[(k^2-\beta^2)/\beta]\ \psi^e(x,y)\exp(-j\beta z) \tag{2.1}$$

$$H_z = j\,[(k^2-\beta^2)/\beta]\ \psi^h(x,y)\exp(-j\beta z) \tag{2.2}$$

$$E_t = [\nabla_t\,\psi^e(x,y) - (\omega\mu/\beta)(\hat{z}\times\nabla_t)\,\psi^h(x,y)]\exp(-j\beta z) \tag{2.3}$$

$$H_t = [(\omega\epsilon/\beta)(\hat{z}\times\nabla_t)\,\psi^e(x,y) + \nabla_t\,\psi^h(x,y)]\exp(-j\beta z) \tag{2.4}$$

where β is the unknown propagation constant and $k = \omega(\epsilon_o\epsilon_r\mu_o)^{1/2}$. Subscript 't' refers to transverse coordinates (x, y), and $\hat{z}$ is a unit vector in the z-direction. These relations hold good for both the regions 1 and 2, shown in Figure 2.1, when a suitable value of ϵ_r is used in the wavenumber k. Appropriate expressions for ψ^e and ψ^h are chosen for regions 1 and 2. It has been assumed that the structure is lossless and the substrate is non-magnetic. The field representation of Equations (2.1) to (2.4) is valid for enclosed microstrip structure also.

The modes of propagation can be divided into two orthogonal sets of modes because the structure is symmetrical about the y-z plane. One of these sets has a symmetric E_z and an antisymmetric H_z component

($E_z$even-$H_z$odd), while the other set is designated as $E_z$odd-$H_z$even. The dominant mode is lowest order $E_z$even-$H_z$odd mode which approaches the quasi-TEM solution at low frequencies.

2.2 ANALYSIS OF OPEN MICROSTRIP

Fullwave analysis of an open microstrip may be carried out by using a Fourier transformation along the x-direction (parallel to the substrate and perpendicular to the strip). The two methods for analysis described in this section employ such a transformation and to that extent resemble the variational method in the Fourier transform domain used for quasi-static analysis of microstrip in Chapter 1.

As illustrated in the previous section, components of E and H fields are expressed in terms of two potentials ψ^h and ψ^e. Fourier transformation is taken along the x-direction. Solutions for the transforms of ψ^e and ψ^h are obtained by matching the boundary conditions in the transform domain. The interface condition in the y = h plane is written in terms of longitudinal and transverse electric currents on the strip conductor. The two methods described in this section differ mainly with regard to the manner in which the boundary conditions at the dielectric-air interface (y = h) are applied.

In the Fourier transform domain, potentials $\tilde{\psi}^e$ and $\tilde{\psi}^h$ may be written as

$$\tilde{\psi}_i^e(\alpha, y) = \int_{-\infty}^{\infty} \psi_i^e(x,y)\, e^{j\alpha x}\, dx \tag{2.5}$$

and a similar relation holds for $\tilde{\psi}_i^h$. The subscript i = 1,2 designates the regions 1 (substrate) and 2 (air), respectively. $\tilde{\psi}_i$'s satisfy the transformed wave equation which may be written as

$$(d^2/dy^2 - \gamma_i^2)\, \tilde{\psi}_i(\alpha, y) = 0 \tag{2.6}$$

where $\gamma_i^2 = \alpha^2 + \beta^2 - k_i^2 \qquad i = 1,2$

$$k_1^2 = \omega^2 \epsilon_r \mu_r \epsilon_o \mu_o; \quad k_2^2 = \omega^2 \epsilon_o \mu_o$$

The next step is to write expressions for $\tilde{\psi}_i$ in the two regions such that boundary conditions at y = 0 and at y → ∞ are satisfied. These expressions may be taken as

$$\tilde{\psi}_1^e(\alpha, y) = A(\alpha) \sinh(\gamma_1 y) \tag{2.7}$$

$$\tilde{\psi}_2^e(\alpha, y) = B(\alpha) \exp[-\gamma_2 (y-h)] \tag{2.8}$$

$$\tilde{\psi}_1^h(\alpha, y) = C(\alpha) \cosh(\gamma_1 y) \tag{2.9}$$

$$\tilde{\psi}_2^h(\alpha, y) = D(\alpha) \exp[-\gamma_2 (y-h)] \tag{2.10}$$

The coefficients A, B, C and D are to be determined by applying continuity conditions at the interface y = h. These conditions are

$$\tilde{E}_{z1}(\alpha, h) = \tilde{E}_{z2}(\alpha, h) \tag{2.11}$$

$$\tilde{E}_{x1}(\alpha, h) = \tilde{E}_{x2}(\alpha, h) \tag{2.12}$$

$$\tilde{H}_{z1}(\alpha, h) - \tilde{H}_{z2}(\alpha, h) = -\tilde{J}_x(\alpha) \tag{2.13}$$

$$\tilde{H}_{x1}(\alpha, h) - \tilde{H}_{x2}(\alpha, h) = \tilde{J}_z(\alpha) \tag{2.14}$$

where $\tilde{J}_x(\alpha)$ and $\tilde{J}_z(\alpha)$ are the Fourier transforms of the unknown current components on the strip, and the second subscript (1 or 2) indicates the regions 1 or 2. In addition, the boundary conditions to be satisfied on the strip may be written as

$$E_{z2}(x, h) = 0 \qquad |x| < W/2 \tag{2.15a}$$

$$(d/dy)\, H_{z2}(x, h) = 0 \qquad |x| < W/2 \tag{2.15b}$$

Two methods of analyzing open microstrip lines by using the abovementioned formulation will now be described. These methods differ because of the manner in which the boundary conditions (2.15) are applied. In one of the methods, called the integral equation method as given by Denlinger [1], boundary conditions (2.15) are applied in the space domain (x-y plane). In the other method, called Galerkin's method in FTD [2,3], the boundary conditions (2.15) are applied in the Fourier transform domain (α-y plane).

2.2.1 Integral Equation Method

Equations (2.7 - 2.15) lead to a set of coupled integral equations for the currents $\tilde{J}_x(\alpha)$ and $\tilde{J}_z(\alpha)$. These integral equations are derived to be [1]

$$I_{xo} \int_{-\infty}^{\infty} G_{11}(\alpha, \beta)\, \tilde{I}_x(\alpha) e^{-j\alpha x}\, d\alpha + I_{zo} \int_{-\infty}^{\infty} G_{12}(\alpha, \beta)\, \tilde{I}_z(\alpha) e^{-j\alpha x}\, d\alpha = 0 \tag{2.16a}$$

and

$$I_{xo} \int_{-\infty}^{\infty} G_{21}(\alpha,\beta)\, \tilde{I}_x(\alpha) e^{-j\alpha x}\, d\alpha + I_{zo} \int_{-\infty}^{\infty} G_{22}(\alpha,\beta)\, \tilde{I}_z(\alpha) e^{-j\alpha x}\, d\alpha = 0 \tag{2.16b}$$

where $-W/2 < x < W/2$, $\mu_r = 1$, $k_0 = k_2$,

$$G_{11}(\alpha,\beta) = \frac{1}{det}\left[F_1\, b_{22} + \frac{\alpha\beta}{k_1^2 - \beta^2}\, b_{12}\right] \tag{2.17}$$

$$G_{12}(\alpha,\beta) = b_{12}/det \tag{2.18}$$

$$G_{21}(\alpha,\beta) = \frac{\gamma_2}{det}\left[F_1\, b_{21} + \frac{\alpha\beta}{k_1^2 - \beta^2}\, b_{11}\right] \tag{2.19}$$

$$G_{22}(\alpha,\beta) = \gamma_2\, b_{11}/det \tag{2.20}$$

$$b_{11} = -b_{22} = j\alpha \left\{ \frac{k_0^2 - \beta^2}{k_1^2 - \beta^2} - 1 \right\} \tag{2.21}$$

$$b_{12} = \frac{\omega\mu_o\gamma_1}{\beta}\left[\frac{\gamma_2}{\gamma_1} + \frac{k_0^2 - \beta^2}{k_1^2 - \beta^2} \tanh \gamma_1 h\right] \tag{2.22}$$

$$b_{21} = \frac{\omega\epsilon_o\gamma_1}{\beta}\left[\frac{\gamma_2}{\gamma_1} + \epsilon_r \frac{k_2^2 - \beta^2}{k_1^2 - \beta^2} \coth \gamma_1 h\right] \tag{2.23}$$

$$det = b_{11} b_{22} - b_{12} b_{21} \tag{2.24}$$

$$F_1 = \omega\mu_o\gamma_1 \tanh(\gamma_1 h)/[j(k_0^2 - \beta^2)] \tag{2.25}$$

In deriving Equations (2.16), a one-term approximation has been used for unknown current distributions $\tilde{J}_x(\alpha)$ and $\tilde{J}_z(\alpha)$. These approximations are given below

$$\tilde{J}_x(\alpha) = I_{xo}\tilde{I}_x(\alpha) \tag{2.26a}$$

$$\tilde{J}_z(\alpha) = I_{zo}\tilde{I}_z(\alpha) \tag{2.26b}$$

It has been assumed that $\tilde{J}_x$ and $\tilde{J}_z$ have known forms, and the only unknowns in their representation are the amplitude coefficients I_{xo} and I_{zo}.

The unknown propagation constant β can now be solved by equating the determinant of the coefficient matrix for the unknowns I_{xo} and I_{zo} to zero.

The current distributions I_x and I_z, chosen by Denlinger [1], are

$$I_z(x) = \begin{cases} 1 + |2x/W|^3 & |x| \leqslant W/2 \\ 0 & \text{otherwise} \end{cases} \tag{2.27a}$$

$$I_x(x) = \begin{cases} \sin(\pi x/0.7W) & |x| \leqslant 0.8\,W/2 \\ \cos(\pi x/0.2W) & 0.8\,W/2 < |x| \leqslant W/2 \\ 0 & \text{otherwise} \end{cases} \tag{2.27b}$$

It may be pointed out that because of the one-term approximation used here, the results are critically dependent on the choice of the form of the current distribution. This is a disadvantage of the method discussed above.

A considerable simplification in the above analysis results from neglecting the transverse current component J_x. This is a good approximation when the strip width is small as compared to the wavelength (i.e., $W/\lambda_o < 0.1$) and when the lowest order mode is being considered. This approximation reduces the coupled pair of integral equations to a single integral equation containing β as a parameter. The computer time requirement is therefore considerably reduced.

The dispersion curves based on this method will be discussed along with the results of the second method described next.

2.2.2 Galerkin's Method in FTD [2,3]

In this method, formulation of the problem is similar to that in the above method but the boundary conditions on the strip, given by Equations (2.15), are now applied in FTD rather than in the space domain. In place of integral Equations (2.16), one now obtains:

$$G_{11}(\alpha,\beta)\,\tilde{J}_x(\alpha) + G_{12}(\alpha,\beta)\,\tilde{J}_z(\alpha) = \tilde{U}_1(\alpha) + \tilde{U}_2(\alpha) \tag{2.28a}$$

$$G_{21}(\alpha,\beta)\,\tilde{J}_x(\alpha) + G_{22}(\alpha,\beta)\,\tilde{J}_z(\alpha) = \tilde{V}_1(\alpha) + \tilde{V}_2(\alpha) \tag{2.28b}$$

where

$$\tilde{U}_1(\alpha) = \int_{-\infty}^{-W/2} u(x)e^{j\alpha x}\,dx;\ \tilde{U}_2(\alpha) = \int_{W/2}^{\infty} u(x)e^{j\alpha x}\,dx \tag{2.29}$$

$$\tilde{V}_1(\alpha) = \int_{-\infty}^{-W/2} v(x)e^{j\alpha x}\,dx;\ \tilde{V}_2(\alpha) = \int_{W/2}^{\infty} v(x)e^{j\alpha x}\,dx \tag{2.30}$$

Functions G_{11} etc. are defined in Equations (2.17 - 2.20) and $u(x)$, v(x) are defined by

$$E_{z2}(x,h) = \begin{cases} 0 & -W/2 < x < W/2 \\ j[(k_2{}^2 - \beta^2)/\beta]\, u(x) & \text{otherwise} \end{cases} \tag{2.31}$$

$$\frac{d}{dy} H_{z2}(x,h) = \begin{cases} 0 & -W/2 < x < W/2 \\ j[(k_2{}^2 - \beta^2)/\beta]\, v(x) & \text{otherwise} \end{cases} \tag{2.32}$$

Equations (2.28) are solved by the method of moments using Galerkin's approach. As a first step $\tilde{J}_x$ and $\tilde{J}_z$ are expanded in terms of known basis functions $\tilde{J}_{xn}$ and $\tilde{J}_{zn}$ as follows:

$$\tilde{J}_x(\alpha) = \sum_{n=1}^{M} c_n \tilde{J}_{xn}(\alpha) \;;\quad \tilde{J}_z(\alpha) = \sum_{n=1}^{N} d_n \tilde{J}_{zn}(\alpha) \tag{2.33}$$

The basis functions $\tilde{J}_{xn}(\alpha)$ and $\tilde{J}_{zn}(\alpha)$ are chosen such that their inverse Fourier transforms are nonzero only on the strip $-W/2 < x < W/2$. After substituting Equation (2.33) in Equations (2.28) and taking the inner product with the basis functions $\tilde{J}_{zn}$ and $\tilde{J}_{xn}$ for different values of n, we obtain the matrix equation

$$\sum_{n=1}^{M} K^{1,1}_{m,n}\, c_n + \sum_{n=1}^{N} K^{1,2}_{m,n}\, d_n = 0 \qquad m = 1, 2, \ldots, N \tag{2.34a}$$

$$\sum_{n=1}^{M} K^{2,1}_{m,n}\, c_n + \sum_{n=1}^{N} K^{2,2}_{m,n}\, d_n = 0 \qquad m = 1, 2, \ldots, M \tag{2.34b}$$

where

$$K^{1,1}_{m,n} = \int_{-\infty}^{\infty} \tilde{J}_{zm}(\alpha)\, G_{11}(\alpha,\beta)\, \tilde{J}_{xn}(\alpha)\, d\alpha \tag{2.35}$$

and similar relations hold for other $K_{m,n}$'s. The simultaneous Equations (2.34) are solved for the propagation constant β by setting the determinant of this set of equations equal to zero. In this method also, the results depend on the choice of basis functions and the values of M and N selected, and the accuracy of the results can be increased by selecting higher values of M and N.

Galerkin's method in FTD has several advantages as compared with the integral equation method discussed in the previous subsection:

(a) the method is simpler since the solution is extracted from algebraic equations and not from the coupled integral equations and (b) the physical nature of the mode for each solution can be easily recognized via the corresponding selection made for the basis functions.

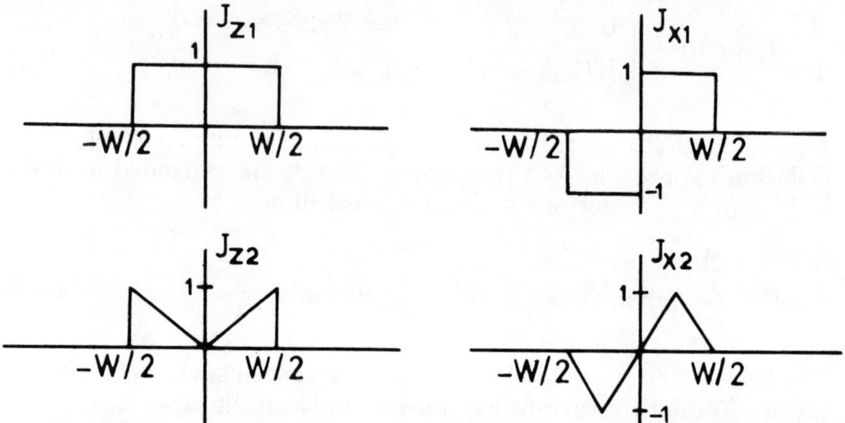

Figure 2.2(a) Basis Functions for Currents in Microstrip (used for Analysis by using Galerkin's Method in FTD)

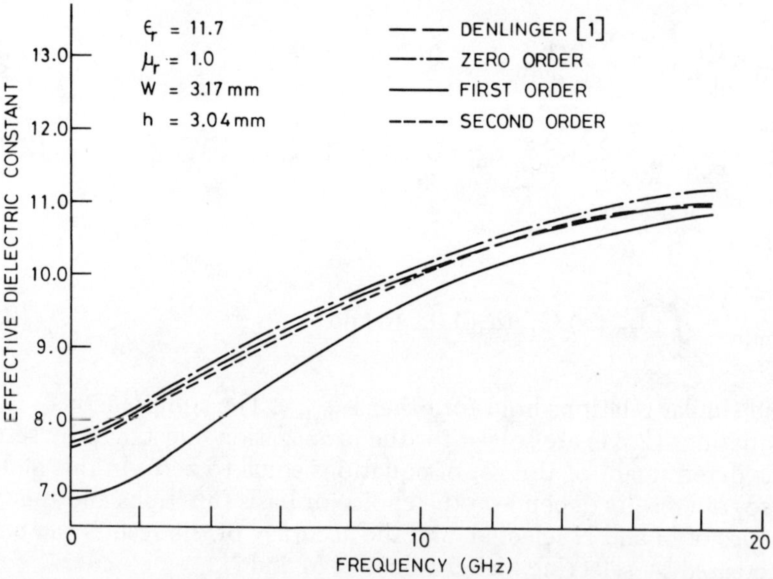

Figure 2.2(b) Variation of Effective Dielectric Constant with Frequency for an Open Microstrip (from [2])

2.2.3 Discussion of Results

The results for the effective dielectric constant found from Galerkin's method in FTD by considering two different sets of M and N are shown in Figure 2.2. The basis functions chosen are also shown in this figure. The results (effective dielectric constant versus frequency) are compared with Denlinger's results [1] based on the method described in Section 2.2.1. It may be noted that the first order solution (N=M=1) does not give satisfactory values since J_{x1} shown in Figure 2.2(a) is not a good choice for J_x.

Fullwave analysis of an open microstrip has been extended for the calculation of characteristic impedance by Knorr and Tufekcioglu [3]. Galerkin's approach in FTD, discussed in Section 2.2.2, is used for this computation.

When the transverse component of current is ignored, we can define characteristic impedance Z_{oi} as

$$Z_{oi} = 2P_{avg}/I_z^2 \tag{2.36}$$

where I_z is the total z-directed strip current. Average power is calculated as

$$P_{avg} = \tfrac{1}{2}\mathrm{Re} \iint (E_x H_y^* - E_y H_x^*)\, dx\, dy \tag{2.37}$$

This relation can be written in FTD by using Parseval's theorem as

$$P_{avg} = \frac{1}{4\pi}\, \mathrm{Re} \int_{-\infty}^{\infty}\int_{-\infty}^{\infty} [\tilde{E}_x(\alpha,y)\, \tilde{H}_y^*(\alpha,y) - \tilde{E}_y(\alpha,y)\, \tilde{H}_x^*(\alpha,y)]\; dy\, d\alpha \tag{2.38}$$

Integration with respect to y can be carried out analytically. This leaves an equation of the form

$$P_{avg} = \frac{1}{4\pi} \int_{-\infty}^{\infty} g(\alpha)\; d\alpha \tag{2.39}$$

which is evaluated numerically in each of the two regions.

As in case of waveguides, alternative definitions of characteristic impedance are possible. One can write

$$Z_{ov} = \frac{V^2(0)}{2\, P_{avg}} \tag{2.40}$$

where V(0) is given by

$$V(0) = -\int_0^h E_y(0, y)\, dy \tag{2.41}$$

and is the voltage between the center of the strip and the ground plane.

Results based on these two definitions are shown in Figure 2.3(a). The quasi-static value of impedance is also shown. We note that the impedance based on current (i.e., Z_{oi}) converges to quasi-static value whereas Z_{ov} does not. This is perhaps due to the fact that V(0) is a sensitive function of assumed current distribution whereas the total current used in Equation (2.36) is not.

Results in Figure 2.3(b) show that characteristic impedance increases with frequency. It may be added that for 1 mm thick substrate $h/\lambda_o = 0.4$ corresponds to 120 GHz, and over this frequency range impedance increases by about 16 percent of the quasi-static value.

The increase in the characteristic impedance with frequency can be interpreted qualitatively as follows. When frequency increases, the effective dielectric constant for the microstrip increases. This has been observed from the results based on fullwave analysis. An increase in the effective dielectric constant implies that the fields are getting concentrated below the strip which also amounts to a decrease in the effective width of the microstrip. The characteristic impedance of microstrip should decrease with the increase of ϵ_{re}. On the other hand, a decrease in effective strip width should increase the characteristic impedance. The fullwave analysis described above shows that the latter effect is more pronounced. The planar waveguide model discussed in Chapter 1 agrees with this interpretation.

2.3 ANALYSIS OF ENCLOSED MICROSTRIP

Four different methods of fullwave analysis for an enclosed microstrip structure have been illustrated in Figure 1.6 in the previous chapter. Of these, the finite difference method is conceptually the simplest. The other three methods involve formulation and solution of integral equations and are listed in the increasing order of their analytical complexity.

2.3.1 Finite Difference Methods

In this method the microstrip cross-section is divided into small rectangles by means of a rectangular net. Wave equations for ψ^e and ψ^h are solved for values of the potentials at the net points, and for

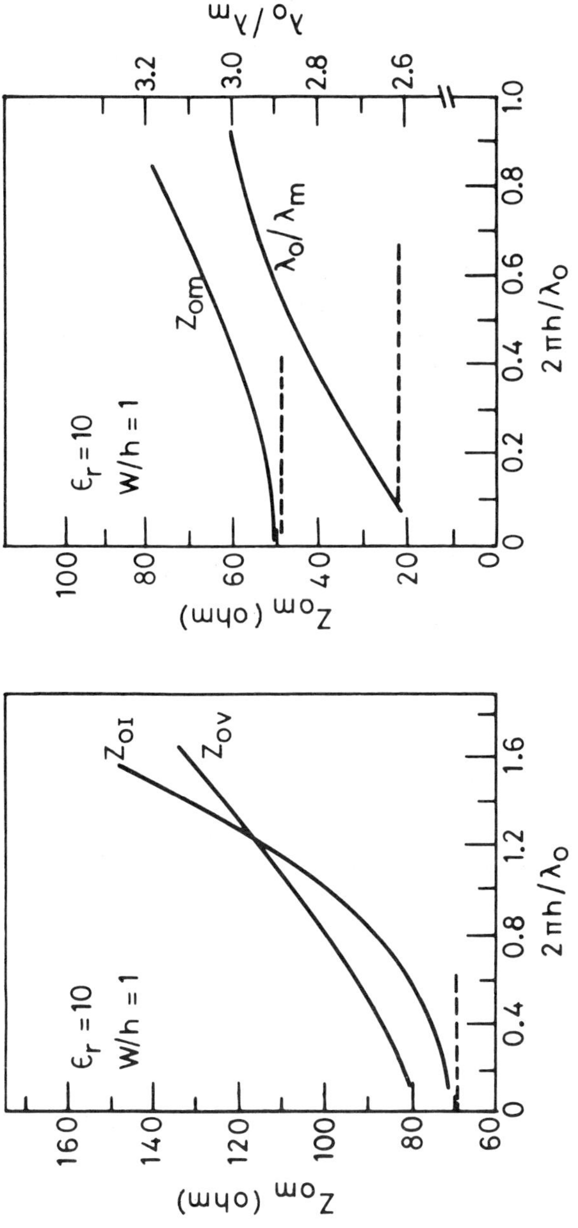

Figure 2.3 Variation of Microstrip Impedance and Wavelength with Frequency. Dotted lines (----) show Quasi-Static Values (from [3])

this purpose the wave equations for ψ^e and ψ^h may be written in finite difference form as [4]

$$\lambda\psi^e_{m,n} = 2(1+R^2)\,\psi^e_{m,n} - \psi^e_{m+1,n} - \psi^e_{m-1,n} - R^2\,\psi^e_{m,n+1} - R^2\,\psi^e_{m,n-1} \tag{2.42}$$

$$\lambda\psi^h_{m,n} = 2(1+R^2)\,\psi^h_{m,n} - \psi^h_{m+1,n} - \psi^h_{m-1,n} - R^2\,\psi^h_{m,n+1} - R^2\,\psi^h_{m,n-1} \tag{2.43}$$

where $\lambda = (k^2-\beta^2)(\Delta x)^2$, $\psi^e_{m,n} = \psi^e(m\Delta x, n\Delta y)$, $\psi^h_{m,n} = \psi^h(m\Delta x, n\Delta y)$ and $R = \Delta x/\Delta y$. Integers m and n in subscripts refer to the coordinates of the grid point. The configuration and the coordinate system are shown in Figure 2.4. After applying boundary and interface

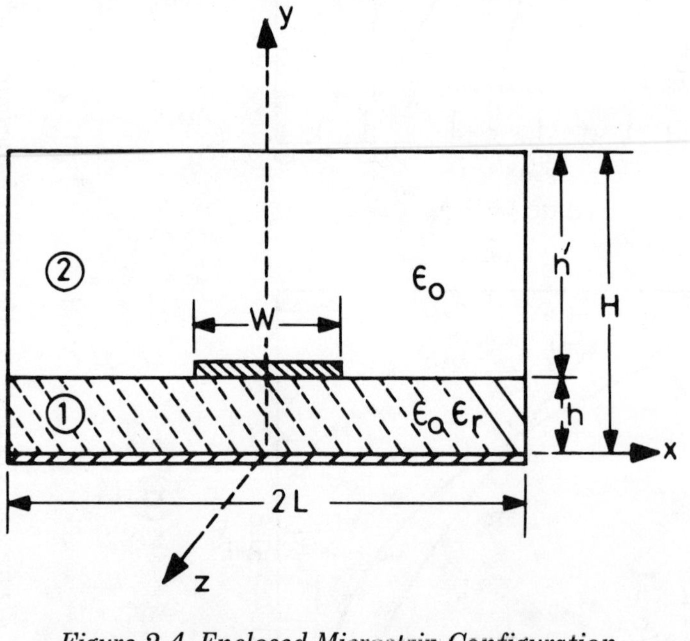

Figure 2.4 Enclosed Microstrip Configuration

conditions the finite difference Equations (2.42) and (2.43) may be written in the form of a matrix equation

$$[A]\,[\phi] = \lambda[\phi] \tag{2.44}$$

where [A] is the coefficient matrix, which is sparse and has the size

2(MN-1) by 2(MN-1) with $M\Delta x = L$ and $N\Delta y = H$ (as shown in Figure 2.4). Potentials $\psi^e_{m,n}$ and $\psi^h_{m,n}$ are elements of vector ϕ. It may be pointed out that λ has different values in regions 1 and 2.

There are several methods of solving Equation (2.44) and a discussion of these techniques is given in references [4] and [5]. It may be pointed out that the relaxation method used for quasi-static analysis becomes prohibitively slow in the present case. The method suitable in the present case has been described by Martin and Wilkinson [6]. Also, the matrix resulting from Equations (2.42) and (2.43) is asymmetric whereas efficient methods are available for the solution of symmetric matrix eigenvalue problems. A symmetric matrix can be obtained by the use of the variational method [5]. Another advantage of the variational method is that a graded mesh (with closer spacings near the strip and wider spacings near the enclosure walls) can be used. This allows the analysis of structures of realistic dimensions without prohibitively large computer storage requirements.

The derivation of a variational expression suitable for finite difference equations proceeds from a general variational formulation for an inhomogeneously filled structure. The general expression is obtained directly from Maxwell's curl equations [7] and can be written in terms of the longitudinal field components as

$$\iint \left[\frac{1}{\epsilon_r} \frac{1}{k_o^2} (\omega\epsilon_o\epsilon_r E_z \nabla_t^{\,2} E_z + \omega\mu_o H_z \nabla_t^2 H_z) + \omega\epsilon_o\epsilon_r E_z^2 + \omega\mu_o H_z^2 \right] dS = 0 \tag{2.45}$$

By application of the divergence theorem, one may obtain a variational expression for J as [5]

$$J = \iint_S \left\{ A\tau\, \epsilon_r |\nabla_t \psi^e|^2 + \tau |\nabla_t \psi^h|^2 + 2A\tau \left\{ \frac{\partial\psi^e}{\partial x}\frac{\partial\psi^h}{\partial y} - \frac{\partial\psi^h}{\partial x}\frac{\partial\psi^e}{\partial y} \right\} - k_o^2 \left[(\psi^h)^2 + A\epsilon_r (\psi^e)^2 \right] \right\} dS \tag{2.46}$$

where

$$\psi^h = H_z,\ \psi^e = \frac{\omega\epsilon_o}{\beta} E_z,\ \tau = \frac{\omega^2\mu_o\epsilon_o - \beta^2}{\omega^2\mu_o\epsilon_o\epsilon_r - \beta^2} \text{ and } A = (\beta c/\omega)^2.$$

Since Equation (2.46) does not involve derivatives higher than the first order, it can be put in finite difference form using the following formulas (refer to Figure 2.5 with $\Delta_1 = \Delta_2 = \Delta$).

$$\iint_S |\nabla_t \phi|^2 \, dS \simeq \left\{ \left[\frac{\phi_1 - \phi_0}{\Delta}\right]^2 + \left[\frac{\phi_2 - \phi_0}{\Delta}\right]^2 \right\} \frac{\Delta^2}{2} \qquad (2.47)$$

and

$$\iint_S \phi^2 \, dS \simeq \frac{1}{3} (\phi_0^2 + \phi_1^2 + \phi_2^2) \frac{\Delta^2}{2} \qquad (2.48)$$

where $\phi_0, \phi_1 \ldots$ represent values of potential ψ^e or ψ^h at points 0, 1, ... By the use of approximations described by Equations (2.47) and (2.48), it is possible to arrive at an approximation for the contribution from the elementary triangular region of Figure 2.5 to the

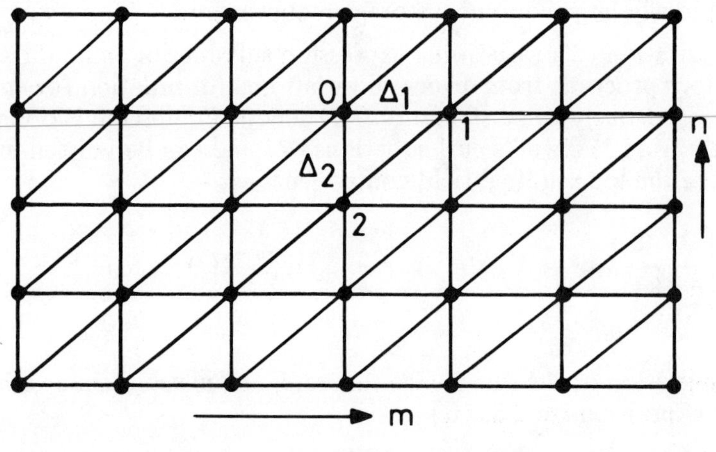

Figure 2.5 A Typical Region Within the Finite Difference Mesh

integral of Equation (2.46). The surface integral J of Equation (2.46) is then computed as the sum of such approximations for each elemental region in the structure. The stationary property of J is utilized after differentiating with respect to each of the variables $\psi_1^h, \psi_2^h, \ldots, \psi_i^h, \psi_1^e, \psi_2^e, \ldots \psi_i^e$. In this way N linear equations are derived for the system where N is the total number of variables ψ_i^h and ψ_i^e. These relations are put in form of a matrix Equation (2.44), which now becomes a symmetric band structured matrix. The solution of such a matrix may be arrived at in the following three steps: (i) [A] is reduced to tridiagonal form [8], (ii) the eigenvalues of the tridiagonal matrix are found by the method of bisection [9], and (iii) the eigenvector associated with a specific eigenvalue is found by the method of inverse iterations [10]. References [8-10] give details of these three steps.

A disadvantage of the finite difference method is the large size of the matrix to be handled and the resulting computer storage requirement.

Equation (2.46) can also be solved by the finite elements method in place of the finite difference method discussed above. Corr and Davies [5] have tried this technique and found that there are no advantages to be gained by the use of the finite elements method.

2.3.2 Integral Equation Methods [11-13]

The other group of methods for the fullwave analysis of enclosed microstrip uses integral equation formulation. The common features of these methods are as follows: Expressions for potentials ψ^e and ψ^h, in regions 1 and 2, are written in the form of series expansion such that the boundary conditions on the metallic periphery of the enclosure are satisifed. Also, since the main interest lies in the dominant mode which is $E_z$even-$H_z$odd, the total magnetic field is made to vanish at the plane of symmetry x = 0. The appropriate expressions are

$$\psi_1^e = \sum_{n=1}^{\infty} A_n^e \sinh \alpha_n^{(1)} y \cos k_n x \qquad (2.49)$$

$$\psi_2^e = \sum_{n=1}^{\infty} B_n^e \sinh \alpha_n^{(2)} (H-y) \cos k_n x \qquad (2.50)$$

$$\psi_1^h = \sum_{n=1}^{\infty} A_n^h \cosh \alpha_n^{(1)} y \sin k_n x \qquad (2.51)$$

$$\psi_2^h = \sum_{n=1}^{\infty} B_n^h \cosh \alpha_n^{(2)} (H-y) \sin k_n x \qquad (2.52)$$

where

$$k_n = [n-(1/2)]\pi/L \qquad (2.53)$$

$$\alpha_n^{(1)} = (k_n^2 + \beta^2 - \epsilon_r k_0^2)^{1/2} \qquad (2.54)$$

$$\alpha_n^{(2)} = (k_n^2 + \beta^2 - k_0^2)^{1/2} \qquad (2.55)$$

k_0 is the free space wavenumber, and the coefficients A_n's and B_n's are as yet unknown.

Interface conditions in the plane y = h are applied to the field components derived from Equations (2.49 - 2.52). This results in relations equating the series of infinite terms. These equations are converted to an infinite set of homogeneous simultaneous equations for coefficients A_n's and B_n's by taking scalar products with a complete set of functions appropriate to the various ranges of x. The resulting equations may be written either in terms of integral equations or in terms of a matrix equation and solved for β. The various methods differ in the manner in which the interface conditions are applied and in the method of solving resulting equations. Three such methods are discussed next.

i) Integral Equation Method [11]

This method by Zysman and Varon [11] is the straightforward implementation of the steps outlined above. Four mutually independent interface conditions at y = h are written as (Figure 2.4)

$$E_{x1} = E_{x2}, \quad 0 < |x| < L \tag{2.56}$$

$$E_{z1} = E_{z2}, \quad 0 < |x| < L \tag{2.57}$$

$$E_{x1} = 0, \quad 0 < |x| < W/2; \quad H_{x1} = H_{x2}, \quad W/2 < |x| < L \tag{2.58}$$

$$E_{z1} = 0, \quad 0 < |x| < W/2; \quad H_{z1} = H_{z2}, \quad W/2 < |x| < L \tag{2.59}$$

These conditions are now imposed on the field components derivable from Equations (2.49-2.52). One obtains a pair of coupled homogeneous Fredholm integral equations of first kind [11].

$$\sum_{n=1}^{\infty} [G_n^{(1)} \int_o^{W/2} h_1(\xi) \cos k_n \xi d\xi + G_n^{(2)} \int_{W/2}^{L} h_2(\xi) \sin k_n \xi d\xi] \sin k_n x = 0 \tag{2.60}$$

$$\sum_{n=1}^{\infty} [G_n^{(3)} \int_o^{W/2} h_1(\xi) \cos k_n \xi d\xi + G_n^{(4)} \int_{W/2}^{L} h_2(\xi) \sin k_n \xi d\xi] \cos k_n x = 0 \tag{2.61}$$

Here G_n's are known functions of β, and $h_1(\xi)$, $h_2(\xi)$ are unknown functions of ξ. These equations may be transformed into a matrix equation algorithm. The roots of the determinantal equation of the resulting matrix can be obtained numerically.

ii) Fourier Analysis Method [12]

This method differs from the previous one mainly in the manner in which the interface conditions at y = h are applied. The continuity condition on E_z for $0 < |x| < L$ is satisfied by choosing

$$(k_1^2 - \beta^2) A_n^e \sinh \alpha_n^{(1)} h = (k_2^2 - \beta^2) B_n^e \sinh \alpha_n^{(2)} (H-h) \qquad (2.62)$$

The remaining conditions are rewritten by constructing three functions F_1, F_2 and F_3 such that these functions are zero at y = h all across the width of the microstrip structure ($0 \leqslant |x| \leqslant L$). These functions may be written as

$$F_1(x) = (H_{z1} - H_{z2}) D(x) + (\partial H_{z1}/\partial y)[1 - D(x)] \qquad (2.63)$$

$$F_2(x) = (H_{y1} - H_{y2}) D(x) + (\partial H_{z2}/\partial y)[1 - D(x)] \qquad (2.64)$$

$$F_3(x) = (H_{x1} - H_{x2}) D(x) + E_z[1 - D(x)] \qquad (2.65)$$

where D(x) is a function which is zero on the strip ($0 \leqslant |x| \leqslant W/2$) and unity outside the strip ($W/2 < |x| \leqslant L$). The fact that F's are dimensionally incompatible is of no consequence since no physical significance is attached to these functions. The required interface conditions are met by constructing a complete set of functions and requiring each F to be orthogonal to every member of the set. A suitable complete set of functions may be chosen as sin $(m\pi x/L)$ and cos$(m\pi x/L)$, m = 0, 1, 2, . . . and the orthogonality condition is

$$\int_{-L}^{L} F_i(x) \begin{cases} \sin(m\pi x/L)dx \\ \cos(m\pi x/L)dx \end{cases} = 0 \qquad i = 1, 2, 3 \qquad (2.66)$$

In the actual computation the infinite series for ψ^e and ψ^h, given by Equations (2.49-2.52), are truncated at some finite value of n (say N). Substituting the expressions for F's into Equation (2.66) and performing the necessary differentiations and integrations, one obtains a homogeneous set of 3(N+1)/2 linear equations for the unknowns A_n^e, A_n^h and B_n^h. In order for a nontrivial solution to exist, the determinant of the coefficient matrix must vanish. Since this matrix is a known function of β, the dispersion relation can be solved by seeking the value of β that makes the determinant vanish. In actual calculation by Hornsby and Gopinath [12], N was chosen to be 10 and 20. The difference in results obtained for these two choices of N was found to be less than 2 percent.

iii) Singular Integral Equation Method [13]

This is a modification over the two integral equation methods discussed earlier. The motivation for the modification is to improve the computational efficiency; i.e., to reduce the size of matrix without sacrificing the accuracy of the results.

The key step in this method involves the transformation of the equations obtained by applying boundary conditions into an auxiliary set of equations that can be solved by methods used for solving singular integral equations. The use of singular integral equations in the solution of waveguide problems has been discussed in detail by Lewin [14]. The final result of this transformation is a determinantal equation which has the property of more rapid convergence as compared to the determinantal equation corresponding to the original set of equations.

When the determinantal equation obtained by this method is studied for suitable truncation size, it is found that a 2 by 2 size is adequate for commonly used values of parameters. The resulting equation is then solved for the wavenumber β as a function of the free-space wavenumber k_o. The final equation obtained by the application of this method is given in Appendix 2-A. Some of the results based on this method are discussed in Section 2.3.4.

2.3.3 Galerkin's Method in FTD

This method is similar to Galerkin's method in FTD used for open microstrip in Section 2.2.2. The bounded nature of the geometry (Figure 2.4) requires the use of the finite Fourier transform instead of the conventional Fourier transform over an infinite range. The latter type of transform was used for open microstrip analysis in Section 2.2.2 The transform used in the present analysis is defined as

$$\tilde{\psi}_i(\alpha_n, y) = \int_{-L}^{L} \psi_i(x, y) \exp(j\alpha_n x) \, dx \tag{2.67}$$

where $\alpha_n = (n-1/2)\pi/L$ for $E_z$even-$H_z$odd modes and $\alpha_n = (n\pi/L)$ for $E_z$odd-$H_z$even modes ($n = 1, 2, \ldots$). The next step is to transform all the field components and apply boundary and interface conditions in the transform domain. This leads to [15]:

$$G_{11}(\alpha_n, \beta) \, \tilde{J}_x(\alpha_n) + G_{12}(\alpha_n, \beta) \, \tilde{J}_z(\alpha_n) = K_z \tilde{E}_z(\alpha_n) \tag{2.68a}$$

$$G_{21}(\alpha_n, \beta) \, \tilde{J}_x(\alpha_n) + G_{22}(\alpha_n, \beta) \, \tilde{J}_z(\alpha_n) = K_x \tilde{E}_x(\alpha_n) \tag{2.68b}$$

where

$$G_{11} = G_{22} = \alpha_n \beta (\gamma_{n,2} \tanh \gamma_{n,2} h' + \gamma_{n,1} \tanh \gamma_{n,1} h)/\det \qquad (2.69a)$$

$$G_{12} = [(\epsilon_r k_o^2 - \beta^2)\gamma_{n,2} \tanh \gamma_{n,2} h' + (k_o^2 - \beta^2)\gamma_{n,1} \tanh \gamma_{n,1} h]/\det \qquad (2.69b)$$

$$G_{21} = [(\epsilon_r k_o^2 - \alpha_n^2)\gamma_{n,2} \tanh \gamma_{n,2} h' + (k_o^2 - \alpha_n^2)\gamma_{n,1} \tanh \gamma_{n,1} h]/\det \qquad (2.69c)$$

$$\det = (\gamma_{n,1} \tanh \gamma_{n,1} h + \epsilon_r \gamma_{n,2} \tanh \gamma_{n,2} h')(\gamma_{n,1} \coth \gamma_{n,1} h + \gamma_{n,2} \coth \gamma_{n,2} h') \qquad (2.69d)$$

and K_z and K_x are known constants. Also

$\gamma_{n,1}^2 = \alpha_n^2 + \beta^2 - k_o^2\, \epsilon_r$ and $\gamma_{n,2}^2 = \alpha_n^2 + \beta^2 - k_o^2$ and $h' = H - h$

$\tilde{J}_x(\alpha_n)$ and $\tilde{J}_z(\alpha_n)$ represent transforms of strip currents $J_x(x)$ and $J_z(x)$, respectively, and $\tilde{E}_z(\alpha_n)$ and $\tilde{E}_x(\alpha_n)$ are transforms of electric field components in the plane $y = h$. The electric field components are unknown for $W/2 < |x| < L$, though they are zero on the strip. These two unknowns are eliminated by applying Galerkin's method. For this purpose, currents are written in terms of known basis functions $\tilde{J}_{xm}$ and $\tilde{J}_{zm}$ as:

$$\tilde{J}_x(\alpha_n) = \sum_{m=1}^{M} c_m \tilde{J}_{xm}(\alpha_n) \qquad (2.70a)$$

$$\tilde{J}_z(\alpha_n) = \sum_{m=1}^{N} d_m \tilde{J}_{zm}(\alpha_n) \qquad (2.70b)$$

where c_m and d_m are unknown coefficients. These expressions for currents are substituted in Equations (2.68). Taking inner products of both sides of Equations (2.68) with the basis functions $\tilde{J}_{zi}$ and $\tilde{J}_{xi}$ for different values of i, one obtains

$$\sum_{m=1}^{M} K_{im}^{1,1} c_m + \sum_{m=1}^{N} K_{im}^{1,2} d_m = 0 \quad i = 1, 2, \ldots N \qquad (2.71a)$$

$$\sum_{m=1}^{M} K_{im}^{2,1} c_m + \sum_{m=1}^{N} K_{im}^{2,2} d_m = 0 \quad i = 1, 2, \ldots M \qquad (2.71b)$$

The coefficients K_{im}, obtained by inner products, are written as

$$K_{im}^{1,1} = \sum_{n=1}^{\infty} \tilde{J}_{zi}(\alpha_n)\, G(\alpha_n, \beta)\, \tilde{J}_{xm}(\alpha_n), \text{ etc.} \tag{2.72}$$

It is seen that the right-hand sides of Equations (2.68) are eliminated through the use of Parseval's theorem, because the currents $J_{zi}(x)$, $J_{xi}(x)$ and the field components $E_z(x,h)$, $E_x(x,h)$ are zero in the complementary regions of x.

The simultaneous Equations (2.71) are solved for the propagation constant β at each frequency ω by setting the determinant of the coefficient matrix equal to zero and by seeking the root of the resulting equation. The dispersion characteristics of microstrip are derived from the values of β.

The choice of the basis functions is important for the numerical efficiency of the method. The accuracy can be improved systematically by increasing the number of basis functions M or N. However, if the first few basis functions approximate the actual unknown current reasonably well, the necessary size of the matrix can be held small for a given accuracy of the solution. For the dominant mode, the following forms for J_{z1} and J_{x1} are suitable

$$J_{z1}(x) = \begin{cases} \dfrac{1}{W}\left[1 + \left|\dfrac{2x}{W}\right|^3\right] & |x| \leqslant W/2 \\ 0 & W/2 < |x| < L \end{cases} \tag{2.73}$$

$$J_{x1}(x) = \begin{cases} \dfrac{2}{W}\sin\dfrac{2\pi x}{W} & |x| \leqslant W/2 \\ 0 & W/2 < |x| < L \end{cases} \tag{2.74}$$

The Fourier transforms of the above current distributions are given by

$$\tilde{J}_{z1}(\alpha_n) = \frac{2\sin(\alpha_n W/2)}{\alpha_n W/2} + \frac{3}{(\alpha_n W/2)^3}\left\{\cos(k_n W/2) - \frac{2\sin(\alpha_n W/2)}{\alpha_n W/2} + \frac{2[1-\cos(\alpha_n W/2)]}{(\alpha_n W/2)^2}\right\} \tag{2.75}$$

and

$$\widetilde{J}_{x1}(\alpha_n) = \frac{2\pi \sin(\alpha_n W/2)}{(\alpha_n W/2)^2 - \pi^2} \tag{2.76}$$

Results based on this analysis [15] have been compared with the results of singular integral equation method discussed earlier, and the agreement is good.

2.3.4 Discussion of Results

Methods for fullwave analysis of microstrip provide information about two aspects of wave propagation along microstrip, namely, dispersion and higher order modes. Main features of these results are discussed in this section.

i) Dispersion

Information regarding the dispersive nature of propagation in a microstrip can be expressed in different ways. Figures (2.6) and (2.7) indicate two ways of representing dispersion. In Figure (2.6) frequency

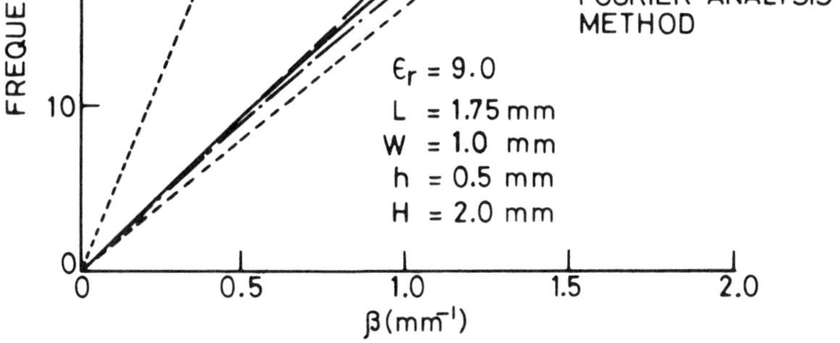

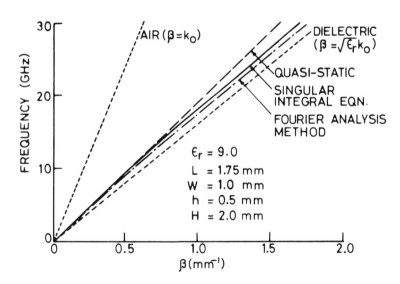

Figure 2.6 Dispersion Behavior of Microstrip as Computed by Different Methods (from [13])

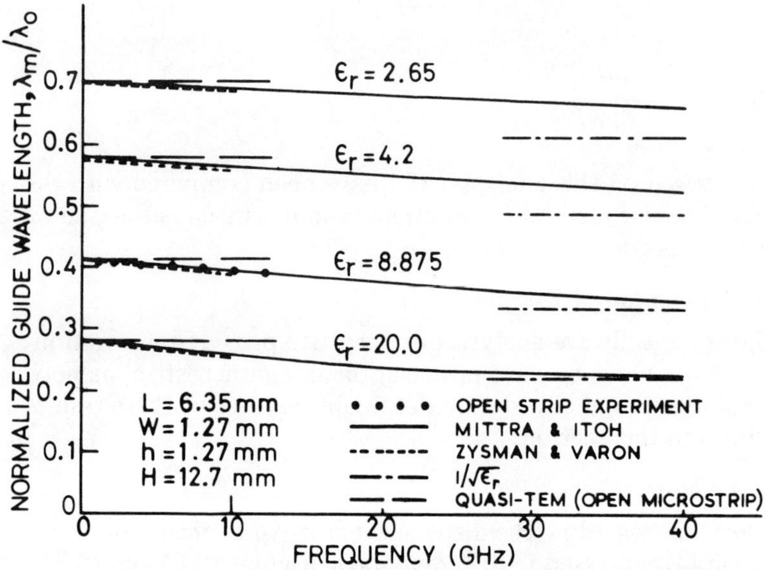

Figure 2.7 Variation of Microstrip Guide Wavelength with Frequency (from [13])

is plotted against phase constant β leading to the traditional ω-β diagram. This figure also includes a ω-β curve based on quasi-static analysis (which is a straight line). Results of fullwave analysis based on two different methods are shown. These two curves are not straight but lie between the two straight lines, one corresponding to quasi-static analysis and the other for a homogeneously filled line. At lower frequencies (less than 5 GHz) results given by both the methods coincide with quasi-static results.

Figure (2.7) presents the same results in a different manner. Here normalized guide wavelength λ_m/λ_o is plotted as a function of frequency. Two different methods (the integral equation method and the singular integral equation method) are compared. Experimental results for open microstrip are also included. It is observed that λ_m/λ_o decreases with an increase in frequency and tends to $1/\sqrt{\epsilon_r}$. It implies that at higher frequencies more and more energy propagates inside the substrate and below the strip.

ii) Higher Order Modes

Plotting the ω-β diagram for higher order modes requires considerable computation time. Thus only limited results are available.

The singular integral equation method has been used for investigation of higher order modes [13]. The results for a substrate dielectric constant of 8.875 (alumina) are shown in Figure 2.8. Similar results are

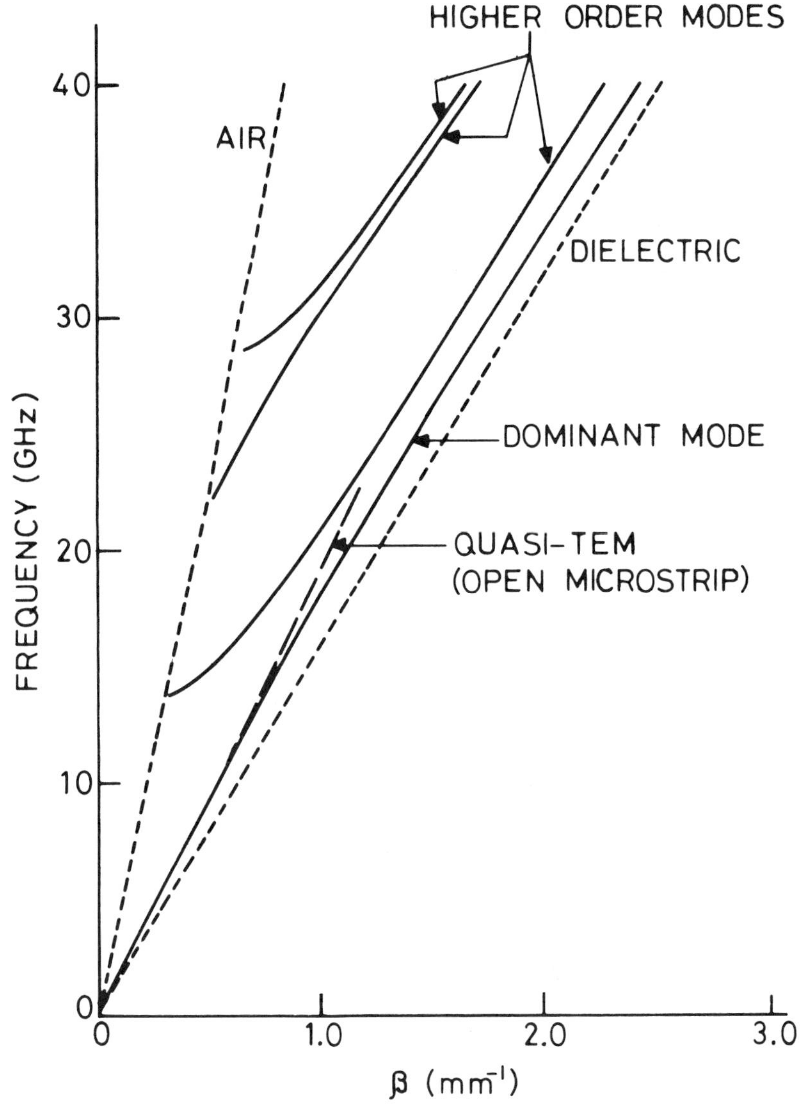

Figure 2.8 Higher Order Modes in a Microstrip (Computed by Using Singular Integral Equation Method) $\epsilon_r = 8.875$, *L = 6.35 mm, W = 1.27 mm, h = 1.27 mm and H = 12.7 mm (from [13])*

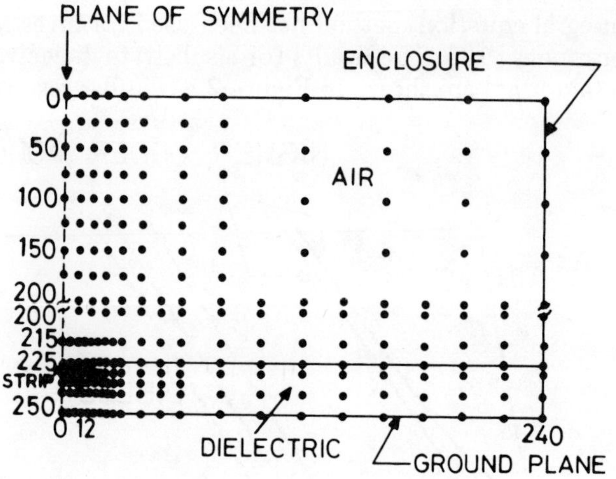

(a)

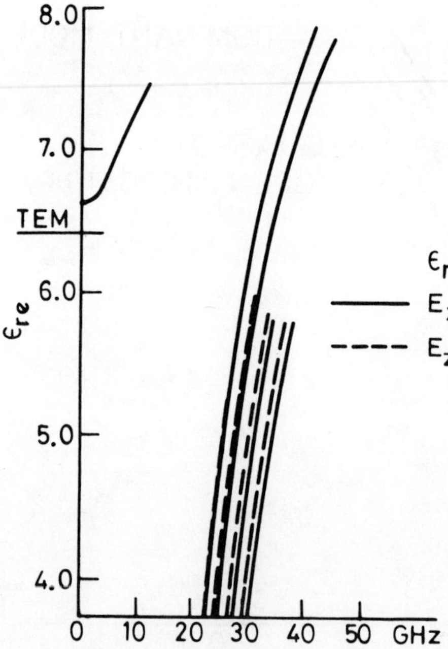

(b)

Figure 2.9(a) Mesh Points for Microstrip Anaysis by Using Finite Difference Method. Scale 1 unit = 0.002 inch, (b) Higher Order Modes, Computed by Using Finite Difference Method (from [5])

available [13] for three other dielectric constant values (2.62, 4.2 and 20.0). The existence of a number of higher order modes is evident in these plots. It should be noted that this mode spectrum is not complete since only the $E_z$even-$H_z$odd type of modes are shown. Comparison with similar curves for other values of ϵ_r indicates that the frequency at which the first higher order mode begins to appear is lower for higher values of ϵ_r.

Dispersion curves for higher order modes have also been calculated by Corr and Davies [5] using the finite difference method discussed earlier. Their results are presented in Figure 2.9(b) for the microstrip configuration shown in Figure 2.9(a). This plot includes $E_z$odd-$H_z$even type of modes also. It is seen that the dispersion curves tend to group in pairs of $E_z$even and $E_z$odd modes of the same order. The difference between the static limiting value of ϵ_{re} for the lowest mode and the TEM value is attributed entirely to discretization errors in the finite difference method.

Higher order microstrip modes have been compared with LSM and LSE modes of the slab line structure formed by the removal of the microstrip conductor [5]. A very close similarity between the power density distributions of $E_z$odd and LSM modes is noted. Also higher order $E_z$even and $E_z$odd modes have very similar power density distributions. It is concluded that because the plane of symmetry makes so little difference to the higher order modes with the same subscript, these modes are strongly associated not with the strip, but with the dielectric-air interface. In view of their close similarity to the LSM modes, they can be considered as distorted LSM modes. The specific type of mode correspondences may be grouped together. Using the notation E for $E_z$even and M for $E_z$odd modes, it can be said that modes E_1, M_1 and LSM_{12} are similar, modes E_2, M_2 and LSM_{14} are similar and so on. Thus, for enclosed microstrip the approximate cut-off frequency for higher order modes may be obtained from the cut-off frequency of LSM modes.

Considerable information about higher order modes can also be obtained from the planar waveguide model for microstrip discussed in Chapter 1. Cut-off frequencies and guide wavelengths for various modes are given by Equations (1.65) and (1.66), respectively.

2.4 DESIGN CONSIDERATIONS

In this section various important design parameters of microstrip lines are discussed. These include attenuation constant, power handling capability, effect of tolerances and dielectric anisotropy. Various expressions, useful for microstrip design, are summarized in the last subsection.

2.4.1 Microstrip Losses

Attenuation in a microstrip structure is caused by two loss components: conductor loss and dielectric loss. If a magnetic substrate is used, a magnetic loss component will also be present. We will discuss losses for nonmagnetic substrates in this subsection.

Conductor Loss

A comprehensive treatment of conductor loss in microstrip structure is given by Pucel *et. al.* [16] and by Schneider [17]. Both of these analyses are based on the "incremental inductance rule" of Wheeler [18]. In this method the series surface resistance R per unit length is expressed in terms of that part of the total inductance per unit length which is attributable to the skin effect, i.e., the inductance L_i produced by the magnetic field within the conductors.

It is well known that for a conductor the surface impedance, Z_s (=R + jX), has a real part R (surface resistance per unit length) which is equal to the imaginary part X. That is

$$R = X = \omega L_i \tag{2.77}$$

According to Wheeler, L_i can be found from the external inductance L per unit length. L_i is obtained as the incremental increase in L caused by an incremental recession of all metallic walls due to skin effect. This situation is shown in Figure 2.10. The amount of recession is

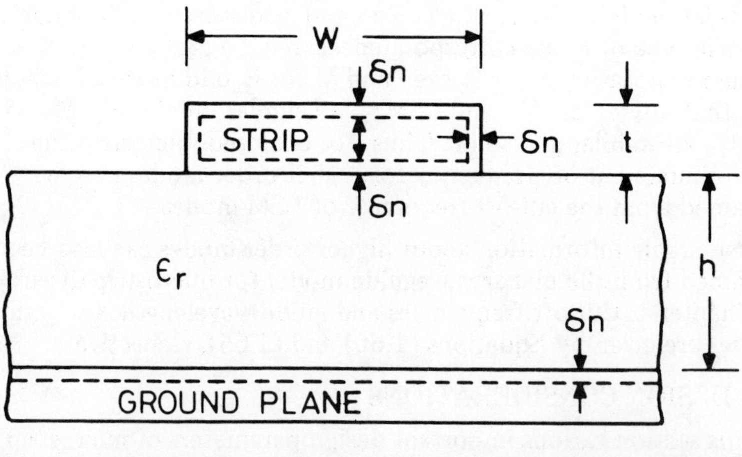

Figure 2.10 Recession of Conducting Walls of Microstrip for Loss Calculation Using 'Incremental Inductance Rule'

equal to half the skin depth $\delta = (2/\omega\mu\sigma_c)^{1/2}$. An assumption underlying this rule is that the radius of curvature and the thickness of the conductors exposed to the electromagnetic fields be greater than skin depth, preferably several skin depths. According to Wheeler [18], we have

$$L_i = \sum_m \frac{\mu_m}{\mu_o} \frac{\partial L}{\partial n_m} \frac{\delta_m}{2} \quad (2.78)$$

$$R = \sum_m \frac{R_{sm}}{\mu_o} \frac{\partial L}{\partial n_m} \quad (2.79)$$

where $\partial L/\partial n_m$ denotes the derivative of L with respect to incremental recession of wall m, n_m is the normal direction to this wall, and $R_{sm} = \omega\mu_m \delta_m/2$ the surface resistance of the wall m.

The attenuation constant because of conductor (ohmic) loss is defined as

$$\alpha_c \simeq \frac{P_c}{2P(z)} = \frac{\text{Power loss in conductors}}{2\,(\text{Power transmitted})} \quad \text{(nepers/unit length)} \quad (2.80)$$

In terms of R and Z_{om} (characteristic impedance), α_c may be written as

$$\alpha_c = \frac{|I|^2 R}{2\,|I|^2 Z_{om}} = \frac{1}{2\mu_o Z_{om}} \sum_m R_{sm} \frac{\partial L}{\partial n_m} \quad (2.81)$$

Inductance L of the microstrip structure can be expressed in terms of the characteristic impedance for the microstrip with the substrate replaced by air (Z_{om}^a) and is given as

$$L = Z_{om}^a/c \quad (2.82)$$

where c is the velocity of electromagnetic waves in free space.

Wheeler's incremental inductance rule requires the thickness of conductors to be greater than about four times the skin depth. The effect of using smaller thicknesses has also been reported [19-21]. It is observed that the conductor losses are reduced by about 9 percent when the conductor thickness is $\pi/2$ times the skin depth.

Expression for attenuation constant based on Equation (2.81) is presented later in subsection 2.4.5 where all other design information is also summarized.

Dielectric Loss

For a uniformly filled transmission line the dielectric loss α_{du} is independent of the geometry of the line and may be written as

$$\alpha_{du} = \frac{gZ_o}{2} = \frac{\omega}{2}\sqrt{\frac{\mu}{\epsilon'}}\,\epsilon'' = \frac{\omega}{2}\sqrt{\mu\epsilon'}\tan\delta \tag{2.83}$$

where g is the shunt conductance per unit length of the line, ϵ' is the real part and ϵ'' is the imaginary part of the permittivity of the dielectric. However, when the dielectric is not uniform over the cross-section of the line, the above expression does not apply. Calculation of loss for the mixed dielectric case has been considered by Welch and Pratt [19] and by Schneider [22]. In both of these analyses, an effective loss tangent $(\tan\delta)_e$ is derived. The results obtained in these two analyses can be shown to be identical when the difference in the definition of filling factor q in the two cases is taken into account.

When the upper dielectric (air) is assumed to be lossless, the following expression for α_d (attenuation constant considering mixed dielectrics) is obtained [19]

$$\begin{aligned}\alpha_d &= \frac{\omega}{2}\sqrt{\mu\epsilon_{re}}\,(\tan\delta)_e \\ &= \frac{\omega}{2}\sqrt{\mu\epsilon_{re}}\,\frac{\sigma_e}{\omega\epsilon_{re}}\end{aligned} \tag{2.84}$$

If σ is the conductivity of the dielectric and σ_o the conductivity of air, we can write

$$\sigma_e = q\sigma + (1-q)\,\sigma_o \simeq q\sigma \qquad (\text{since } \sigma_o \ll \sigma)$$

Also,

$$\epsilon_o\,\epsilon_{re} = q\epsilon + (1-q)\,\epsilon_o \qquad \text{with } \epsilon = \epsilon_o\epsilon_r$$

Therefore, Equation (2.84) becomes

$$\alpha_d = q\left\{\frac{\epsilon}{q\epsilon+(1-q)\epsilon_o}\right\}^{1/2}\alpha_{du} = \left(\frac{\epsilon_r}{\epsilon_{re}}\right)^{1/2} q\alpha_{du} \tag{2.85}$$

where q is the dielectric filling fraction (see Section 1.2.1), and α_{du} is the attenuation constant for a line uniformly filled with the dielectric ϵ_r, given by Equation (2.83). Since,

$$q = \frac{\partial \epsilon_{re}}{\partial \epsilon_r} = \frac{\epsilon_{re} - 1}{\epsilon_r - 1}$$

the attenuation constant α_d may be written as

$$\alpha_d = 27.3 \frac{\epsilon_r}{\sqrt{\epsilon_{re}}} \frac{\epsilon_{re} - 1}{\epsilon_r - 1} \frac{\tan \delta}{\lambda_o} \text{ dB/unit length} \tag{2.86}$$

For microstrip lines on alumina substrate the dielectric loss α_d is negligible compared to the total loss α. But for microstrip lines utilizing semiconductor substrates such as Si, the dielectric loss factor is dominant. For example, a 50 ohm line on silicon substrate ($\epsilon_r = 11.7$) with a resistivity of 10^3 ohm-cm has a dielectric loss of the order of 0.36 dB/cm while conductor loss is about 0.19 dB/cm [19]. For these substrates the dielectric conductivity σ is non-zero. In this case Equation (2.86) can be used with some modification; the final expression is given below [19]

$$\alpha_d = 4.34 \frac{1}{\sqrt{\epsilon_{re}}} \frac{\epsilon_{re} - 1}{\epsilon_r - 1} \left(\frac{\mu_o}{\epsilon_o}\right)^{1/2} \sigma \quad \text{dB/unit length} \tag{2.87}$$

Dielectric loss in a microstrip has also been computed numerically using the moment method [23]. In this case α_d is written as

$$\alpha_d = \frac{\frac{\sigma}{2} \int E^2 \cdot ds}{2P} = \frac{\sigma \int E^2\, ds}{2V^2/Z_{om}} \tag{2.88}$$

Equations (2.86) and (2.87) give a value of α_d which is about 1 percent higher than that predicted by the numerical method of Simpson and Tseng [23]. Values of the conductor and the dielectric losses per unit length in 50 ohm microstrip lines on various substrates have been calculated using results given in [24] and are shown in Figure 2.11 as functions of frequency. Attenuation for lines on quartz substrate has been discussed by Van Heuven [25].

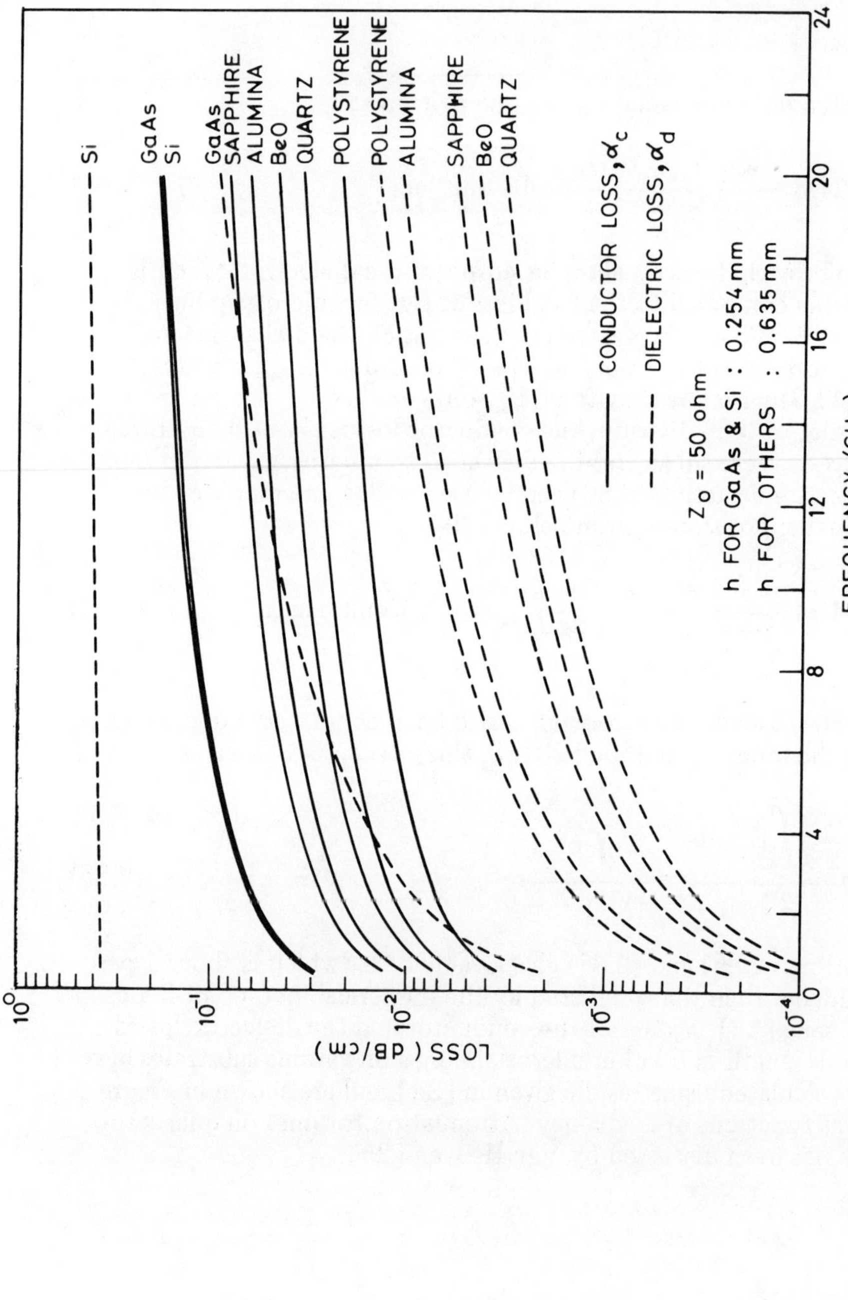

Figure 2.11 Conductor and Dielectric Losses as Functions of Frequency for Microstrip Lines on Various Substrates

2.4.2 Power Handling Capability [26]

There is a widespread impression that microstrip lines are suitable only for low power components. Although, microstrip lines are not as well suited for high power applications such as waveguides or coaxial lines of comparable cross-sections, they could certainly be used for several medium power applications. A 50 ohm microstrip on 25 mil thick alumina substrate can handle a few kilowatts of power.

The power handling capability of a microstrip, like that of any other dielectric filled transmission line, is limited by heating caused because of ohmic and dielectric losses and by dielectric breakdown. Increase in temperature due to conductor and dielectric losses limits the average power of the microstrip line, while the breakdown between the strip conductor and ground plane limits the peak power.

Average Power

The average power handling capability (APHC) of microstrip is determined by the temperature rise of the strip conductor and the supporting substrate. The parameters which play major roles in the calculation of average power capability are: (i) transmission line losses, (ii) thermal conductivity of the substrate material, (iii) surface area of the strip conductor, and (iv) ambient temperature; i.e. temperature of the medium surrounding the microstrip. Therefore, dielectric substrates with low loss tangent and large thermal conductivity will increase the average power capability of microstrip lines.

The rise of the temperature of the strip conductor can be calculated from heat flow field in the cross-section. An analogy between the heat flow field and the electric field is described in Table 2.1. The heat generated by the conductor loss and the dielectric loss is discussed separately in the following paragraphs.

Density of Heat Flow Due to Conductor Loss

Loss of electromagnetic power in the strip conductor generates heat in the strip. Because of the good heat conductivity of the strip metal, heat generation is uniform along the width of the conductor.
Since the ground plane is held at ambient temperature (i.e. acts as a heat sink), this heat flows from the strip conductor to the ground plane through the substrate. The heat flow can be calculated by considering analogous electric field distribution. The heat flow field in the microstrip structure corresponds to the electrostatic field (without any dispersion) of the microstrip. From Figure 1.4 we note that

the electric field lines (the thermal field in the case of heat flow) spread near the ground plane.

Table 2.1 Analogy between heat flow field and electric field

Heat Flow Field	Electric Field
1. Temperature, T (°C)	Potential, V (volt)
2. Temperature gradient, T_g (°C/m)	Electric field, E (V/m)
3. Heat flow rate, Q (watt)	Flux, ϕ (coulomb)
4. Density of heat flow, q (watt/m^2)	Flux density, D (columb/m^2)
5. Thermal conductivity, K (watt/m/°C)	Permittivity, ϵ (coulomb/m/volt)
6. Density of heat generated, ρ_h (watt/m^3)	Charge density, ρ (coulomb/m^3)
7. $q = -K\nabla T$	$D = -\epsilon\nabla V$
8. $\nabla \cdot q = \rho_h$	$\nabla \cdot D = \rho$

In order to account for the increase in area normal to heat flow lines, the parallel plate model of microstrip is used. For these calculations ϵ_r (in electrical analogue) is taken equal to the ratio of the thermal conductivity of the substrate (Table 2.2) to that of the air. The equivalent width of the strip (W_e) in the parallel plate model is calculated from the electrical analogue as

$$W_e = \frac{120\,\pi h}{Z'_{om}\sqrt{\epsilon'_{re}}} \tag{2.89a}$$

where h is the thickness of the substrate and Z'_{om} is the characteristic impedance of the microstrip (in ohms). Microstrip parameters Z'_{om} and ϵ'_{re} are calculated with ϵ_r replaced by K_d/K_a (the ratio of thermal conductivity of the dielectric to that of the air). When the impedance of a microstrip with air as the dielectric is written as

Table 2.2 Properties of Various Dielectric Substrates

Material	ϵ_r	Loss tangent at 10 GHz	K W/cm/°C	Dielectric strength KV/cm
Sapphire	11.7	10^{-4}	0.4	4×10^3
Alumina	9.7	2×10^{-4}	0.3	4×10^3
Quartz (fused)	3.8	10^{-4}	0.01	10×10^3
Polystyrene	2.53	4.7×10^{-4}	0.0015	280
Beryllium oxide (Be0)	6.6	10^{-4}	2.5	—
GaAs ($\rho=10^7$ Ω–cm)	12.3	16×10^{-4}	0.3	350
Si ($\rho=10^3$ Ω–cm)	11.7	50×10^{-4}	0.9	300
Air	1	$\simeq 0$	0.00024	30

Z^a_{om} $(= Z'_{om}\sqrt{\epsilon'_{re}})$, Equation (2.89a) becomes

$$W_e = \frac{120\,\pi h}{Z^a_{om}} \tag{2.89b}$$

Consider a unit length of the line. The power absorbed (ΔP) in the line, due to conductor loss in the strip when one watt of power is incident, is given by

$$\Delta P = 0.2303\,\alpha_c \quad \text{(Watts/m)} \tag{2.90}$$

where α_c (dB/m), the attenuation coefficient due to loss in the strip conductor is assumed small. The density of heat flow, due to the conductor loss may be written as

$$q_c = \frac{0.2303\,\alpha_c \ \text{(Watt/m}^2\text{)}}{W_e} \tag{2.91}$$

Density of Heat Flow Due to Dielectric Loss

In addition to the conductor loss, heat is generated by dielectric loss in the substrate. The density of the heat generated is proportional to the square of the electric field. However, we can consider a parallel plate model wherein the electric field is uniform and the density of the heat generated can also be considered uniform. This assumption ignores the increased dielectric loss in regions of high electric field near the strip edges. However, as the dielectric loss is a small fraction of total loss (except for semiconductor substrates like Si) the above assumption should hold. The effective width for this parallel plate model depends on the spread of electric field lines and is a function of frequency. The effective width, $W_{eff}(f)$, is given by [27, 28],

$$W_{eff}(f) = W + \frac{W_{eff}(0) - W}{1 + (f/f_p)^2} \tag{2.92}$$

where

$$f_p = \frac{Z_{om}}{2\mu_o h}$$

and $W_{eff}(0)$ is equal to W_e of Equations (2.89). μ_o is the permeability of free space, ϵ_{re} is the static value of effective dielectric constant [29], and Z_{om} is the characteristic impedance of microstrip (in ohms).

The heat flow in the y-direction caused by a sheet of heat sources can be evaluated by considering the configuration in Figure 2.12.

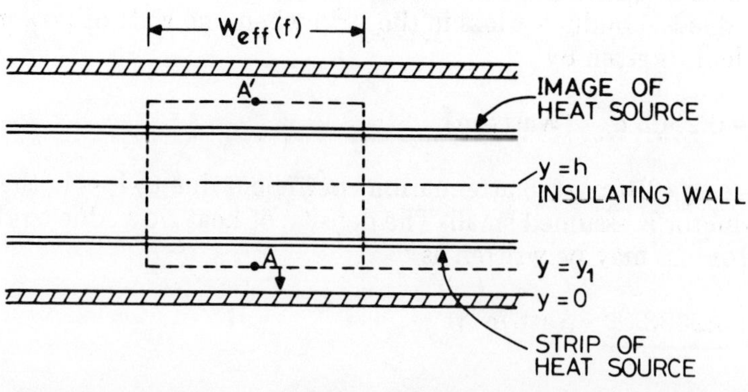

Figure 2.12 Geometry for Calculating the Density of Heat Flow Due to Dielectric Loss in Microstrip Lines

The heat conducted away by air is negligible and the air-dielectric boundary can be considered an insulating wall (corresponding to a magentic wall in electrical analogue). Therefore, the configuration is modified by removing the insulating wall and incorporating an image source of heat and an image of the ground plane as shown. The space between the two ground planes is filled homogeneously by the dielectric medium. Now heat flow at a point A is obtained by applying the divergence theorem (for heat flow field) to the volume shown by the dotted lines, that is,

$$\iiint (\nabla \cdot q_d)\, dv = \oiint_s q_d \cdot ds = \iiint \rho_h\, dv \tag{2.93}$$

where s is the enclosed area. Total q_d at $y = y_1$ is contributed by the heat sources lying between $y = y_1$ and $y = h$ (and their images). It may be noted that sources located at $y < y_1$ (and their images) do not contribute to heat flow at $y = y_1$. Thus,

$$q_d(y) = -(h-y)\,\rho_h \tag{2.94}$$

The negative sign implies that the heat flow is in the -y direction (for $y < h$). If α_d (dB/m) is the attenuation coefficient due to dielectric loss, the density of heat generated, ρ_h, may be written as

$$\rho_h = \frac{0.2303\,\alpha_d}{W_{eff}(f)h} \tag{2.95}$$

From Equations (2.94) and (2.95)

$$q_d(y) = -\frac{0.2303\,\alpha_d}{W_{eff}(f)}(1 - y/h) \tag{2.96}$$

Temperature Rise

The total density of heat flow due to conductor and dielectric losses may be expressed in terms of temperature gradient as

$$q = q_c + q_d(y) = -K\frac{\partial T}{\partial y} \tag{2.97}$$

where K is the thermal conductivity of the substrate. Therefore, the temperature at $y = h$ (i.e. at the strip conductor) is given by

$$T = \frac{0.2303}{K} \int_0^h \left\{ \frac{\alpha_c}{W_e}\, dy - \frac{\alpha_d}{W_{eff}(f)} (1 - y/h) \right\} dy + T_{amb} \qquad (2.98)$$

The corresponding rise in temperature is

$$\Delta T = \frac{0.2303\,h}{K} \left\{ \frac{\alpha_c}{W_e} + \frac{\alpha_d}{2\,W_{eff}(f)} \right\} \; (°C/watt) \qquad (2.99)$$

This relation is used for calculating the average power handling capability of the microstrip line.

The properties of various substrates are given in Table 2.2. Strip conductors, except in the case of polystyrene substrates, are of gold (t = 0.01 mm) while in the case of polystyrene substrates copper (t = 0.035 mm) is used. Conductor loss in the ground plane does not contribute to APHC limitation. However, the ground plane loss is very small compared to the strip loss [30] and formulas for the total loss could be used to calculate APHC. Results shown in Figure 2.13 for variations of ΔT with frequency are based on this assumption. The following interesting observations are noted from this figure. (a) The temperature rise ΔT increases with frequency. (b) The beryllium oxide (Be0) substrate has a smaller temperature rise due to its higher value of thermal conductivity. Alumina and sapphire have nearly same ΔT variation, although alumina has about 25 percent lower thermal conductivity compared to sapphire. This is due to the fact that sapphire line has slightly more loss due to a higher dielectric constant. Also W_e and W_{eff} in the case of sapphire are smaller. Therefore, the combined effect of these parameters on ΔT is almost equal in sapphire and alumina. (c) We note that for frequencies less than 2.6 GHz, ΔT for Si (1000 ohm-cm) is larger than that for GaAs (10^7 ohm-cm). At 2.6 GHz two ΔTs are equal, and for frequencies above 2.6 GHz ΔT is smaller for Si. (d) Plastic substrates (polystyrene etc.) have higher values of ΔT due to poor thermal conductivity although losses are small (Figure 2.11).

It may be pointed out that the effect of any thermal resistance barriers which may exist between the bonding of the strip and the microstrip dielectric, between the microstrip dielectric and the ground plane and any heat sink has not been taken into account in this analysis. This effect can limit average power handling capability of microstrip.

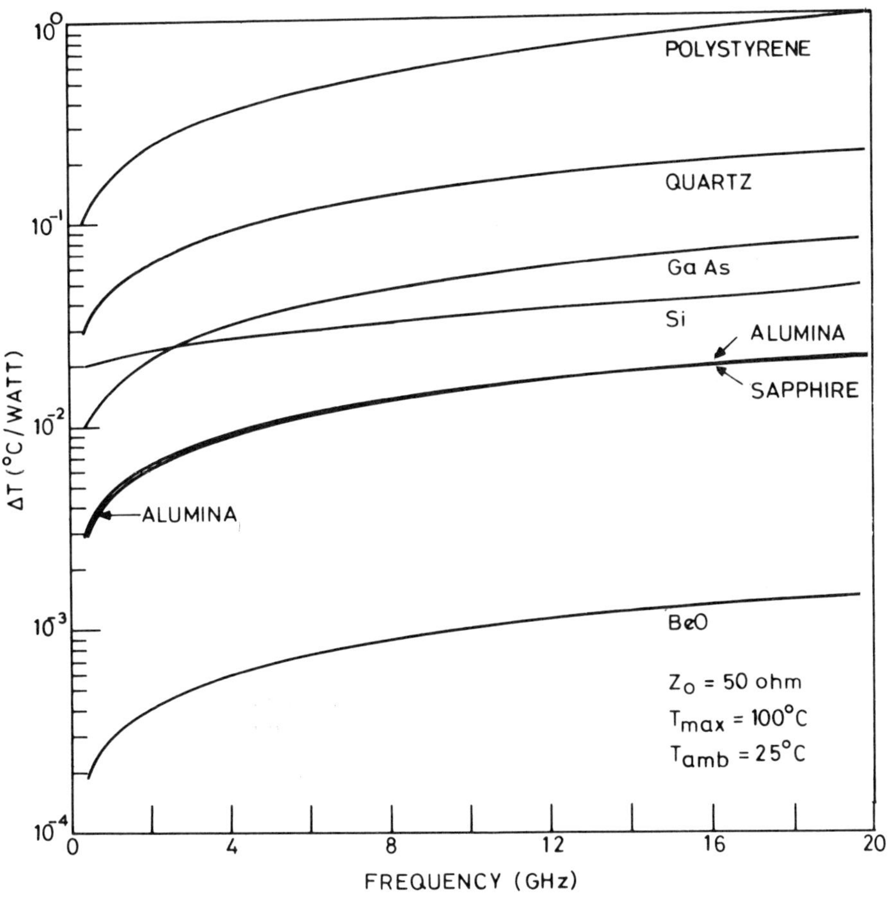

Figure 2.13 Rise in Temperature of the Strip Conductor as a Function of Frequency for Various Substrates

Average Power Handling Capability

The maximum average power for a given line may be calculated from

$$P_{avg} = (T_{max} - T_{amb})/\Delta T \qquad (2.100)$$

where ΔT denotes rise in temperature per watt and T_{max} is the maximum operating temperature. For polystyrene, maximum operating temperature is 100°C, whereas for the rest of the dielectrics (in Table 2.2) it is much more than 100°C. The maximum operating temperature of microstrip circuits is limited due to (i) change of substrate properties with temperature, (ii) change of physical dimensions with temperature and (iii) connectors. One can take maximum operating temperature of microstrip circuits where its electrical and physical characteristics remain unchanged. The circuits on alumina and glassifiber reinforced teflon substrates have been tested upto 150°C for about 2000 hours. It has been found [31] that the electrical and physical characteristics remain unchanged.

For T_{max} = 100°C, T_{amb} = 25°C and Z_{om} = 50 ohm, values of APHC for various substrates at 2 GHz, 10 GHz and 20 GHz are calculated and given in Table 2.3. Among the dielectrics considered, APHC is lowest for polystyrene and it is maximum for Be0. At lower frequencies GaAs microstrip lines have better APHC than Si microstrip lines, but at higher frequencies (> 2.6 GHz) APHC is better in the case of Si. For commonly used alumina (or sapphire) substrates, a 50 ohm microstrip can carry about 5.14 KW of CW power at 10 GHz.

Table 2.3 Comparison of APHC for Various Substrates

Substrate	Maximum Average Power (Kilowatts)		
	2.0 GHz	10 GHz	20 GHz
Polystyrene	0.321	0.124	0.075
Quartz	1.200	0.523	0.357
Si	3.19	2.23	1.64
GaAs	3.55	1.47	0.934
Sapphire	11.65	5.10	3.46
Alumina	12.12	5.17	3.40
Be0	174.5	75.7	51.5

Peak Power Handling Capability

The calculation of peak power handling capability of microstrip lines is more complicated. The peak voltage which can be applied without causing dielectric breakdown determines the peak power handling capability (PPHC) of the microstrip. If Z_{om} is the characteristic impedance of the microstrip and V_o is the maximum voltage the line can withstand, the maximum peak power is given by

$$P_p = \frac{V_o^2}{2Z_{om}} \tag{2.101}$$

Thick substrates can support higher voltages (for the same breakdown field). Therefore, low impedance lines and lines on thick substrates have higher peak power handling capability.

The sharp edges of the strip conductor serve as field concentrators. The electric field tends to a large value at the sharp edges of the conductor if it is a flat strip and decreases as the edge of the conductor is rounded off more and more. Therefore, thick and rounded strip conductors will increase breakdown voltage.

The dielectric strength of the substrate material as well as of the air plays an important role. The breakdown strength of dry air is approximately 30 kV/cm. Thus the maximum electric field (tangential) near the strip edge should be less than 30 kV/cm. In order to avoid air breakdown near the strip edge, the edge of the strip conductor is painted with a dielectric paint which has the same dielectric constant as that of the substrate and is lossless. The dielectric strength of various dielectrics is also given in Table 2.2. This table shows that, among the dielectrics considered, fused quartz has the maximum dielectric strength while polystyrene has the minimum.

In some cases connectors or launchers decide the PPHC of the microstrip line. The 3 mm sub-miniature connectors and their transitions will breakdown before the line [32] itself. N-type connectors and transitions have higher PPHC. An additional factor, which may reduce PPHC is the effect of internal mismatches. Data for PPHC is not readily available. Howe [32] has reported successful operation of microstrip lines upto 10 kW at S-band and 4 kW at X-band.

2.4.3 Effect of Tolerances [33]

Characteristics of microstrip lines (namely, Z_{om} and ϵ_{re}) are primarily functions of strip width W and substrate parameters ϵ_r and

h. These are also influenced by factors such as strip thickness, frequency of operation (dispersion), size of enclosure etc. Any changes in the values of W, ϵ_r or h give rise to corresponding changes in Z_{om} and ϵ_{re}.

The substrate properties, like surface finish, metallization thickness, the fabrication process, and so on, determine the accuracy of fabrication of strip width. In addition to the error in fabrication of strip width, the thickness and the dielectric constant of the substrate have some manufacturing tolerances. All these factors contribute to variations in Z_{om} and ϵ_{re} of the microstrip. Since in MICs it is very difficult to incorporate arrangements for post fabrication adjustments, it is necessary to take into account the effect of tolerances at the design stage itself. However, unlike the effects of deterministic parameters like dispersion, strip thickness etc., the effect of tolerances cannot be incorporated exactly because of the uncertainty in Z_{om} and ϵ_{re} arising from tolerances.

The effect of tolerances on the performance of microstrip can be analyzed using the sensitivity approach. This approach is the easiest method of predicting the worst case behavior, corresponding to a given set of tolerances. It does not require the actual statistical distribution of tolerances. Only their maximum absolute values are needed. Sensitivity analysis is useful in situations where deviations in parameter can be considered incremental. This implies that the circuit characteristics should be slowly varying functions in the domain of parameter variations around the exact parameter values.

It has been observed that the maximum change in the characteristics of microstrip due to tolerances can be evaluted using the following equations,

$$\frac{|\Delta Z_{om}|_{max}}{Z_{om}} = \left|\frac{\Delta W}{W} S_W^{Z_{om}}\right| + \left|\frac{\Delta h}{h} S_h^{Z_{om}}\right| + \left|\frac{\Delta \epsilon_r}{\epsilon_r} S_{\epsilon_r}^{Z_{om}}\right|, \text{ and} \tag{2.102}$$

$$\frac{|\Delta \epsilon_{re}|_{max}}{\epsilon_{re}} = \left|\frac{\Delta W}{W} S_W^{\epsilon_{re}}\right| + \left|\frac{\Delta h}{h} S_h^{\epsilon_{re}}\right| + \left|\frac{\Delta \epsilon_r}{\epsilon_r} S_{\epsilon_r}^{\epsilon_{re}}\right| \tag{2.103}$$

where ΔW, Δh and $\Delta \epsilon_r$ are the tolerances in W, h and ϵ_r, respectively. The sensitivity S_B^A is defined as

$$S_B^A = \frac{B}{A} \frac{\partial A}{\partial B} \tag{2.104}$$

The influence of tolerances can be reduced by using improved fabrication techniques and using substrates with better tolerances. The required fabrication accuracy for the strip width will be a function of specified accuracy in transmission line characteristics and given tolerances in substrate parameters.

It can be determined from the following equations

$$|S_W^{Z_{om}}| \frac{|\Delta W|}{W} = \frac{|\Delta Z_{om}|}{Z_{om}} - |\frac{\Delta h}{h} S_h^{Z_{om}}| - |\frac{\Delta \epsilon_r}{\epsilon_r} S_{\epsilon_r}^{Z_{om}}| \qquad (2.105)$$

$$|S_W^{\epsilon_{re}}| \frac{|\Delta W|}{W} = \frac{|\Delta \epsilon_{re}|}{\epsilon_{re}} - |\frac{\Delta h}{h} S_h^{\epsilon_{re}}| - |\frac{\Delta \epsilon_r}{\epsilon_r} S_{\epsilon_r}^{\epsilon_{re}}| \qquad (2.106)$$

The required fabrication accuracy for strip width is the minimum of the two values of ΔW obtained from the above equations. The fabrication accuracy of h or tolerance in ϵ_r can be determined in a similar manner, provided that the tolerances for the other two parameters are known.

Expressions for sensitivity of microstrip characteristics (Z_{om} and ϵ_{re}) with respect to various parameters (W, h, ϵ_r, etc) can be calculated using the closed form expressions for Z_{om} and ϵ_{re} given by Schneider [17] and the definition of sensitivity given in Equation (2.104). Various sensitivities may thus be written as

$$S_W^{Z_{om}} = -S_h^{Z_{om}} = \frac{-1}{Z_{om}\sqrt{\epsilon_{re}}} \left\{ \frac{60\,(8h/W - W/4h)}{8h/W + W/4h} + 1.25\, Z_{om} \frac{\epsilon_r - 1}{\sqrt{\epsilon_{re}}} \frac{h/W}{(1+10h/W)^{3/2}} \right\} \quad \text{for } (W/h \leqslant 1) \qquad (2.107)$$

$$S_W^{Z_{om}} = -S_h^{Z_{om}} = -\left[\frac{Z_{om}\sqrt{\epsilon_{re}}}{120\pi} \left\{ \frac{W}{h} + 0.44\frac{h}{W} + 6\frac{h}{W}\left(1 - \frac{h}{W}\right)^5 \right\} + 1.25\, \frac{\epsilon_r - 1}{\epsilon_{re}} \frac{h/W}{(1+10h/W)^{3/2}} \right] \quad \text{for } (W/h \geqslant 1) \qquad (2.108)$$

$$S_W^{\epsilon_{re}} = -S_h^{\epsilon_{re}} = \frac{2.5}{W/h} \frac{\epsilon_r - 1}{\epsilon_{re}} (1 + 10\, h/W)^{-3/2} \qquad (2.109)$$

$$S_{\epsilon_r}^{Z_{om}} = -0.25 \frac{\epsilon_r}{\epsilon_{re}} [1 + (1 + 10h/W)^{-1/2}] \tag{2.110}$$

$$S_{\epsilon_r}^{\epsilon_{re}} = 0.5 \frac{\epsilon_r}{\epsilon_{re}} [1 + (1 + 10h/W)^{-1/2}] \tag{2.111}$$

The sensitivity curves for impedance and effective dielectric constant are shown in Figure 2.14 and Figure 2.15 respectively for $\epsilon_r = 9.7$.

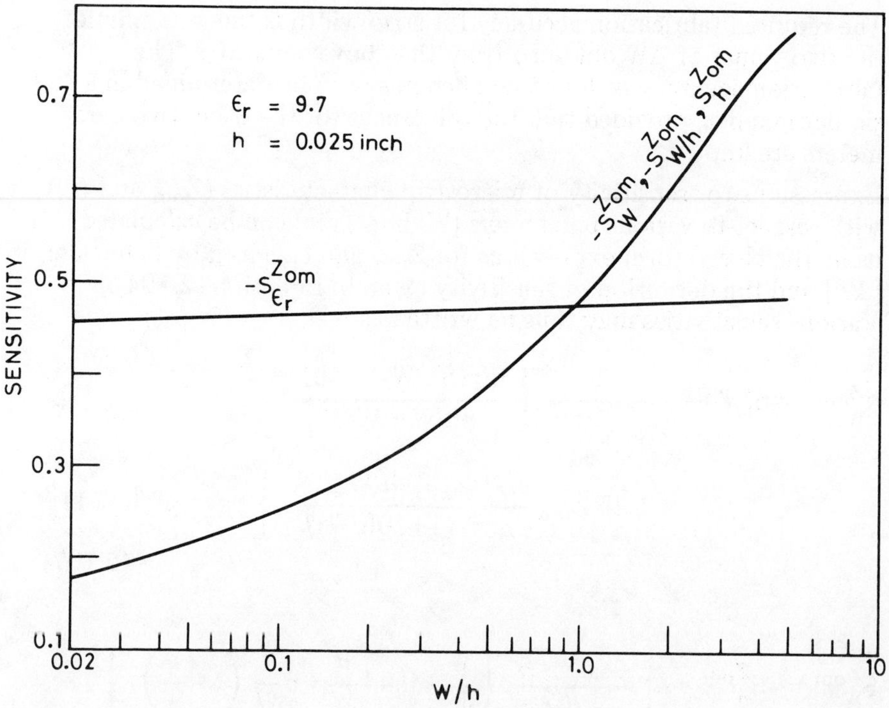

Figure 2.14 Sensitivities of Microstrip Impedance With Respect to W, h and ϵ_r (from [33])

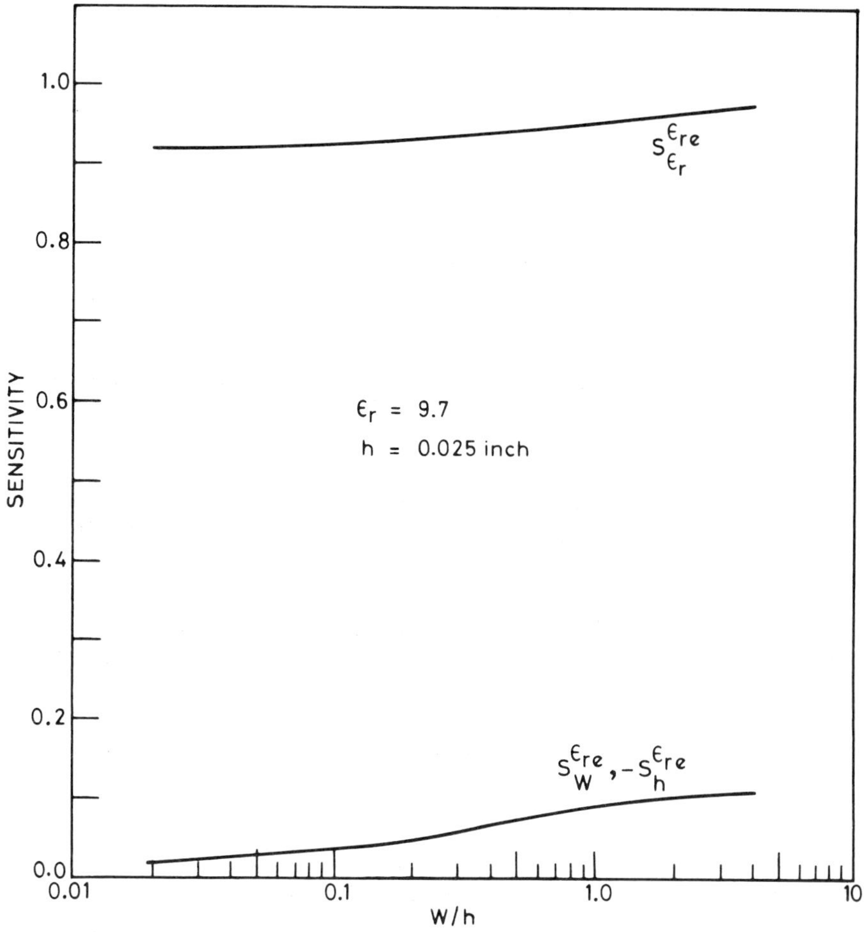

Figure 2.15 Sensitivities of Effective Dielectric Constant of Microstrip With Respect to W, h and ϵ_r (from [33])

The sensitivity values thus obtained are used in Equation (2.102) to determine the maximum change in Z_{om}. From $(\Delta Z_{om})_{max}$ the maximum value of VSWR is obtained using the relation

$$VSWR = \left[1 - \frac{|\Delta Z_{om}|_{max}}{Z_{om}} \right]^{-1} \quad (2.112)$$

The VSWR values are plotted in Figure 2.16 for the set of tolerances

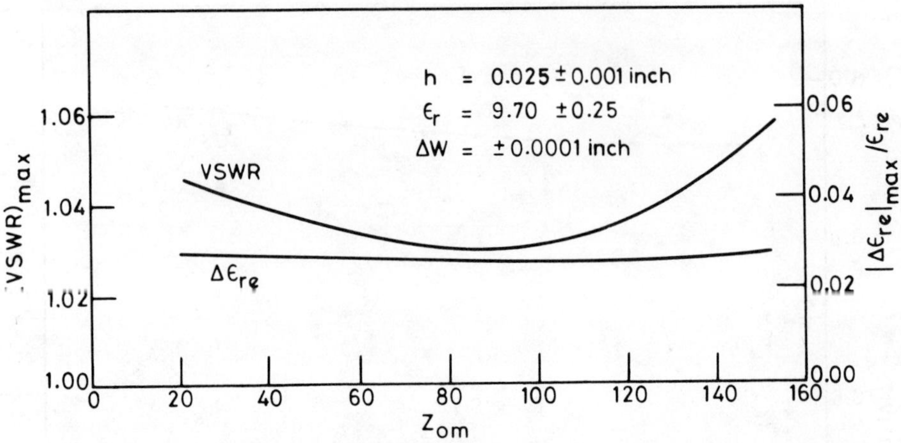

Figure 2.16 VSWR and Change in Effective Dielectric Constant Because of Tolerances in Microstrip Parameters (from [33])

mentioned therein. The alternative problem of determining the fabrication accuracy of the strip width is evaluated using Equation (2.105). It is plotted in Figure 2.17 for a VSWR value of 1.05.

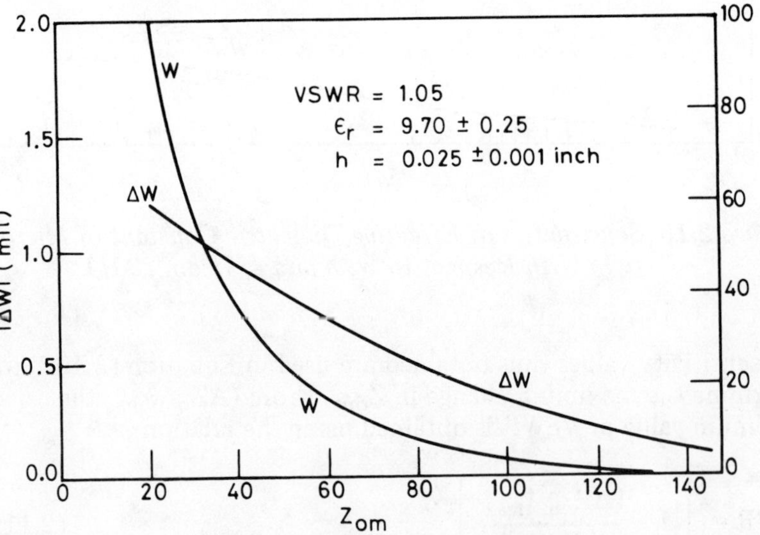

Figure 2.17 Tolerance in Microstrip Width Allowed for a VSWR Value of 1.05 (from [33])

It may be observed from Equation (2.102) that there is a tradeoff between tolerances; i.e., the tolerance value for one parameter can be increased or decreased at the cost of other parameters. This helps in optimum use of fabrication technologies.

The effect of tolerances on the characteristics of microstrip has been compared with the effects of finite thickness of metal strip, dispersion, discontinuity and an imperfect measurement system, detailed later in Section 2.4.5.

2.4.4 Effect of Dielectric Anisotropy

Some of the dielectric substrates used for microstrip circuits exhibit anisotropy in permittivity. The most common examples are sapphire (especially when single crystal) and Epsilam-10 (trade name for a ceramic loaded resin). In both these cases, the substrates are manufactured such that one of the principal axes of the permittivity tensor is perpendicular to the dielectric interface y = h. If there were no fringing of electric fields (in microstrip configuration) all the field lines will coincide with this axis, and the capacitance will be determined by the value of permittivity in this direction. In such a case there is no effect of anisotropy.

If the line parameters are to be independent of line orientation in the xz-plane, permittivity tensor in x and z direction must be equal. For sapphire we take $\epsilon_x = \epsilon_z = 11.6$ and $\epsilon_y = 9.4$ whereas for Epsilam-10 $\epsilon_x = \epsilon_z = 15.0$ and $\epsilon_y = 10.0$.

Quasi-static analysis of microstrip on anisotropic substrates has been carried out by using the finite difference method [34] and also by using a transformation [35] which enables capacitance for anisotropic substrates to be derived from microstrip formulas for isotropic substrates.

Finite Difference Method [34]

This method is a straightforward solution of the Laplace equation by finite difference techniques. When the dielectric is anisotropic, the Laplace equation may be written as

$$\epsilon_x \frac{\partial^2 \phi(x,y)}{\partial x^2} + \epsilon_y \frac{\partial^2 \phi(x,y)}{\partial y^2} = 0 \qquad (2.113)$$

In finite difference form this may be written as follows. For all net points in the dielectric material (see Figure 1.9).

$$\epsilon_x(\phi_B+\phi_A)+\epsilon_y(\phi_D+\phi_C)-2(\epsilon_x+\epsilon_y)\phi_P=0 \qquad (2.114)$$

and when the point P lies on the dielectric-air interface

$$\tfrac{1}{2}(1+\epsilon_x)(\phi_B+\phi_A)+\phi_D+\epsilon_y\phi_C-(2+\epsilon_x+\epsilon_y)\phi_P=0 \qquad (2.115)$$

The rest of the procedure for evaluating capacitances is the same as outlined in Section 1.2.2.

Transform Method [35]

A simple, but rigorous transformation which converts the anisotropic electrostatic field into an isotropic one with similar shape has been reported by Szentkuti [35]. This transformation may be described as follows:

For the substrate ($y \leqslant h$) let

$$\bar{x}=x,\ \bar{y}=y\sqrt{(\epsilon_x/\epsilon_y)},\ \text{i.e.}\ \ \bar{h}=h\sqrt{(\epsilon_x/\epsilon_y)} \qquad (2.116)$$

$$\bar{\epsilon}_r=\bar{\epsilon}_x=\bar{\epsilon}_y=\sqrt{(\epsilon_x\,\epsilon_y)} \qquad (2.117)$$

Potentials and their derivatives at original and transformed points (P and $\bar{P}$) are related by

$$\phi_P=\bar{\phi}_{\bar{P}} \qquad (2.118)$$

$$\partial\phi_P/\partial y=(\partial\bar{\phi}_{\bar{P}}/\partial\bar{y}/\partial y)\ \ \text{etc.} \qquad (2.119)$$

Expressing Equation (2.113) in terms of $\bar{x}$ and $\bar{y}$ leads to an isotropic Laplace equation for $\bar{\phi}(\bar{x},\bar{y})$. Also

$$E_x=-\partial\bar{\phi}/\partial\bar{x}=\bar{E}_{\bar{x}} \qquad D_y=-\bar{\epsilon}_r\,\epsilon_o\,\partial\bar{\phi}/\partial\bar{y}=\bar{D}_{\bar{y}} \qquad (2.120)$$

Thus we note that: (a) values of the tangential component of E and the normal component of flux at the interface $y = h$ are not affected by the transformation, (b) all potential and charges are not altered within the region $y \leqslant h$, and (c) the potential of the transformed ground plane is conserved. Therefore, capacitances of the original anisotropic and the transformed isotropic structures are equal.

Effective dielectric constants for anisotropic substrates are compared with the corresponding values for isotropic substrates ($\epsilon_r = \epsilon_y$) as a function of W/h in Figure 2.18. We note that considerable difference exists for thin lines (small W/h) whereas the two results tend to

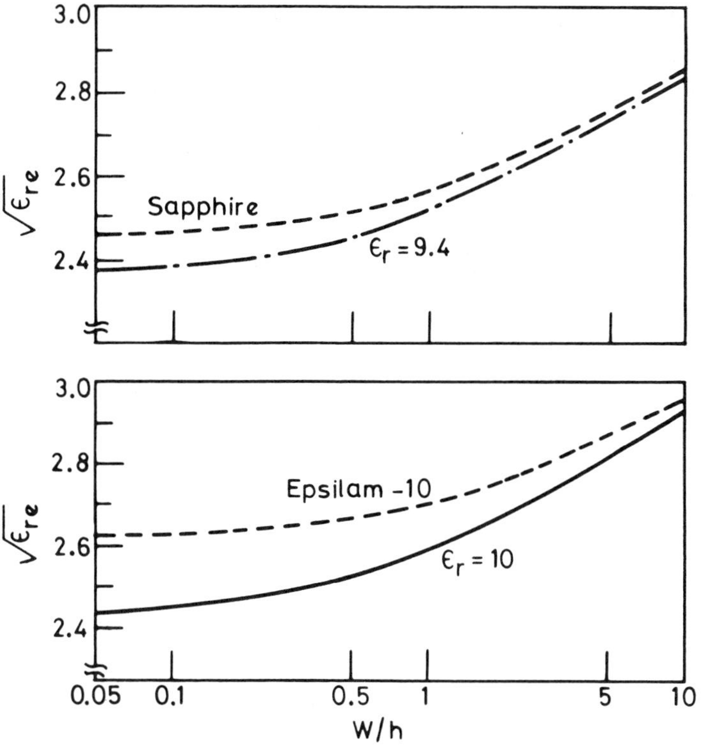

Figure 2.18 Effect of Dielectric Anisotropy on Effective Dielectric Constants of Microstrip Lines on Sapphire ($\epsilon_x = \epsilon_z = 11.6$, $\epsilon_y = 9.9$) and Epsilam-10 Substrates (from [35])

identical values as W/h increases. This can be explained by noting that the fringing field values are larger for narrow strips, and it is only the E_x component of the fringing field that is affected by ϵ_x.

2.4.5 Design Equations

The numerical methods for the characteri. .on of microstrip lines discussed so far involve extensive computations. Closed form expressions are necessary for optimization and computer-aided-design of microstrip circuits. A complete set of design equations for microstrip are presented in this section. These include closed form expressions for the characteristic impedance and effective dielectric constant, and their variation with metal strip thickness, enclosure size and dispersion. Expressions for microstrip loss and quality factor Q are also described.

Characteristic Impedance and Effective Dielectric Constant

The closed form expressions for Z_{om} and ϵ_{re} have been reported by Wheeler [36], Schneider [17] and Hammerstad [37]. Wheeler and Hammerstad have also given synthesis expressions for Z_{om}. The closed form expressions based on the works of Wheeler and Schneider are given below [37]:

$$Z_{om} = \frac{\eta}{2\pi\sqrt{\epsilon_{re}}} \ln\left(\frac{8h}{W} + 0.25\frac{W}{h}\right) \quad (W/h \leqslant 1) \qquad (2.121a)$$

$$Z_{om} = \frac{\eta}{\sqrt{\epsilon_{re}}} \left\{\frac{W}{h} + 1.393 + 0.667 \ln\left(\frac{W}{h} + 1.444\right)\right\}^{-1} \quad (W/h \geqslant 1) \qquad (2.121b)$$

where $\eta = 120\,\pi$ ohm

$$\epsilon_{re} = \frac{\epsilon_r+1}{2} + \frac{\epsilon_r-1}{2} F(W/h) \qquad (2.122)$$

$$F(W/h) = \begin{cases} (1 + 12\,h/W)^{-1/2} + 0.04\,(1-W/h)^2 & (W/h \leqslant 1) \\ (1 + 12\,h/W)^{-1/2} & (W/h \geqslant 1) \end{cases}$$

Hammerstad noted [38] that the maximum relative error in ϵ_{re} and Z_{om} is less than 1 percent. The expressions for W/h in terms of Z_{om} and ϵ_r are as follows:

For $Z_{om}\sqrt{\epsilon_{re}} > 8.991$, i.e., $A > 1.52$

$$W/h = \frac{8\exp(A)}{\exp(2A)-2} \qquad (2.123a)$$

for $Z_{om}\sqrt{\epsilon_{re}} \leq 8.991$, i.e., $A \leq 1.52$

$$W/h = \frac{2}{\pi}\left\{B-1-\ln(2B-1) + \frac{\epsilon_r-1}{2\,\epsilon_r}\left[\ln(B-1) + 0.39 - \frac{0.61}{\epsilon_r}\right]\right\} \qquad (2.123b)$$

where

$$A = \frac{Z_{om}}{60}\left\{\frac{\epsilon_r+1}{2}\right\}^{1/2} + \frac{\epsilon_r-1}{\epsilon_r+1}\left\{0.23 + \frac{0.11}{\epsilon_r}\right\}$$

$$B = \frac{60\,\pi^2}{Z_{om}\sqrt{\epsilon_r}}$$

These expressions also provide an accuracy better than one percent.

The results discussed above are based on the assumption that the thickness of the strip conductor is negligible. But in practice, the strip has a finite thickness "t" which affects the characteristics.

Effect of Strip Thickness

The effect of strip thickness on Z_{om} and ϵ_{re} of microstrip lines has been reported by a number of investigators [17, 29, 36, 39-51]. Simple and accurate formulas for Z_{om} and ϵ_{re} with finite strip thickness are [29]:

$$Z_{om} = \frac{\eta}{2\pi\sqrt{\epsilon_{re}}}\,\ln\left\{\frac{8h}{W_e} + 0.25\frac{W_e}{h}\right\} \qquad (W/h \leqslant 1) \qquad (2.124a)$$

$$Z_{om} = \frac{\eta}{\sqrt{\epsilon_{re}}}\left\{\frac{W_e}{h} + 1.393 + 0.667\,\ln\left(\frac{W_e}{h} + 1.444\right)\right\}^{-1} \qquad (2.124b)$$

$$(W/h \geqslant 1)$$

where

$$\frac{W_e}{h} = \frac{W}{h} + \frac{1.25}{\pi}\frac{t}{h}\left(1 + \ln\frac{4\pi W}{t}\right) \qquad (W/h \leqslant 1/2\pi) \qquad (2.125a)$$

$$\frac{W_e}{h} = \frac{W}{h} + \frac{1.25}{\pi}\frac{t}{h}\left(1 + \ln\frac{2h}{t}\right) \qquad (W/h \geqslant 1/2\pi) \qquad (2.125b)$$

$$\epsilon_{re} = \frac{\epsilon_r+1}{2} + \frac{\epsilon_r-1}{2}F(W/h) - C \qquad (2.126)$$

in which

$$C = \frac{\epsilon_r - 1}{4.6} \frac{t/h}{\sqrt{W/h}} \tag{2.127}$$

It can be observed that the effect of thickness on Z_{om} and ϵ_{re} is insignificant for small values of t/h. This agrees with the experimental results reported in [39] for $t/h \leqslant 0.005$, $2 \leqslant \epsilon_r \leqslant 10$ and $W/h \geqslant 0.1$. However, the effect of strip thickness is significant on conductor loss in the microstrip line.

Effect of Enclosure

Most of microstrip circuit applications require a metallic enclosure for hermetic sealing, mechanical strength, electromagnetic shielding, mounting connectors and ease of handling. The effect of the top cover alone [52, 53] as well as of the top cover and side walls [48, 54] has been reported in the literature. Both the top cover and side walls tend to lower impedance and effective dielectric constant. This is because the fringing flux lines are prematurely terminated on the enclosure walls. This increases the electric flux in air. The closed form equations for a microstrip with top cover (without side walls) are obtained as follows [53]

$$Z_{om} = \frac{1}{\sqrt{\epsilon_{re}}} \left[\frac{\eta}{2\pi} \ell n \left\{ \frac{8h}{W} + 0.25 \frac{W}{h} \right\} - P \right] (W/h \leq 1) \tag{2.128a}$$

$$Z_{om} = \frac{1}{\sqrt{\epsilon_{re}}} \left[\eta \left\{ \frac{W}{h} + 1.393 + 0.667 \ell n \left(\frac{W}{h} + 1.444 \right) \right\}^{-1} - \left\{ 1 - \tanh \left(\frac{0.48 \sqrt{W/h - 1}}{(1 + h'/h)^2} \right) \right\} \cdot P \right]$$
$$(W/h \geq 1) \tag{2.128b}$$

where

$$\epsilon_{re} = \frac{\epsilon_r + 1}{2} + \left[\frac{\epsilon_r - 1}{2} F(W/h) \right] \tanh \left\{ 0.18 + 0.235\, h'/h - \frac{0.415}{(h'/h)^2} \right\} \tag{2.129}$$

$$P = 270 \left[1 - \tanh \left(0.28 + 1.2 \sqrt{h'/h} \right) \right]$$

The factor F (W/h) has been defined in Equation (2.122); h′ is the spacing between the strip and the top cover and $h'/h \geqslant 1$.

The accuracy of these equations has been verified by comparison with numerical results generated using the variational method [52]. It is found that the error is within 1 percent for $0.05 \leqslant W/h \leqslant 5$.

Effect of Dispersion

The effect of frequency (dispersion) on ϵ_{re} is described accurately by the dispersion model given by Getsinger [55] and modified by Edwards and Owens [56], as discussed in Section 1.3.3. The effect of frequency on Z_{om} has been described by several investigators [3, 27, 28, 57]. Comparison of the approximate results of Bianco *et. al.* [28], and Owens [27] with the numerical results of Krage and Haddad [57] and Knorr and Tufekcioglu [3] shows that the results of Bianco *et. al.* [28] are closer to numerical values.

The results of Bianco *et. al.* for $Z_{om}(f)$, and Edwards and Owen for $\epsilon_{re}(f)$ may be stated as follows:

$$Z_{om}(f) = Z_{oT} - \frac{Z_{oT} - Z_{om}}{1+G(f/f_p)^2} \tag{2.130}$$

$$\epsilon_{re}(f) = \epsilon_r - \frac{\epsilon_r - \epsilon_{re}}{1+G(f/f_p)^2} \tag{2.131}$$

where

$$G = \left[\frac{Z_{om} - 5}{60}\right]^{1/2} + 0.004\, Z_{om}$$

$$f_p(\text{GHz}) = 15.66\, Z_{om}/h$$

Here h is in mils, Z_{om} in ohms and Z_{oT} is twice the characteristic impedance of a stripline of width W and height 2h. Z_{om} and ϵ_{re} are quasi-static values obtained earlier.

Losses

The closed form expressions for total loss have been reported in the literature [16,17]. An expression for loss, derived using Equations (2.124-2.127), may be written as

$$\alpha_T = \alpha_c + \alpha_d \tag{2.132}$$

The two components α_c and α_d are given by

$$\alpha_c = \begin{cases} 1.38\,A\,\dfrac{R_s}{hZ_{om}}\,\dfrac{32-(W_e/h)^2}{32+(W_e/h)^2}\ \text{dB/unit length}\ (W/h \le 1) \\ \\ 6.1\times10^{-5}\,A\,\dfrac{R_s Z_{om}\,\epsilon_{re}}{h}\left[W_e/h + \dfrac{0.667\,W_e/h}{W_e/h + 1.444}\right]\ \text{dB/unit length} \\ \qquad (W/h \geqslant 1) \end{cases} \tag{2.133}$$

and

$$\alpha_d = \begin{cases} 4.34\,\eta\sigma\,\dfrac{\epsilon_{re}-1}{\sqrt{\epsilon_{re}}\,(\epsilon_r-1)}\ \text{dB/unit length} \qquad \text{or} \\ \\ 27.3\,\dfrac{\epsilon_r}{\epsilon_r-1}\,\dfrac{\epsilon_{re}-1}{\sqrt{\epsilon_{re}}}\,\dfrac{\tan\delta}{\lambda_o}\ \text{dB/unit length} \end{cases} \tag{2.134}$$

where

$$A = 1 + \frac{h}{W_e}\left\{1 + \frac{1.25}{\pi}\,\ell n\,\frac{2B}{t}\right\}$$

$R_s = \sqrt{\pi f \mu_o \rho_c}$; ρ_c = resistivity of the strip conductor

$\sigma = \omega\epsilon_o\epsilon_r\tan\delta$ = conductivity of the dielectric substrate

and

$$B = \begin{cases} h & \left(W/h \geqslant \dfrac{1}{2\pi}\right) \\ \\ 2\pi W & \left(W/h \leqslant \dfrac{1}{2\pi}\right) \end{cases}$$

The dielectric loss is normally very small compared with the conductor loss for dielectric substrates. The dielectric loss in silicon substrate (used for monolithic MICs), however, is usually of the same order, or even larger than the conductor loss. This is because of lower resistivity available in silicon wafers. However, higher resistivity can be obtained in GaAs, and therefore the dielectric loss is lower for this material. Values of conductor and dielectric losses per unit length for 50 ohm microstrip lines on various substrates (dielectric as well as semiconductor) are plotted in Figure 2.11 (given in Section 2.4.1) as functions of frequency. At a given frequency the total loss can be obtained by adding the two values.

Quality Factor-Q

The quality factor, Q, of a microstrip can be related to the total loss in the line by [58]

$$Q_T = \frac{\beta}{2\alpha_T} \tag{2.135}$$

where Q_T is the total Q of the resonator (quarter wavelength), α_T is the total loss in the resonator, and $\beta = 2\pi/\lambda_m$. When losses in a resonant line are considered, another loss factor, α_r, due to radiation at the open end discontinuities must also be taken into account [58, 59]. The corresponding radiation Q-factor is given by [58]

$$Q_r = \frac{Z_{om}}{480\pi(h/\lambda_o)^2 R} \tag{2.136}$$

where

$$R = \frac{\epsilon_{re}(f)+1}{\epsilon_{re}(f)} - \frac{[\epsilon_{re}(f)-1]^2}{2[\epsilon_{re}(f)]^{3/2}} \ln\left\{\frac{\sqrt{\epsilon_{re}(f)}+1}{\sqrt{\epsilon_{re}(f)}-1}\right\} \tag{2.137}$$

Note that the effect of dispersion is considered, as described by Equation (2.131).

The total Q of the resonator can be expressed by

$$\frac{1}{Q_T} = \frac{1}{Q_c} + \frac{1}{Q_d} + \frac{1}{Q_r} \tag{2.138}$$

Here, Q_c, Q_d and Q_r are the quality factors corresponding to conductor, dielectric and radiation losses, respectively. Finally, the circuit quality factor, Q_o, is defined as

$$\frac{1}{Q_o} = \frac{1}{Q_c} + \frac{1}{Q_d} = \frac{\lambda_o(\alpha_c+\alpha_d)}{\pi\sqrt{\epsilon_{re}(f)}} \tag{2.139}$$

The variation with frequency of Q_o, Q_r and Q_T for a quarter wave resonator on GaAs, alumina and quartz substrates is shown in Figure 2.19. A quarter wave 50 ohm resonator on 25 mil thick alumina

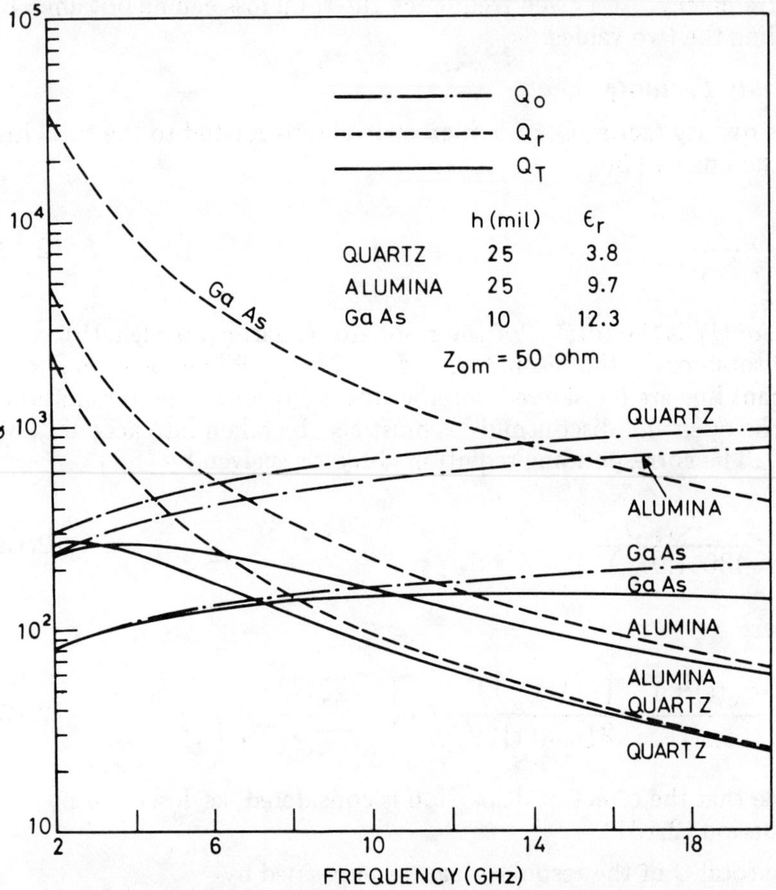

Figure 2.19 Variation of Q-factors With Frequency for Quarterwave Microstrip Resonators on Quartz, Alumina and GaAs Substrates

substrate has a Q_o of about 240 at 2.0 GHz and 550 at 10.0 GHz, whereas Q_T is 230 at 2.0 GHz and nearly 160 at 10.0 GHz. This is due to the fact that the radiation losses are higher than conductor and dielectric losses at higher frequencies. On the other hand, a quarter wave 50 ohm resonator on 10 mil GaAs substrate has Q_o

of about 82 at 2.0 GHz and 160 at 10.0 GHz, whereas Q_T is 82 at 2.0 GHz and nearly 145 at 10.0 GHz. This is explained by smaller radiation losses for thin substrates. Thus, the commonly accepted rule that thick substrates should be used for high Q circuits does not apply to microstrip lines because of high radiation losses incurred under this condition.

Comparison of Various Factors Affecting Microstrip Characteristics

The effect of tolerances on the characteristics of microstrip has been compared in [60] with the effects of finite thickness of metal strip, dispersion, discontinuities and imperfect measurement system. These are included here as Table 2.4 and Table 2.5 for 50 ohm microstrip on alumina and polystyrene substrates, respectively.

Table 2.4 Change in the Characteristics of Microstrip on Alumina Substrate (Z_{om} = 50 ohms, ϵ_r = 9.7, h = 0.025 in)

Effect of various factors		VSWR (due to change in Z_{om})	$\Delta\epsilon_{re}$
Effect of thickness	t/h=0.004	1.013	-0.029
(compared with t=0 case)	t/h=0.040	1.029	-0.075
Effect of dispersion	f=3 GHz	1.003	+0.033
(compared to quasi-static value)	f=10GHz	1.03	+0.303
Effect of dimensional tolerances	$\Delta W = \pm 0.0002$ in	$\leqslant 1.037$	$\leqslant \pm 0.1919$
($\Delta\epsilon_r = \pm 0.25$, $\Delta h = \pm 0.001$ in)	$\Delta W = \pm 0.0020$ in	$\leqslant 1.076$	$\leqslant \pm 0.2347$
Effect of step discontinuity $W_2/W_1 = 2.0$ ($W_1 = 0.025$ in)	f=3 GHz	1.008	
$C_{step} = 8.9 \times 10^{-3}$ pF	f=10 GHz	1.028	—
Launchers, connectors or transitions	f=3 GHz	1.065	
	f=10GHz	1.100	—

Table 2.5 Change in the Characteristics of Microstrip on Polystyrene Substrate (Z_{om} = 50 ohms, ϵ_r = 2.55, h = 0.0625 in)

Effect of various factors		VSWR (due to change in Z_{om})	$\Delta\epsilon_{re}$
Effect of thickness	t/h=0.022	1.009	−0.004
(compared with t=0 case)	t/h=0.044	1.017	−0.009
Effect of dispersion	f = 2GHz	1.007	+0.011
(compared to quasi-static value)	f = 4GHz	1.027	+0.043
Effect of dimensional tolerances	ΔW=±0.0001 in	⩽1.097	⩽±0.1596
($\Delta\epsilon_r$ = ±0.2, Δh = ±0.005 in)	ΔW=±0.0030 in	⩽1.110	⩽±0.1619
Effect of step discontinuity W_2/W_1 = 2.0	f = 2GHz	1.016	—
C_{step} = 2.66×10^{-2} pF	f = 4GHz	1.032	—
Launchers, connectors	f = 2GHz	1.060	—
or transitions	f = 4GHz	1.070	—

It may be observed from the Tables that the change in Z_{om} is relatively higher due to the dimensional tolerances and the imperfect measurement system. For microstrip on polystyrene substrate, the change in characteristics due to dimensional tolerances dominates the change due to other factors. However, at 10 GHz and for microstrip on alumina substrate, dispersion gives rise to the largest change in ϵ_{re}.

APPENDIX 2-A SINGULAR INTEGRAL EQUATION FOR FULL-WAVE ANALYSIS OF AN ENCLOSED MICROSTRIP

The final equation resulting from the singular integral equation method mentioned in Section 2.3.2 may be written as [13],

$$[\alpha_1 - M_1(\bar{\beta})K_1][\alpha_1 - Y_1(\bar{\beta})K_1] - N_1(\bar{\beta})X_1(\bar{\beta})K_1^2 = 0$$

where $\bar{\beta} = \beta/k_o$, $\alpha_n = (n-1/2)\ \pi/L$

$$K_n = \frac{2}{L}\int_{W/2}^{L} \frac{\cos(\pi x/2L)}{\sin\theta} \sin \alpha_n x\, dx$$

and the relationship between x and θ is given by (for $W/2 \leqslant x \leqslant L$ and $0 \leqslant \theta \leqslant \pi$),

$$\cos(\pi x/L) = \tfrac{1}{2}[\cos(\pi W/2L) - 1] + \tfrac{1}{2}[\cos(\pi W/2L) + 1]\cos\theta$$

Functions M_1, Y_1, N_1 and X_1 may be evaluated as follows:

$$M_1 = -a_1/I_h,\ N_1 = -b_1/I_h$$

$$X_1 = \frac{S_1 - M_1 Q I_g - (Qa_1 - Rc_1)E_1}{S - R\,I_g}$$

$$Y_1 = \frac{S_1' - N_1 Q I_g - (Qb_1 - Rd_1)E_1}{S - R\,I_g}$$

$$I_h = \int_0^{\pi} \frac{d\theta}{(1 - r_1 - r_2\cos\theta)^{1/2}}$$

$$r_1 = \tfrac{1}{2}\left(\cos\frac{\pi W}{2L} - 1\right),\quad r_2 = \tfrac{1}{2}\left(\cos\frac{\pi W}{2L} + 1\right)$$

$$S = \sum_{n=1}^{\infty} \frac{\sin\left(\alpha_n \frac{W}{2}\right)}{\alpha_n}(R - R_n)K_n$$

$$S_1 = \sum_{n=1}^{\infty} \frac{\sin\left(\alpha_n \frac{W}{2}\right)}{\alpha_n}\left[D_{n1}\left\{(Q-Q_n)a_1 - (R-R_n)c_1\right\} + K_n(Q-Q_n)M_1\right]$$

$$S'_1 = \sum_{n=1}^{\infty} \frac{\sin\left(\alpha_n \frac{W}{2}\right)}{\alpha_n} [D_{n1} \left\{ (Q-Q_n)\, b_1 - (R-R_n)\, d_1 \right\} + K_n (Q-Q_n)\, N_1]$$

$$Q = Q(\beta) = \frac{1 - \epsilon_r}{1 - \bar{\beta}^2}\ , \quad R = R(\beta) = \frac{\epsilon_r - \bar{\beta}^2}{1 - \bar{\beta}^2} + 1$$

$$I_g = \frac{r_2 L}{\pi^2 \sqrt{2}} \int_o^{\pi} \ell n \left\{ \frac{\sqrt{(1-r_1-r_2 \cos\theta')} + \sqrt{(1-r_1-r_2)}}{\sqrt{(1-r_1-r_2 \cos\theta')} - \sqrt{(1-r_1-r_2)}} \right\} \frac{d\theta'}{\sqrt{(1-r_1-r_2 \cos\theta')}}$$

$$E_1 = \frac{-r_2 L}{\pi^2 \sqrt{2}} \int_o^{\pi} \ell n \left\{ \frac{\sqrt{(1-r_1-r_2 \cos\theta')} + \sqrt{(1-r_1-r_2)}}{\sqrt{(1-r_1-r_2 \cos\theta')} - \sqrt{(1-r_1-r_2)}} \right\} \frac{\cos\theta'\, d\theta'}{\sqrt{(1-r_1-r_2 \cos\theta')}}$$

The functions a_1, b_1, c_1 and d_1 are given by:

$$a_1 = \alpha_1 \left\{ 1 - \frac{P_1(\beta)\, R(\beta) - T(\beta)\, Q_1(\beta)}{P(\beta)\, R(\beta) - T(\beta)\, Q(\beta)} \right\}$$

$$b_1 = \alpha_1 \left\{ \frac{T_1(\beta)\, R(\beta) - T(\beta)\, R_1(\beta)}{P(\beta)\, R(\beta) - T(\beta)\, Q(\beta)} \right\}$$

$$c_1 = \alpha_1 \left\{ \frac{P(\beta)\, Q_1(\beta) - P_1(\beta)\, Q(\beta)}{P(\beta)\, R(\beta) - T(\beta)\, Q(\beta)} \right\}$$

$$d_1 = \alpha_1 \left\{ 1 - \frac{P(\beta)\, R_1(\beta) - T_1(\beta)\, Q(\beta)}{P(\beta)\, R(\beta) - T(\beta)\, Q(\beta)} \right\}$$

where

$$P(\beta) = \epsilon_r + \frac{c_r - \bar{\beta}^2}{1 - \bar{\beta}^2} + \bar{\beta}^2 \frac{1 - c_r}{1 - \bar{\beta}^2}$$

$$T(\beta) = 2\bar{\beta}^2$$

and

$$D_{n1} = - \int_{W/2}^{L} \frac{2}{L} \cos \frac{\pi x}{2L} \cot\theta \sin \alpha_n x\, dx$$

$$P_1(\beta) = \epsilon_r \frac{\gamma_{1,1}}{\alpha_1} \coth \gamma_{1,1} h$$

$$+ \frac{\epsilon_r - \bar{\beta}^2}{1 - \bar{\beta}^2} \frac{\gamma_{1,2}}{\alpha_1} \coth \gamma_{1,2}(H-h)$$

$$+ \bar{\beta}^2 \frac{\alpha_1}{\gamma_{1,2}} \frac{1 - \epsilon_r}{1 - \bar{\beta}^2} \coth \gamma_{1,2}(H-h)$$

$$T_1(\beta) = \bar{\beta}^2 \left\{ \frac{\alpha_1}{\gamma_{1,1}} \coth \gamma_{1,1} h + \frac{\alpha_1}{\gamma_{1,2}} \coth \gamma_{1,2}(H-h) \right\}$$

$$Q_n = Q_n(\beta) = \frac{\alpha_n}{\gamma_{n,2}} \frac{1 - \epsilon_r}{1 - \bar{\beta}^2} \coth \gamma_{n,2}(H-h)$$

$$R_n = R_n(\beta) = \frac{\epsilon_r - \bar{\beta}^2}{1 - \bar{\beta}^2} \frac{\alpha_n}{\gamma_{n,1}} \coth \gamma_{n,1} h + \frac{\alpha_n}{\gamma_{n,2}} \coth \gamma_{n,2}(H-h)$$

$$\gamma_{n,1}^2 = \alpha_n^2 + \beta^2 - \epsilon_r k_o{}^2$$

$$\gamma_{n,2}^2 = \alpha_n^2 + \beta^2 - k_o{}^2$$

REFERENCES

[1] Denlinger, E.J., "A Frequency Dependent Solution for Microstrip Transmission Lines," *IEEE Trans., Vol. MTT-19*, 1971, pp. 30-39.

[2] Itoh, T. and R. Mittra, "Spectral-domain Approach for Calculating Dispersion Characteristics of Microstrip Lines," *IEEE Trans., Vol. MTT-21*, 1973, pp. 496-498.

[3] Knorr, J.B. and A. Tufekcioglu, "Spectral-domain Calculation of Microstrip Characteristics Impedance," *IEEE Trans., Vol. MTT-23*, 1975, pp. 725-728.

[4] Hornsby, J.S. and A. Gopinath, "Numerical Analysis of a Dielectric Loaded Waveguide with a Microstrip Line — Finite Difference Methods," *IEEE Trans., Vol. MTT-17*, 1969, pp. 684-690.

[5] Corr, D.G. and J.B. Davies, "Computer Analysis of the Fundamental and Higher Order Modes in Single and Coupled Microstrip," *IEEE Trans., Vol. MTT-20*, 1972, pp. 669-678.

[6] Martin, R.S. and J.H. Wilkinson, "Reduction of the Symmetric Eigenproblem Ax = λBx and Related Problems to Standard Form," *Numerische Mathematik, Vol. 11*, pp. 99-110, 1968.

[7] Berk, A.D., "Variational Principles for Electromagnetic Resonators and Waveguides," *IRE Trans., Vol. AP-4*, 1956, pp. 104-111.

[8] Schwartz, H.R., "Tridiagonalization of a Symmetric Band Matrix," *Numerische Mathematik, Vol. 12*, 1968, pp. 231-241.

[9] Barth, W. *et. al.*, "Calculation of the Eigenvalues of a Symmetric Tridiagonal Matrix by the Method of Bisection," *Numerische Mathematik, Vol. 9*, 1967, pp. 336-393.

[10] Wilkinson, J.H., "Calculation of the Eigenvectors of a Symmetric Tridiagonal Matrix by Inverse Iteration," *Numerische Mathematik, Vol. 4*, 1962, pp. 368-376.

[11] Zysman, G.I. and D. Varon, "Wave Propagation in Microstrip Transmission Lines," *IEEE G-MTT Int. Microwave Symp. Digest*, 1969, pp. 2-9.

[12] Hornsby, J.S. and A. Gopinath, "Fourier Analysis of a Dielectric-loaded Waveguide with a Microstrip," *Electron. Lett., Vol. 5*, 1969, pp. 265-267.

[13] Mittra, R. and T. Itoh, "A New Technique for the Analysis of the Dispersion Characteristics of Microstrip Lines," *IEEE Trans., Vol. MTT-19,* 1971, pp. 47-56.

[14] Lewin, L., "The Use of Singular Integral Equations in the Solution of Waveguide Problems," in *Advances in Microwaves,* L. Young (ed.), New York: Academic Press, 1966, pp. 211-284.

[15] Itoh, T. and R. Mittra, "A Technique for Computing Dispersion Characteristics of Shielded Microstrip Lines," *IEEE Trans., Vol. MTT-22,* 1974, pp. 896-898.

[16] Pucel, R.A., *et al.*, "Losses in Microstrip," *IEEE Trans., Vol. MTT-16,* 1968, pp. 342-350. Also see correction in *IEEE Trans., Vol. MTT-16,* 1968, p. 1064.

[17] Schneider, M.V., "Microstrip Lines for Microwave Integrated Circuits," *B.S.T.J., Vol. 48,* 1969, pp. 1422-1444.

[18] Wheeler, H.A., "Formulas for the Skin Effect," *Proc. IRE, Vol. 30,* 1942, pp. 412-424.

[19] Welch, J.D. and H.J. Pratt, "Losses in Microstrip Transmission Systems for Integrated Microwave Circuits," *NEREM Rec., Vol. 8,* 1966, pp. 100-101.

[20] Horton, R., *et. al.*, "Variation of Microstrip Losses with Thickness of Strip," *Electron. Lett., Vol. 7,* 1971, p. 490.

[21] Garg, R., *et. al.*, "Optimum Thickness of Metal in Waveguiding Structures, Ground Planes and Reflectors," *Int. J. Electronics, Vol. 39,* 1975, pp. 525-527.

[22] Schneider, M.V., "Dielectric Loss in Integrated Microwave Circuits," *BSTJ, Vol. 48,* 1969, pp. 2325-2332.

[23] Simpson, T.L., and B. Tseng, "Dielectric Loss in Microstrip Lines," *IEEE Trans., Vol. MTT-24,* 1976, pp. 106-108.

[24] Bahl, I.J. and D.K. Trivedi, "A Designer's Guide to Microstrip Line," *Microwaves, Vol. 16,* May 1977, pp. 174-182.

[25] Van Heuven, J., "Properties of Microstrip Lines on Fused Quartz," *IEEE Trans., Vol. MTT-18,* 1970, pp. 113-114.

[26] Bahl, I.J. and K.C. Gupta, "Average Power Handling Capability of Microstrip Lines," *IEE Jour. on Microwaves, Optics and Acoustics,* January, 1979.

[27] Owens, R.P., "Predicted Frequency Dependence of Microstrip Characteristic Impedance Using the Planar-Waveguide Model," *Electron. Lett., Vol. 12,* 1976, pp. 269-270.

[28] Bianco, B., *et. al.*, "Frequency Dependence of Microstrip Parameters," *Alta Frequenza, Vol. 43,* 1974, pp. 413-416.

[29] Bahl, I.J. and Ramesh Garg, "Simple and Accurate Formulas for Microstrip with Finite Strip Thickness," *Proc. IEEE, Vol. 65,* 1977, pp. 1611-1612.

[30] Frey, J., "Hybrid and Monolithic Microwave Integrated Circuits," in *Microwave Integrated Circuits,* J. Frey (Ed.), Artech House, 1975, pp. xvii-xxi.

[31] Heckl, H. and O. Schweiger, "Evaluation and Space Qualification of MIC on Alumina and Glass Fiber Reinforced Teflon Substrates," ESA session on 'Space Qualified MIC' at *6th European Microwave Conf.*, 1976, Rome.

[32] Howe, Jr., H., "Stripline is Alive and Well -----," *Microwave Journal, Vol. 14,* July 1971, p. 25.

[33] Garg, Ramesh, "The Effect of Tolerances on Microstrip Line and Slotline Performance," *IEEE Trans., Vol. MTT-26,* 1978, pp. 16-19.

[34] Owens, R.P., *et. al.*, "Quasi-static Characteristics of Microstrips on an Anistropic Sapphire Substrate," *IEEE Trans., Vol. MTT-24,* 1976, pp. 499-505.

[35] Szentkuti, B.T., "Simple Analysis of Anisotropic Microstrip Lines by a Transform Method," *Electron. Lett., Vol. 12,* 1976, pp. 672-673.

[36] Wheeler, H.A., "Transmission Line Properties of Parallel Strips Separated by a Dielectric Sheet," *IEEE Trans., Vol. MTT-13,* 1965, pp. 172-185. Also see: Wheeler, H.A., "Transmission Line Properties of a Strip on a Dielectric Sheet on a Plane," *IEEE Trans., Vol. MTT-25,* 1977, pp. 631-647.

[37] Hammerstad, E.O., "Equations for Microstrip Circuit Design," *Proc. European Microwave Conf.*, 1975, pp. 268-272.

[38] Hammerstad, E.O., Private communication.

[39] Gunston, M.A.R. and J.R. Weale, "Variation of Microstrip Impedances with Strip Thickness," *Electron. Lett., Vol. 5,* 1969, pp. 697-698.

[40] Kaupp, H.R., "Characteristics of Microstrip Transmission Lines," *IEEE Trans., Vol. EC-16,* 1967, pp. 185-193.

[41] Schwarzmann, A., "Microstrip Plus Equations Add Up to Fast Designs," *Electronics, Vol. 40,* Oct. 1967, pp. 109-112.

[42] John, S. and P. Arlett, "Simple Method for the Calculation of the Characteristic Impedance of Microstrip," *Electron. Lett., Vol. 10,* 1974, pp. 188-190.

[43] Kumar, A., *et. al.,* "A Method for the Calculation of the Characteristic Impedance of Microstrip," *Int. J. Electronics, Vol. 40,* 1976, pp. 45-47.

[44] Ross, R.F.G. and M.J. Howes, "Simple Formulas for Microstrip Lines," *Electron. Lett., Vol. 12,* 1976, p. 410.

[45] Gunston, M.A.R. and J.R. Weale, "The Transmission Characteristics of Microstrip," *The Marconi Review,* 1969, pp. 226-244.

[46] Gunston, M.A.R., *Microwave Transmission-line Impedance Data,* London: Van Nostrand, 1972, p. 48.

[47] Yamashita, E. and R. Mittra, "Variation Method for the Analysis of Microstrip Lines," *IEEE Trans., Vol. MTT-16,* 1968, pp. 251-256.

[48] Stinehelfer, H.E., "An Accurate Calculation of Uniform Microstrip Transmission Lines," *IEEE Trans., Vol. MTT-16,* 1968, pp. 439-444.

[49] Kowalski, G. and R. Pregla, "Dispersion Characteristics of Shielded Microstrips with Finite Thickness," *AEU, Vol. 25,* 1971, pp. 193-196.

[50] Pregla, R. and S. Nokes, "Calculation of the Capacitance of Thick Microstrip Using a Variational Expression," *AEU, Vol. 29,* 1975, pp. 125-128.

[51] Silvester, P., "TEM Wave Properties of Microstrip Transmission Lines," *Proc. IEE, Vol. 115,* 1968, pp. 43-48.

[52] Yamashita, E., "Variation Method for the Analysis of Microstrip Line Transmission Lines," *IEEE Trans., Vol. MTT-16,* 1968, pp. 529-539.

[53] Bahl, I.J., "Easy and Exact Methods for Shielded Microstrip Design" *Microwaves,* Vol. 17, December, 1978.

[54] Gish, D.L. and O. Graham, "Characteristic Impedance and Phase Velocity of a Dielectric Supported Air Strip Transmission Line with Side Walls," *IEEE Trans., Vol. MTT-18*, 1970, pp. 131-148.

[55] Getsinger, W.J., "Microstrip Dispersion Model," *IEEE Trans., Vol. MTT-21*, 1973, pp. 34-39.

[56] Edwards, T.C. and R.P. Owens, "2-18 GHz Dispersion Measurements on 10-100 ohm Microstrip Line on Sapphire," *IEEE Trans., Vol. MTT-24*, 1976, pp. 506-513.

[57] Krage, M.K. and G.I. Haddad, "Frequency Dependent Characteristics of Microstrip Transmission Lines," *IEEE Trans., Vol. MTT-20*, 1972, pp. 678-688.

[58] Belohoubek, E. and E.J. Denlinger, "Loss Considerations for Microstrip Resonators," *IEEE Trans., Vol. MTT-23*, 1975, pp. 522-526.

[59] Denlinger, E., "Radiation from Microstrip Resonators," *IEEE Trans., Vol. MTT-16*, 1969, pp. 235-236.

[60] Garg, Ramesh, "Microstrip Design Guides," *Int. J. Electronics* (To appear).

Chapter 3

Microstrip Discontinuities I:

Quasi-static Analysis and Characterization

3.1 INTRODUCTION

Microstrip circuits are invariably accompanied by discontinuities of one type or another. Some of the most common forms of microstrip discontinuities are open ends, gaps, steps in width, right-angled bends, T and cross junctions. These are shown in Figure 3.1. Examples of circuits or circuit elements, wherein these discontinuities occur frequently, are also listed in this figure. A complete understanding and design of microstrip circuits require characterization of various discontinuities included in the circuit. Since discontinuity dimensions are usually much smaller than the wavelength in microstrip, they may be approximated by lumped element equivalent circuits. A more complete characterization involves determination of frequency dependent scattering matrix coefficients associated with the discontinuity. Various methods of characterization of microstrip discontinuities are discussed in the present and the next chapter.

Discontinuities appear in conventional microwave circuits (using coaxial lines and waveguides) also. However, it may be pointed out that it is much more important to characterize discontinuities in microstrip circuits accurately. This is because of the fact that the microstrip circuits do not lend themselves to easy adjustments or tuning after the fabrication of the circuit is completed. If a provision is made for adjustments, the main advantages of compactness and reliability gained by the use of microstrip circuits are lost (at least partially).

A discontinuity in microstrip is caused by abrupt change in the geometry of the strip conductor. Therefore, electric and magnetic field distributions are modified near the discontinuity. The altered electric field distribution gives rise to a change in capacitance, and

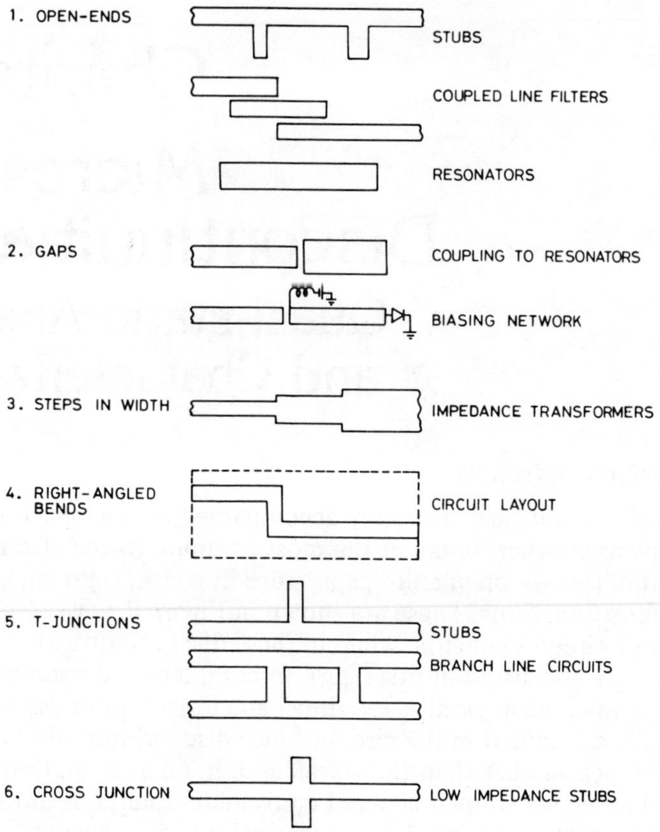

Figure 3.1 Various Types of Microstrip Discontinuities and their Typical Applications

the changed magnetic field distribution can be written in terms of an equivalent inductance. The analysis of microstrip discontinuity involves the evaluation of these capacitances and inductances. Analysis of microstrip discontinuities can either be based on quasi-static considerations or carried out more rigorously by fullwave analysis.

Quasi-static analysis involves calculations of static capacitances and low frequency inductances. Equivalent circuits for discontinuities may be derived from these results. Alternatively, a waveguide type dynamic analysis taking dispersion (and possibly higher order modes also) into account may be carried out. This leads to a frequency dependent scattering matrix. Again, equivalent circuits for discontinuities can be based on these results. Methods for calculation of quasi-static capacitance and inductance for the discontinuity will be discussed in the present chapter. Fullwave analysis of the discontinuities is included in Chapter 4.

3.2 DISCONTINUITY CAPACITANCE EVALUATION

The static values of capacitances associated with discontinuities can be evaluated by finding the excess charge distribution near the discontinuity. The quasi-static methods for the evaluation of discontinuity capacitance have been treated by Farrar and Adams [1 - 3], Maeda [4], Itoh *et al.* [5,6], Silvester and Benedek [7,9], Benedek and Silvester [8] and Horton [10,11]. Different methods used for these calculations are listed below:

1. Matrix inversion method [1 - 3],
2. Variational method [4],
3. Galerkin's method in the spectral domain [5,6], and
4. Use of line sources with charge reversal [7 - 9].

These methods are discussed briefly in the following subsections. In all these methods, the following assumptions are implied: the size of the discontinuity is small compared to the wavelength so that the phase variation across the discontinuity can be neglected; the current on the strip has zero divergence; and the strip conductor is infinitely thin.

3.2.1 Matrix Inversion Method

The matrix inversion method [3] is a very general approach for finding the static capacitance of a conductor of any arbitrary shape on the top surface of the microstrip substrate. The total conductor area is divided into small sub-sections over which the charge density can be assumed to be uniform. This sub-division for a microstrip rectangular section of length L and width W is shown in Figure 3.2. The typical sub-section Δs_j, of sides Δx_j and Δz_j, is assumed to bear a uniform surface charge density σ_j. The potential at subsection Δs_i due to n number of subsections may be written as

$$V_i = \sum_{j=1}^{n} \sigma_j D_{ij} \tag{3.1}$$

where D_{ij} is a function representing potential at sub-section Δs_i, due to a uniform charge density of magnitude unity on Δs_j. One can write a Green's function expressing potential due to a unit charge at Δs_j. Since the potential varies in all three directions, the

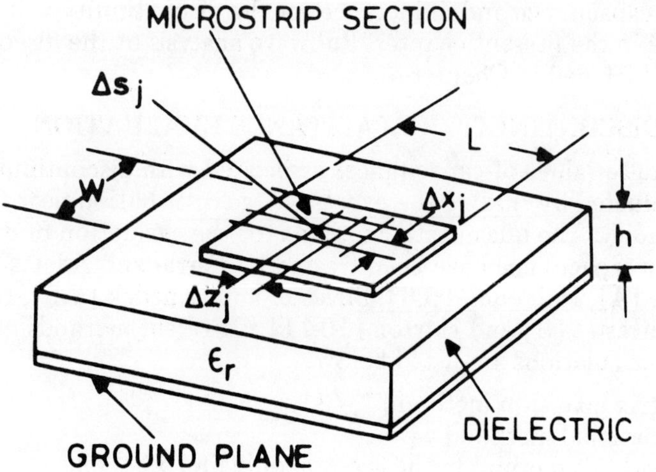

Figure 3.2 A Typical Microstrip Discontinuity Area Divided into Small Sections

Green's function becomes three-dimensional. Values of D_{ij} correspond to values of this Green's function at y = h. Equation (3.1) may be put in matrix form as

$$[V] = [D]\ [\sigma] \tag{3.2}$$

The unknown charge densities $[\sigma]$ are obtained by matrix inversion

$$[\sigma] = [D]^{-1}\ [V] \tag{3.3}$$

If the voltage over the conductor with respect to the ground plane is taken as unity, the total capacitance of the conductor may be written as

$$C = \sum_{j=1}^{n} \sigma_j = \sum_{i=1}^{n} \sum_{j=1}^{n} D'_{ij} \tag{3.4}$$

where D'_{ij} represents an element of matrix $[D]^{-1}$.

In order to implement this method, an expression for D_{ij} is needed. D_{ij} for a rectangular subsection is derived by using the theory of images [3]. A rectangular subsection has been selected because of its frequent occurence in discontinuity problems. For evaluation of D_{ij}, the potential due to a uniformly charged plate in free space is obtained first. D_{ij} for the microstrip section is then evaluated by using the principle of multiple images. The resulting expression is a series, each term of which is contributed by an image of the charge. This series expression may be written as

$$D_{ij} = \sum_{n=1}^{\infty} \frac{K^{n-1}}{2\pi \epsilon_o (1+\epsilon_r)} \cdot$$

$$\left\{ (z_j - z_i) \ln \frac{(c+A)(d+B)(d+G)(c+H)}{(d+C)(c+D)(c+E)(d+F)} \right.$$

$$+ \frac{\Delta z_j}{2} \ln \frac{(d+B)(d+C)(c+E)(c+H)}{(c+D)(c+A)(d+G)(d+F)}$$

$$+ (x_j - x_i) \ln \frac{(a+A)(b+B)(b+H)(a+G)}{(b+D)(a+C)(a+E)(b+F)}$$

$$+ \frac{\Delta x_j}{2} \ln \frac{(b+B(b+D)(a+E)(a+G)}{(a+C)(a+A)(b+G)(b+F)}$$

$$- (2n-2)\,h \left[\tan^{-1} \frac{ac}{(2n-2)\,hA} \right.$$

$$\left. + \tan^{-1} \frac{bd}{(2n-2)\,hB} \right] + (2n-2)h \cdot$$

$$\left[\tan^{-1} \frac{ad}{(2n-2)\,hC} + \tan^{-1} \frac{bc}{(2n-2)\,hD} \right]$$

$$+ 2nh \left[\tan^{-1} \frac{ac}{2nhE} + \tan^{-1} \frac{bd}{2nhF} \right]$$

$$\left. - 2nh \left[\tan^{-1} \frac{ad}{2nhG} + \tan^{-1} \frac{bc}{2nhH} \right] \right\} \qquad (3.5)$$

where

$A = \sqrt{a^2 + c^2 + (2n-2)^2 h^2}$ $\qquad$ $E = \sqrt{a^2 + c^2 + (2nh)^2}$

$B = \sqrt{b^2 + d^2 + (2n-2)^2 h^2}$ $\qquad$ $F = \sqrt{b^2 + d^2 + (2nh)^2}$

$C = \sqrt{a^2 + d^2 + (2n-2)^2 h^2}$ $\qquad$ $G = \sqrt{a^2 + d^2 + (2nh)^2}$

$D = \sqrt{b^2 + c^2 + (2n-2)^2 h^2}$ $\qquad$ $H = \sqrt{b^2 + c^2 + (2nh)^2}$

and

$$a = z_j - \frac{\Delta z_j}{2} - z_i \qquad b = z_j + \frac{\Delta z_j}{2} - z_i$$

$$c = x_j - \frac{\Delta x_j}{2} - x_i \qquad d = x_j + \frac{\Delta x_j}{2} - x_i$$

$$K = \frac{1 - \epsilon_r}{1 + \epsilon_r}$$

Slow convergence of the series in Equation (3.5) is a draw back of this method. About 40 terms of the series have been used in the computation of discontinuity capacitances [3].

The method has been used for finding capacitances associated with microstrip open-ends, steps and gaps. The capacitance associated with an open-end (shown in Figure 3.3) may be written as

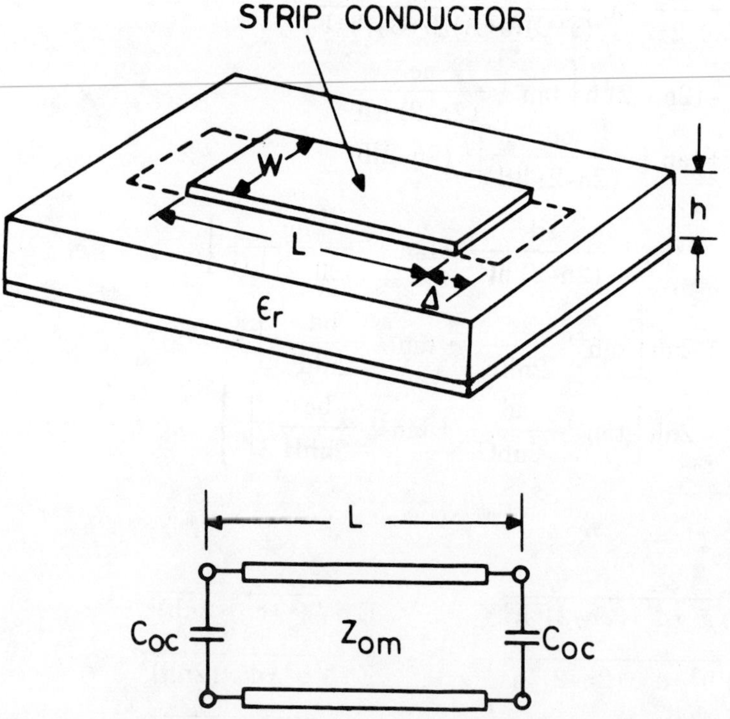

Figure 3.3 Configuration for Calculation of Microstrip Open-End Capacitance and its Equivalent Circuit

$$C_{oc} = \tfrac{1}{2} \lim_{L \to \infty} [C_t(L) - C\,L] \tag{3.6}$$

$C_t(L)$ is the total capacitance of a microstrip section of total length L, and C is the capacitance per unit length of an infinite line of the same width. In order to find out the limit in Equation (3.6), the length L is increased iteratively and the total capacitance is computed everytime until the open-end capacitance given by Equation (3.6) converges. A difficulty with this procedure is that Equation (3.6) involves subtraction of two nearly equal large numbers, and therefore very accurate computations of $C_t(L)$ and CL are necessary.

The configuration for calculation of capacitance associated with a step in the width of microstrip is shown in Figure 3.4. Its equivalent

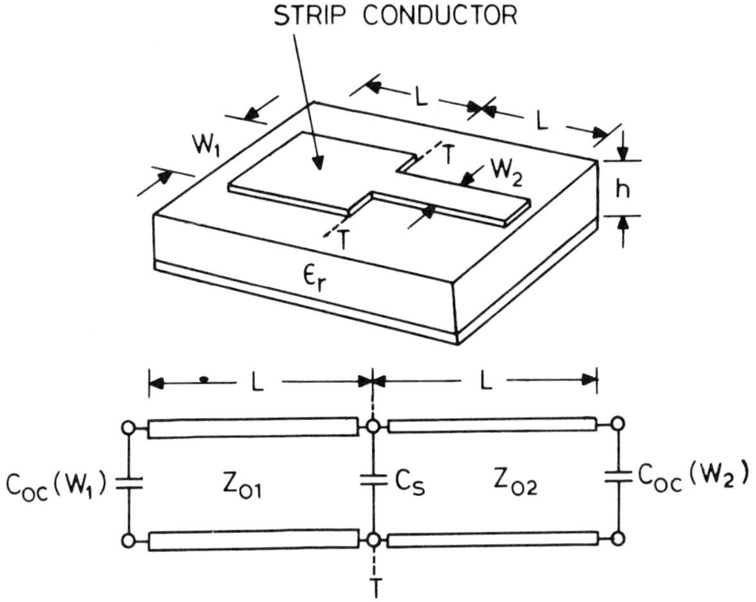

Figure 3.4 Geometry for Calculating Capacitance of a Step Discontinuity and its Equivalent Circuit

circuit is also shown in this figure. The capacitance associated with the step is evaluated as

$$C_s = \lim_{L \to \infty} [C_t(L) - C_{oc}(W_1) - C_{oc}(W_2) - C_1\,L - C_2\,L] \tag{3.7}$$

where $C_{oc}(W_1)$ and $C_{oc}(W_2)$ are open-end capacitances of lines of width W_1 and W_2 respectively, and C_1 and C_2 are capacitances per unit length for these lines.

In the case of a microstrip gap, the equivalent circuit consists of three capacitances in a pi-configuration as shown in Figure 3.5.

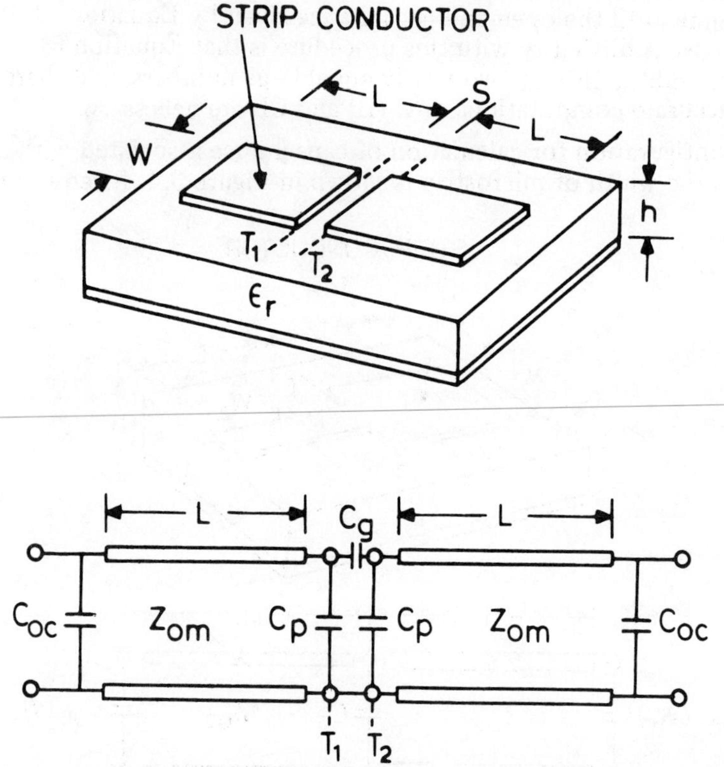

Figure 3.5 Configuration for Characterization of a Microstrip Gap and its Equivalent Circuit

For evaluation of these capacitances, a capacitance matrix $[C(L)]$ is computed as

$$[C(L)] = \begin{bmatrix} C_{11}(L) & C_{12}(L) \\ C_{21}(L) & C_{22}(L) \end{bmatrix} \tag{3.8}$$

where $C_{ij}(L)$ are related to the elements of admittance matrix of the two port network (shown in Figure 3.5) by

$$C_{ij}(L) = Y_{ij}/j\omega \tag{3.9}$$

Capacitances C_p and C_g are then computed by using

$$C_p = \lim_{L\to\infty} [C_{11}(L) - CL - C_{oc}] \tag{3.10a}$$

$$C_g = \lim_{L\to\infty} C_{12}(L) \tag{3.10b}$$

It may be noted that the subtraction of two nearly equal large numbers is involved in Equations (3.7) and (3.10a). But such a subtraction is not involved in the computation of C_g and thus an accurate computation of C_g is much less time consuming.

One can conclude that the method described above is a general one and can be used to compute the excess capacitance of any microstrip discontinuity. The difficulties faced in this method are: slow convergence of infinite series in the three-dimensional Green's function and the subtraction of two nearly equal large numbers. The accuracy of capacitance results can be improved at the expense of increased computer time.

3.2.2 Variational Method

This method [4] uses the variational principle for formulating the capacitance problem. It is known that the capacitance can be expressed by a variational expression which is stationary with respect to arbitrary first order variations in the charge distribution on the strip conductor [12]. If the charge distribution is $\rho(r)$, the capacitance C may be expressed as

$$\frac{1}{C} = \frac{\iint \rho(r)\, G(r;r')\, \rho(r')\, dv'\, dv}{\left[\int \rho(r')\, dv'\right]^2} \tag{3.11}$$

where the integrals are taken through all the volume in which the charge is distributed. Source and observation point coordinates are shown in Figure 3.6. Since Equation (3.11) is a lower bound type of expression, the capacitance can be obtained by maximizing with a suitable choice of charge distribution as a trial function.

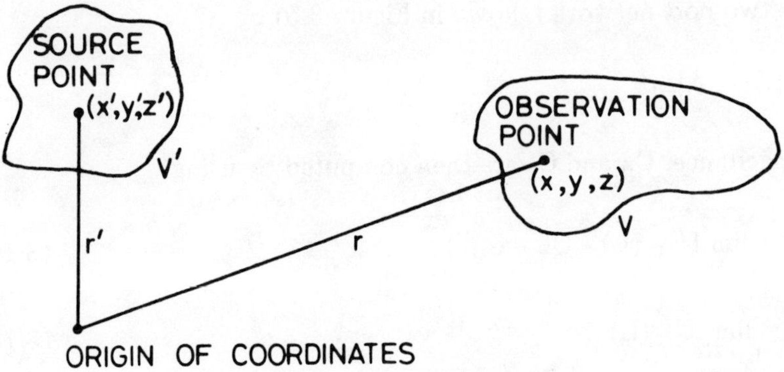

Figure 3.6 Coordinate System for Source and Observation Points

Therefore, charge distribution need not be known exactly when using this method. G is a three dimensional Green's function for potential and satisfies the following relation

$$\nabla^2 G(x,y,z; x',y',z') = -\frac{1}{\epsilon_o \epsilon_r} \delta(x - x')\, \delta(y - y')\, \delta(z - z') \tag{3.12}$$

where δ indicates a Dirac's delta function. Green's functions for the case $y = h$ are adequate for the evaluation of excess capacitance of a discontinuity using the variational expression (3.11).

The variational method has been used for characterizing two types of discontinuities, an open-end and a gap, for which suitable Green's functions have been developed. As shown in Figure 3.7(a), a gap in the strip conductor of microstrip line which is represented by a pi equivalent circuit can be analyzed by placing an electric wall and a magnetic wall successively along the plane of symmetry A. This corresponds to a short circuit and an open circuit, respectively, in the equivalent circuit representation. The capacitance between the microstrip end and the plane A is called C_e for electric wall and C_m for magnetic wall. The parameters of the equivalent pi circuit, C_p (shunt gap capacitance) and C_g (coupling capacitance between the adjacent strip conductors) may be written in terms of C_e and C_m as

$$C_e = C_p + 2C_g \qquad \text{and} \qquad C_m = C_p \tag{3.13}$$

The capacitances C_e and C_m can be evaluated using Equation (3.11)

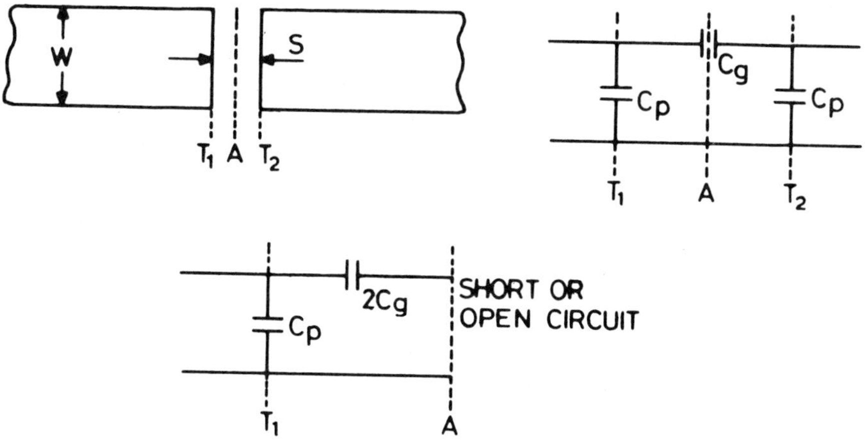

Figure 3.7(a) Representation of a Gap in Microstrip and its Equivalent Circuit

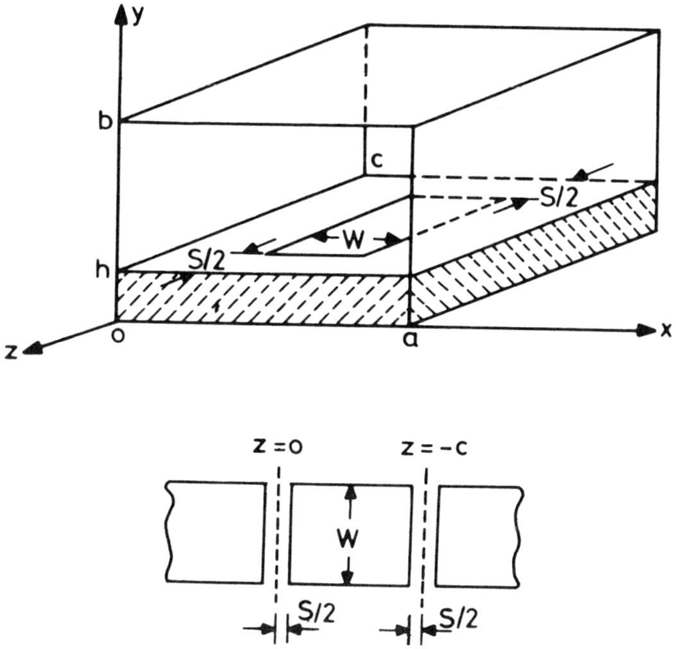

Figure 3.7(b) Configuration for Evaluation of Green's Functions for Gap Capacitances

with suitable G and ρ. The configuration considered for evaluation of G for the two cases is shown in Figure 3.7(b). The portion of microstrip between the planes of symmetry located at z = 0 and z = -c is enclosed in a box as shown in this figure. Two Green's functions G_e and G_m are evaluated for electric wall and magnetic wall cases by writing the solution of Equation (3.12) as a linear combination of hyperbolic sinusoidal functions and applying boundary and continuity conditions. The expressions obtained for G_e and G_m may be written as [4],

$$G_e(x,y,z;x',h,z') = \begin{cases} \sum_{m=1}^{\infty}\sum_{n=1}^{\infty} P.Q.\sinh(\gamma_{mn}y)\sinh[\gamma_{mn}(b-h)] & (0\leqslant y\leqslant h) \quad (3.14a) \\ \sum_{m=1}^{\infty}\sum_{n=1}^{\infty} P.Q.\sinh[\gamma_{mn}(b-y)]\sinh(\gamma_{mn}h) & (h\leqslant y\leqslant b) \quad (3.14b) \end{cases}$$

and

$$G_m(x,y,z;x',h,z') = \begin{cases} \sum_{m=1}^{\infty}\sum_{n=0}^{\infty} \sigma_n P.R.\sinh(\gamma_{mn}y)\sinh[\gamma_{mn}(b-h)] & (0\leqslant y\leqslant h) \quad (3.15a) \\ \sum_{m=1}^{\infty}\sum_{n=0}^{\infty} \sigma_n P.R.\sinh[\gamma_{mn}(b-y)]\sinh(\gamma_{mn}h) & (h\leqslant y\leqslant b) \quad (3.15b) \end{cases}$$

where

$$P = \frac{4}{ac\gamma_{mn}\Gamma_{mn}}\sin\left(\frac{m\pi x}{a}\right)\sin\left(\frac{m\pi x'}{a}\right)$$

$$Q = \sin\left(\frac{n\pi z}{c}\right)\sin\left(\frac{n\pi z'}{c}\right)$$

$$R = \cos\left(\frac{n\pi z}{c}\right)\cos\left(\frac{n\pi z'}{c}\right)$$

$$\gamma_{mn} = \left[\left(\frac{m\pi}{a}\right)^2 + \left(\frac{n\pi}{c}\right)^2\right]^{1/2}$$

$$\Gamma_{mn} = \epsilon_r \cosh(\gamma_{mn}h)\sinh[\gamma_{mn}(b-h)] + \sinh(\gamma_{mn}h)\cosh[\gamma_{mn}(b-h)]$$

and σ_n is ½ for n = 0 and is 1 for n $\neq$ 0. The only additional information required for solving Equation (3.11) is an estimate for charge distribution ρ. If it is assumed that $\rho(x,z)$ is separable in x and z directions we can write,

$$\rho(x,z) = f(x)\, g(z) \tag{3.16}$$

where f(x) corresponds to the charge distribution of a uniform microstrip and may be written as [13]

$$f(x) = \begin{cases} 1 + \left| \dfrac{2}{W}\left(x - \dfrac{a}{2}\right) \right|^3 & \text{for } \left| x - \dfrac{a}{2} \right| \leqslant \dfrac{W}{2} \\ 0 & \text{elsewhere} \end{cases} \tag{3.17}$$

Charge density in the longitudinal direction also increases near the edge of the strip conductor, and g(z) may be assumed to have the form

$$g(z) = \begin{cases} 0 & \dfrac{c}{2} - \dfrac{S}{2} \leqslant \left| z - \dfrac{c}{2} \right| \leqslant \dfrac{c}{2} \\ 1 + \dfrac{K}{h}\left\{ \left| z - \dfrac{c}{2} \right| - \dfrac{c}{2} + \dfrac{S}{2} + h \right\}, & \dfrac{c}{2} - \dfrac{S}{2} - h \leqslant \left| z - \dfrac{c}{2} \right| \leqslant \dfrac{c}{2} - \dfrac{S}{2} \\ 1 & \left| z - \dfrac{c}{2} \right| \leqslant \dfrac{c}{2} - \dfrac{S}{2} - h \end{cases} \tag{3.18}$$

The coefficient K is determined so as to maximize the capacitance. A table of optimum values of coefficient K for the electric and magnetic walls for various values of ϵ_r and S/h is given by Maeda [4]. When S/h is large (or in the case of an open circuit discontinuity), K becomes unity for the electric as well as the magnetic walls.

This method has been used for characterization of gaps and open-ends. The open-end capacitance is evaluated as a limit of gap capacitance C_g when the gap width becomes very large. A fairly good agreement with experimental results is reported in reference [4].

3.2.3 Galerkin's Method in FTD [5,6]

This method is similar to Galerkin's method in FTD used for fullwave analysis of microstrip lines discussed in Chapter 2 and the variational method in FTD used for quasi-static analysis in Chapter 1. The microstrip configuration and the coordinate system are shown in Figure 3.8.

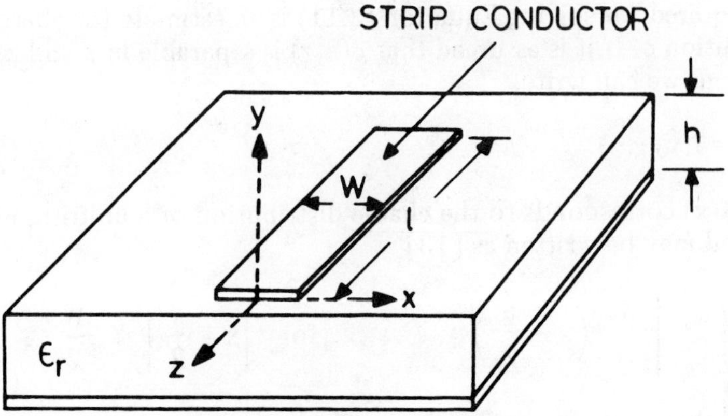

Figure 3.8 Microstrip Geometry and Coordinate System Used for Galerkin's Method in Spectral Domain

In this case a two-dimensional Fourier transform in the x-z plane is used. Transforms of potential and charge are defined by

$$\tilde{\phi}(\alpha,y,\beta) = \int_{-\infty}^{\infty}\int_{-\infty}^{\infty} \phi(x,y,z) \exp(j\{\alpha x + \beta z\})\, dx\, dz \tag{3.19}$$

$$\tilde{\rho}(\alpha,\beta) = \int_{-\ell/2}^{\ell/2}\int_{-W/2}^{W/2} \rho(x,z) \exp(j\{\alpha x+\beta z\})\, dx\, dz \tag{3.20}$$

In spectral domain, Poisson's equation is written as

$$\left[\frac{\partial^2}{\partial y^2} - (\alpha^2 + \beta^2)\right] \tilde{\phi}(\alpha,y,\beta) = -\frac{1}{\epsilon_o}\, \rho(\alpha,\beta)\, \delta(y) \tag{3.21}$$

Boundary conditions at y = -h and y→∞, and the interface conditions at y = 0 are written in spectral domain. When these conditions are applied to Equation (3.21), we obtain

$$G(\alpha,\beta)\, \tilde{\rho}(\alpha,\beta) = \tilde{\phi}_i(\alpha,0,\beta) + \tilde{\phi}_o(\alpha,0,\beta) \tag{3.22}$$

where

$$G(\alpha,\beta) = \frac{1}{\epsilon_o \sqrt{(\alpha^2+\beta^2)}\, [1 + \epsilon_r \coth\{\sqrt{(\alpha^2+\beta^2)}\, h\}]} \tag{3.23}$$

and $\tilde{\phi}_i$ and $\tilde{\phi}_o$ are the transforms of the potential functions on the strip and outside the strip at y = 0, respectively. We assume that the potentials on the strip and the ground plane are 1 and 0 volt, respectively. Using Equation (3.19),

$$\tilde{\phi}_i = \frac{4}{\alpha\beta} \sin\frac{\alpha W}{2} \sin\frac{\beta \ell}{2} \tag{3.24}$$

Now Equation (3.22) contains two unknowns, the transforms of charge on the strip $\tilde{\rho}$ and the potential outside the strip $\tilde{\phi}_o$.

At this stage Galerkin's method is applied which eliminates one of the unknowns ϕ_o and converts Equation (3.22) into a small size matrix equation. This is subsequently solved for the unknown coefficients. The matrix equation is

$$\sum_{n=1}^{N} K_{mn}\, d_n = f_m \qquad m = 1,2,\ldots, N \tag{3.25}$$

where

$$K_{mn} = \int_{-\infty}^{\infty}\int_{-\infty}^{\infty} \tilde{\xi}_m(\alpha,\beta)\, G(\alpha,\beta)\, \tilde{\xi}_n(\alpha,\beta)\, d\alpha\, d\beta$$

$$f_m = \int_{-\infty}^{\infty}\int_{-\infty}^{\infty} \tilde{\xi}_m(\alpha,\beta)\, \tilde{\phi}_i(\alpha,0,\beta)\, d\alpha\, d\beta$$

and $\tilde{\xi}_m$'s are the basis functions for $\tilde{\rho}$. Equation (3.25) is solved for d_n. Finally, the charge distribution in the space domain is expressed in terms of the superposition of the inverse transforms of the basis functions weighted by the coefficients d_n.

The choice of the basis functions is arbitrary as long as they satisfy the required condition that they are zero in the appropriate range. The basis functions chosen are transforms of the following:

$$\xi_m(x,z) = \begin{cases} |x|^{k-1}\, |z|^{j-1} , & \text{on the strip} \\ 0 , & \text{otherwise} \end{cases} \tag{3.26}$$

where m = 1 for k = 1, j = 1; m = 2 for k = 2, j = 1 etc. In actual numerical computations only one or two terms in ζ_m are sufficient. Total capacitance for the strip is obtained form the following expression

$$C = \int_{-\ell/2}^{\ell/2}\int_{-W/2}^{W/2} \rho(x,z)\, dx\, dz = (2\pi)^2 \sum_{n=1}^{N} d_n f_n \tag{3.27}$$

The fringing capacitance at the end of the open-circuited microstrip may again be evaluated by using Equation (3.6).

Comparing with the variational method of the last subsection, one notes that the Green's function in the transform domain is a closed form expression in contrast to a slowly converging series in the space domain.

Although this method could, in principle, be applied to other discontinuities also, the results are available for microstrip open-ends only.

3.2.4 Use of Line Sources with Charge Reversal

All of the three methods for the evaluation of discontinuity capacitance, discussed above, involve subtraction of two nearly equal large quantities. This factor limits the computational accuracy. A method using line sources with charge reversal [7-9] overcomes this difficulty. This method uses line sources (not sub-areas) for developing Green's functions suitable for discontinuity problems. The basic element common to all the discontinuities considered using this method is a semi-infinite line charge. Formulation of the Green's function for a semi-infinite line charge is shown in Figure 3.9. Here, the semi-infinite line charge (c) is considered as superposition of two

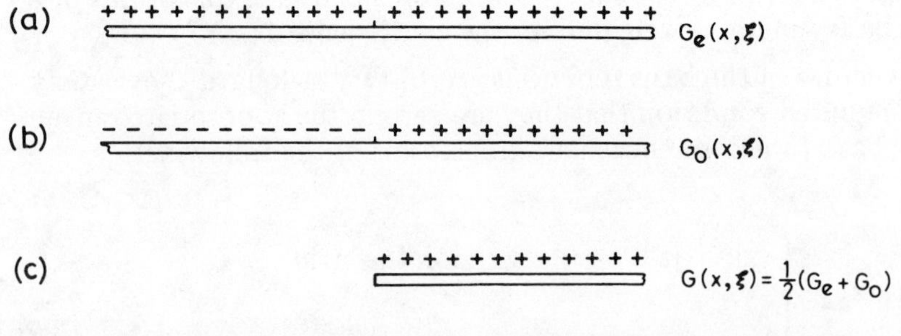

Figure 3.9 Formulation of Green's functions for a Semi-Infinite Line Source

line charges (a) and (b). Figure 3.9(a) shows a uniform and infinitely long line charge such as present in the case of an infinite microstrip. This charge distribution can be obtained by solving

$$\phi_e(x) = \int_{-\infty}^{\infty} \sigma_\infty(\xi) G_e(x, \xi)\, d\xi \tag{3.28}$$

where G_e is the two dimensional Green's function of the microstrip problem discussed in Section 1.2.3 and σ_∞ is the charge density on infinitely extended microstrip line. We also consider a charge distribution shown in Figure 3.9(b) that is exactly similar to $\sigma_\infty(\xi)$ on half the infinite strip and exactly $-\sigma_\infty(\xi)$ on the other half. While this situation is physically difficult to realize, there is no mathematical objection to it, and the potential distribution in this case may be written as

$$\phi_o(x) = \int_{-\infty}^{\infty} \sigma_\infty(\xi)\, G_o(x,\xi)\, d\xi \tag{3.29}$$

where $G_o(x,\xi)$ is the appropriate Green's function. When the charge distributions given by Equations (3.28) and (3.29) are combined, we obtain the configuration of a semi-infinite line charge, Figure 3.9(c), and the potential distribution is now given by

$$\phi_{si} = \tfrac{1}{2}\left\{\phi_e + \phi_o\right\} = \tfrac{1}{2}\int \sigma_\infty(\xi)\left\{G_e(x,\xi) + G_o(x,\xi)\right\} d\xi \tag{3.30}$$

where ϕ_{si} is the potential associated with a charge distribution exactly like that of an infinite microstrip, but terminating at the origin. The potential ϕ_{si} cannot satisfy the requirement of constant potential everywhere on the semi-infinite strip. For obtaining a constant potential, a certain amount of extra charge, say σ_e, must be placed on half the strip. This excess charge σ_e may be obtained from the following equation,

$$\phi - \phi_{si} = \int \sigma_e(\xi)\, G(x;\xi)\, d\xi \tag{3.31}$$

where ϕ is constant potential ($= \phi_e$) over the semi-infinite length and $G = \tfrac{1}{2}(G_e + G_o)$. It may be noted that the excess charge $\sigma_e(\xi)$ is responsible for discontinuity capacitance C, which may now be written as

$$C = \frac{1}{\phi} \int \sigma_e \, dx \tag{3.32}$$

Using the concepts outlined above, computation of the capacitance associated with a microstrip open-end involves the following steps:

i) construction of G_e and G_o
ii) evaluation of ϕ_{si} from Equation (3.30)
iii) solution of integral Equation (3.31) for σ_e, and
iv) finding capacitance from Equation (3.32).

Although the integration (3.31) is over semi-infinite length, it may be noted that both the potential residual and the excess charge approach zero asymptotically (and rather rapidly) for points at increasing distances from the strip end. Also, Equations (3.31) and (3.32) permit the solution for excess charge density and excess capacitance directly, and subtraction of two nearly large quantities is not involved.

Green's functions G_e and G_o are obtained [7] by considering the multiple images of a line charge when placed parallel to a dielectric slab. Green's function G_e for microstrip is given by Equation (1.36) of chapter 1 and G_o may be written as

$$G_o(x,h,z;x_o) = \frac{1-K}{4\pi\epsilon_o\epsilon_r}\left[f(0) - (1-K)\sum_{n=1}^{\infty} K^{n-1} f(n) \right] \tag{3.33}$$

where $K = (1 - \epsilon_r)/(1 + \epsilon_r)$ and

$$f(n) = \ln \frac{\sqrt{z^2 + 4n^2h^2 + (x - x_o)^2} + z}{\sqrt{z^2 + 4n^2h^2 + (x - x_o)^2} - z}$$

The line source configuration used is shown in Figure 3.10 and h is the height of the dielectric substrate.

This method is very general and is used for all types of microstrip discontinuities [8,9] shown in Figure 3.1. Formulation for a microstrip gap is sketched in Figure 3.11. Green's functions G_{even} and G_{odd} are used in equations similar to Equation (3.31) for calculating residual potentials which lead to excess charges and discontinuity capacitances. Similar formulations may be carried out for other discontinuities also.

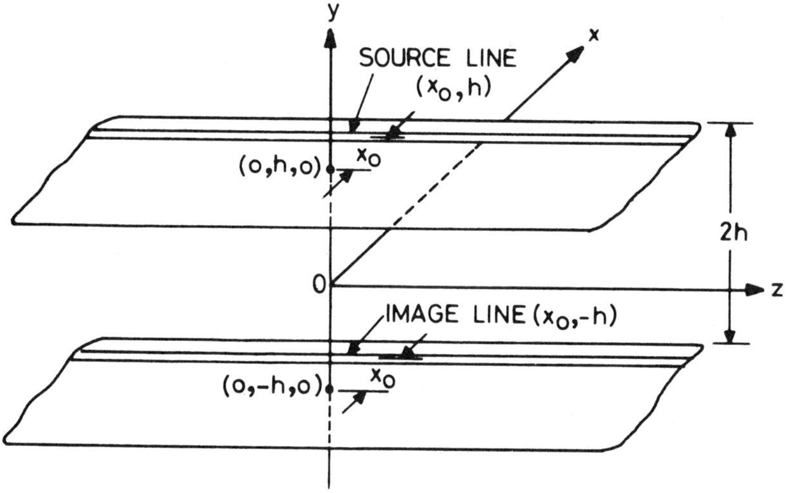

Figure 3.10 Configuration for Calculating G_e and G_o of Figure 3.9

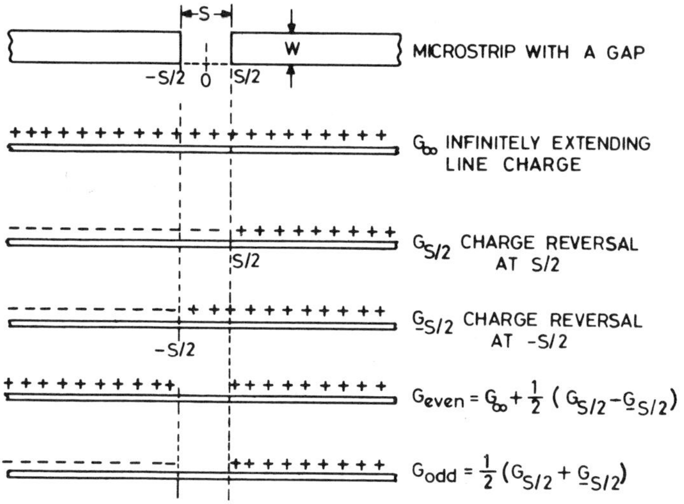

Figure 3.11 Formulation of a Microstrip Gap in Terms of Line Charges

3.3 DISCONTINUITY INDUCTANCE EVALUATION

Calculation of capacitances associated with microstirp discontinuities has been discussed in the above section. However in several cases, e.g. bends, steps, T-junctions etc., inductive effects also become significant. Evaluation of inductive reactances in the equivalent circuit of microstrip discontinuities using the quasi-static method [14, 15] will be discussed in this section. These inductive components are frequency dependent, and quasi-static calculation can provide only their low frequency values.

When inductances are being calculated, the presence of the dielectric substrate (provided it is nonmagnetic) may be disregarded, and only the discontinuity structure and its image in the ground plane are considered. For magnetic substrates it will be necessary to consider the multiple images formed.

The magnetic vector potential A due to the current density J on any section of the line or discontinuity can be written as

$$A = \mu_o \int GJ\, dV \tag{3.34}$$

where G is the Green's function given by

$$G = \frac{1}{4\pi \left[(x-x_o)^2 + (y-y_o)^2 + (z-z_o)^2 \right]^{1/2}} \tag{3.35}$$

From Maxwell's equation, the electric field may be written as

$$E = -\frac{\partial A}{\partial t} - \nabla \phi \tag{3.36}$$

where ϕ is the impressed voltage on the strip which causes current to flow. Also from Ohm's law we have

$$J = \sigma E \tag{3.37}$$

where σ is the strip conductivity. Combining Equations (3.34), (3.36) and (3.37) we may write

$$J + \mu_o \sigma \frac{\partial}{\partial t} \int GJ\, dV = -\sigma \nabla \phi \tag{3.38}$$

For good conductors $\sigma \rightarrow \infty$ and Equation (3.38) may be rewritten as

$$\mu_o \frac{\partial}{\partial t} \int GJ\, dV \simeq -\nabla\phi \tag{3.39}$$

Divergence of Equation (3.39) yields (under quasi-static assumptions)

$$\nabla^2 \phi = 0 \tag{3.40}$$

which implies that the impressed potential satisfies Laplace's equation on the strip conductor. Current density distribution on the microstrip structure can be found by solving Equation (3.40) for ϕ (or $\nabla\phi$) and then Equation (3.38) for J. Knowledge of current density distribution J enables the inductance L of the microstrip structure to be obtained from the following relation

$$\int (A.J)\, dV = I^2 L\,, \qquad \text{where } I = \int J.dS \tag{3.41}$$

A straightforward implementation of the procedure indicated above will yield a value of discontinuity inductance as the difference between two large numbers corresponding to the inductance of the total structure including the discontinuity and the inductance contributed by the uniform line portion of the discontinuity structure. In this procedure it becomes difficult to obtain accurate values of L. This can be overcome using an excess current technique [14] similar to the excess charge formulation [7] used in Section 3.2.4. We will discuss this technique for the case of a right-angled bend.

For the purpose of inductance calculation, the configuration of the right-angled bend is divided into five sections (S1 to S5) as shown in Figure 3.12. The planes PP′ and QQ′ are located such that the currents in S1 and S5 are practically the same as for infinitely long lines; i.e., $J_{z\infty}$ or $J_{x\infty}$ respectively. In S_2 and S_4, the current distribution is considered to consist of two components $J_{z\infty}$ or $J_{x\infty}$ and J_{e2} or J_{e4}, the latter being excess circulating current because of the discontinuity. In S3 the only current component present is the excess circulating current J_{e3}. The magnitude and the distribution of excess circulating currents J_{e2}, J_{e3} and J_{e4} are to be determined. Equation (3.39) becomes (for the configuration in Figure 3.12),

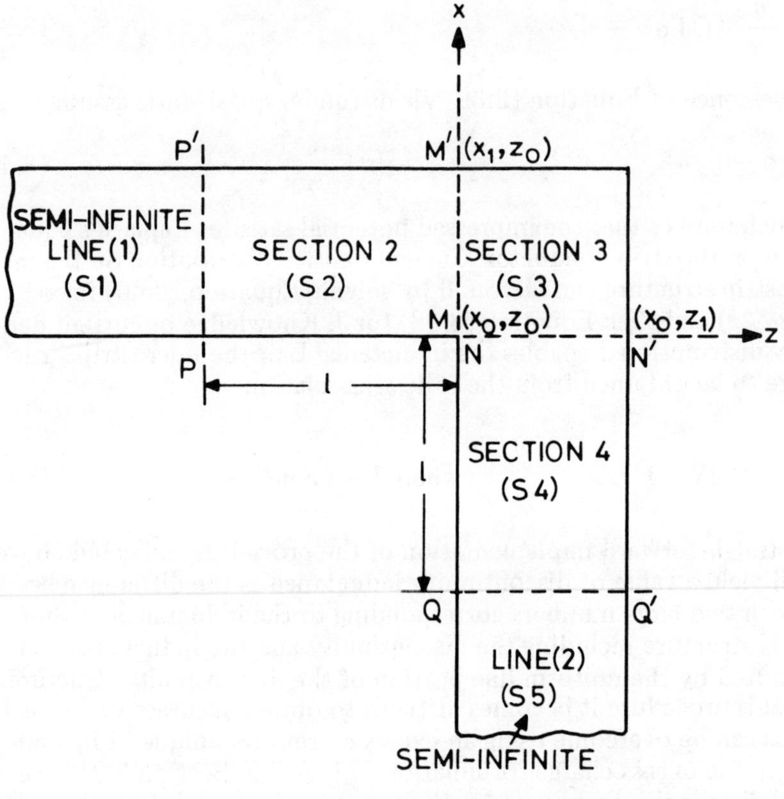

Figure 3.12 Subdivision of a Right-Angled Bend Structure for Calculation of Discontinuity Inductance

$$\int_{s1} G_i\, J_{z\infty}\, dS + \int_{s2} G_i(J_{z\infty} + J_{e2})\, dS + \int_{s3} G_i\, J_{e3}\, dS + \int_{s4} G_i(J_{x\infty} + J_{e4})\, dS$$

$$+ \int_{s5} G_i\, J_{x\infty}\, dS = \frac{-1}{\mu_o} \nabla \Phi \qquad (3.42)$$

where $\Phi = \phi/(jt\omega)$, t is the thickness of the strip conductor, and ω is the angular frequency. $J_{z\infty}$ and $J_{x\infty}$ are current distributions for infinite line and vary only along x and z, respectively. Thus, they can be integrated analytically with respect to x and z, respectively. G_i is the Green's function for the line current element and its image, and may be written as

$$G_i = \frac{1}{4\pi[(x-x_o)^2 + (z-z_o)^2]^{1/2}} - \frac{1}{4\pi[(x-x_o)^2 + (2h)^2 + (z-z_o)^2]^{1/2}} \tag{3.43}$$

When Green's functions for semi-infinite line currents (along with their images in the ground plane) are introduced, Equation (3.42) may be rewritten as

$$\int_{s2+s3+s4} G_i\, J_e\, dS = \frac{-1}{\mu_o} \nabla\Phi - \int_{z_0}^{z_1} G_1\, J_{x\infty}\, dz - \int_{x_0}^{x_1} G_2\, J_{z\infty}\, dx \tag{3.44}$$

Green's functions G_1 and G_2 are given by

$$G_1 = \ell n \left[\frac{(x_o-x) + \{(x_o-x)^2 + (2h)^2 + (z_o-z)^2\}^{1/2}}{(x_o-x) + \{(x_o-x)^2 + (z_o-z)^2\}^{1/2}} \right] \tag{3.45}$$

and

$$G_2 = \ell n \left[\frac{(z_o-z) + \{(x_o-x)^2 + (2h)^2 + (z_o-z)^2\}^{1/2}}{(z_o-z) + \{(x_o-x)^2 + (z_o-z)^2\}^{1/2}} \right] \tag{3.46}$$

Equation (3.44) is solved by Galerkin's method and the solution for J_e in each region is used to calculate the excess inductance.

This method has also been used for a T-junction [14], a step discontinuity and a cross junction [15].

3.4 CHARACTERIZATION OF VARIOUS DISCONTINUITIES

Quasi-static techniques for evaluation of discontinuity capacitances and inductances have been described in previous section. The results of these types of analyses for various microstrip discontinuities will be presented now. Closed form expressions for these discontinuities (wherever available) and ranges of their validity are included here. Techniques of compensation of these discontinuities to obtain better performance are also described in this section.

3.4.1 Open Ends

Open-end discontinuity occurs frequently in a number of circuits such as resonators, matching stubs, and parallel coupled filters. The equivalent circuit of an open-end is represented by an excess capacitance C_{oc} which can be tranformed into an equivalent length of transmission line, $\Delta\ell_{oc}$, as shown in Figure 3.13. Equivalent capacitor shown in Figure 3.13(b) is the one that is usually calculated whereas the equivalent line length (Figure 3.13(c)) is more convenient for circuit design.

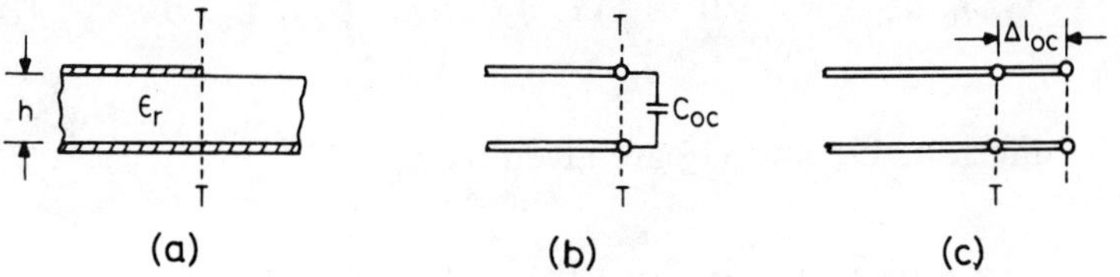

Figure 3.13(a) Microstrip Open-End Discontinuity, (b) Equivalent Capacitance Representation, and (c) Equivalent Line Length Representation

The most extensive data on the microstrip open circuit has been given by Silvester and Benedek [7] using the method of line sources with charge reversal. Their results are presented in Figure 3.14. Also they have given an empirical expression which is very useful for computational purposes and may be written as

$$\frac{C_{oc}}{W} = \exp\left\{2.3026\sum_{i=1}^{5} C_i(\epsilon_r)\left[\log\frac{W}{h}\right]^{i-1}\right\} \quad \text{(pF/m)} \tag{3.47}$$

where C_i's are numerical constants tabulated in reference [7] for ϵ_r = 1.0, 2.5, 4.2, 9.6, 16.0 and 51.0. For ϵ_r = 9.6, values of C_i are 1.738, -0.2538, 0.1308, -0.0087, -0.0113 for i = 1, . . ., 5 respectively.

The equivalent additional line length $\Delta\ell_{oc}$ for an open circuit discontinuity may be obtained from C_{oc} by using the following relation

$$\frac{\Delta\ell_{oc}}{h} = \frac{C_{oc}}{W}\,\frac{cZ_{om}W/h}{\sqrt{\epsilon_{re}}} \tag{3.48}$$

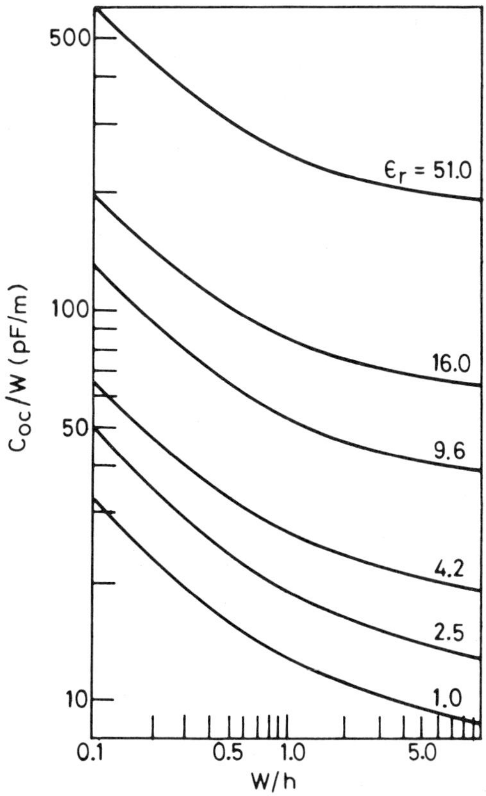

Figure 3.14 Capacitance Associated With an Open-End Discontinuity (from [7])

where c is the velocity of wave propagation in free space. An empirical expression for $\Delta\ell_{oc}/h$ has been obtained by modifying the expression derived by Hammerstad and Bekkadal [16]. The expression is given below [17]

$$\frac{\Delta\ell_{oc}}{h} = 0.412 \frac{\epsilon_{re} + 0.3}{\epsilon_{re} - 0.258} \left[\frac{W/h + 0.264}{W/h + 0.8} \right] \tag{3.49}$$

Maximum relative error in this expression, as compared to Equation (3.47), is less than 4 percent for $W/h \geqslant 0.2$ and $2 \leqslant \epsilon_r \leqslant 50$.

3.4.2 Gaps in Microstrip

The characterization of gaps in microstrip is useful in the design of dc blocks, end coupled filters, coupling elements to resonators, etc. Microstrip gap and its equivalent circuits are shown in Figure 3.15. There are three sets of published data for gap capacitance

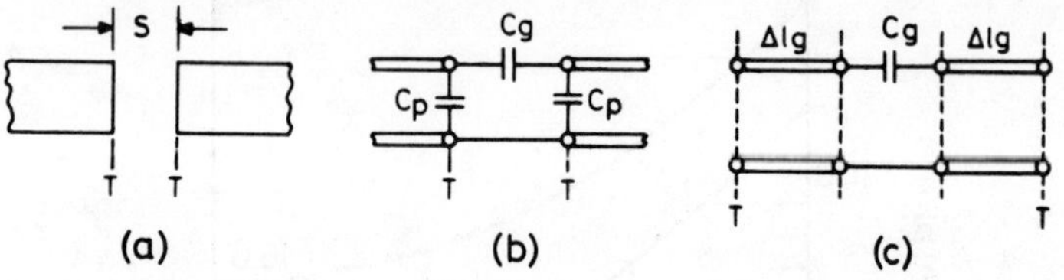

Figure 3.15 A Microstrip Gap and its Equivalent Circuits

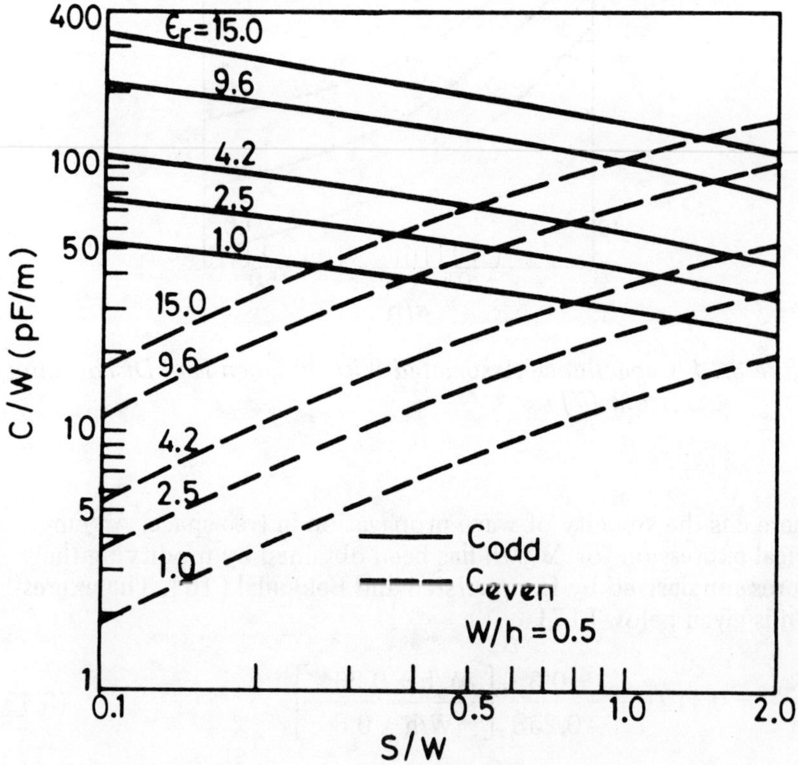

Figure 3.16 (a) Capacitances for Microstrip Gap Evaluated by Using Line Sources With Charge Reversal (W/h = 0.5) (from [8])

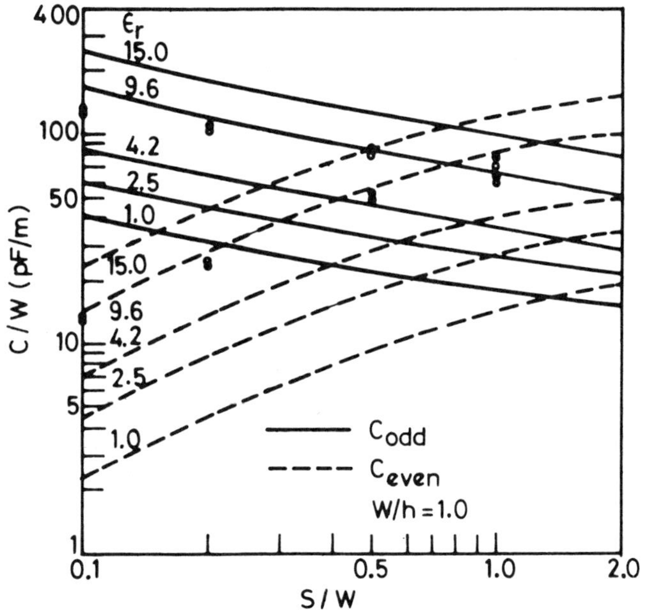

• MAEDA [4], ϵ_r = 10.0, Z_{om} = 50 ohm, h = 0.5mm
∘ FARRAR AND ADAM [1], ϵ_r = 9.6, Z_{om} = 50 ohm, W/h = 1.0

Figure 3.16(b) Capacitances for Microstrip Gap Evaluated by Using Line Sources With Charge Reversal (W/h = 1.0) (from [8])

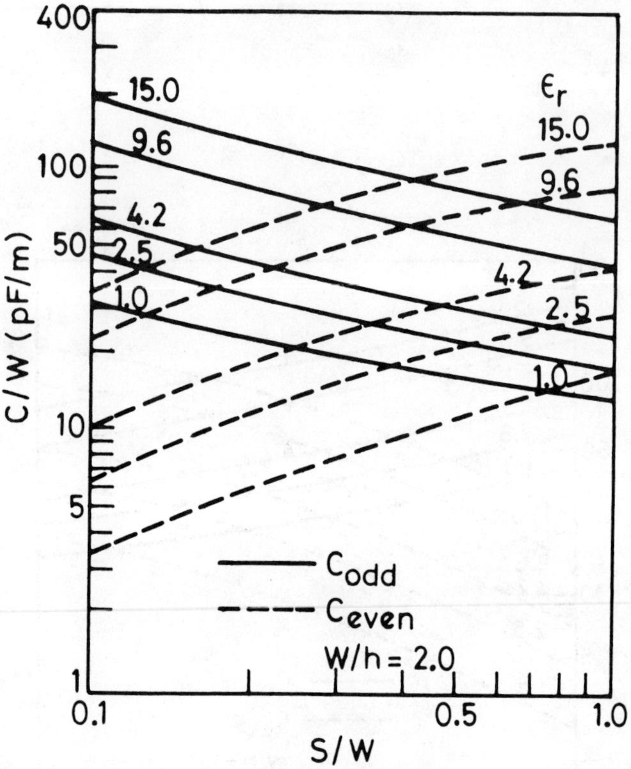

Figure 3.16(c) Capacitances for Microstrip Gap Evaluated by Using Line Sources With Charge Reversal (W/h = 2.0) (from [8])

[1,4,8]. Perhaps the results of Benedek and Silvester are the most accurate as the other two involve the subtraction of nearly equal large numbers. The available results are shown in Figure 3.16. Two sets of points shown in Figure 3.16(b) correspond to result of Maeda [4], and Farrar and Adam [1]. The capacitance C_{odd} and C_{even} are related to C_p and C_g by

$$C_{even} = 2\,C_p$$

$$C_{odd} = 2\,C_g + C_p \tag{3.50}$$

Equivalent line length $\Delta \ell_g$ of Figure (3.15) may be calculated as

$$\frac{\Delta \ell_g}{h} = \frac{C_p}{W} \frac{c\,Z_{om} W/h}{\sqrt{\epsilon_{re}}} \tag{3.51}$$

A comparison of computed and experimental results given by Maeda [4] is shown in Figure 3.17. Experimental results for C_g are derived

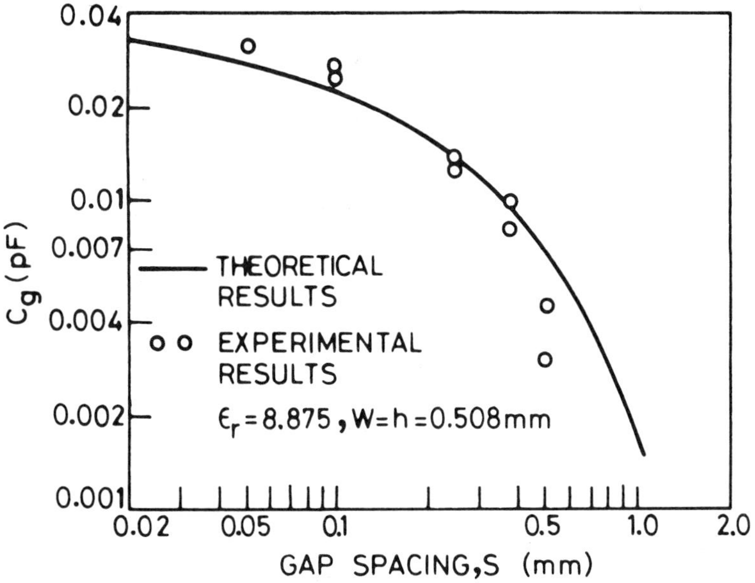

Figure 3.17 Comparison of Theoretical and Experimental Results for Gap Capacitance (from [4])

from reference [18]. The agreement between the experimental results and computed values is reasonably good.

It may be noted that the curves of Figure 3.16 are well suited for polynomial approximation as has been done for the open-end capacitance discussed in the previous subsection. The closed form expression for C_{even} and C_{odd} for ϵ_r = 9.6 and $0.5 \leqslant W/h \leqslant 2$ have been found [17] by curve fitting the available numerical results [8]. The expressions are given below

$$C_{odd}/W\ (\text{pF/m}) = \left(\frac{S}{W}\right)^{m_o} \exp(k_o) \tag{3.52}$$

$$C_{even}/W\ (\text{pF/m}) = 12\left(\frac{S}{W}\right)^{m_e} \exp(k_e) \tag{3.53}$$

where

$$\left.\begin{aligned} m_o &= \frac{W}{h}\,(0.619 \log W/h - 0.3853) \\ k_o &= 4.26 - 1.453 \log W/h \end{aligned}\right\} \quad (0.1 \leqslant S/W \leqslant 1.0)$$

$$m_e \doteq 0.8675, \; k_e = 2.043\left(\frac{W}{h}\right)^{0.12} \qquad (0.1 \leqslant S/W \leqslant 0.3)$$

$$m_e = \frac{1.565}{(W/h)^{0.16}} - 1, \; k_e = 1.97 - \frac{0.03}{W/h} \qquad (0.3 \leqslant S/W \leqslant 1.0)$$

The value of C_{odd} and C_{even} for other values of ϵ_r in the range $2.5 \leqslant \epsilon_r \leqslant 15$ can be calculated by scaling according to the following relations:

$$C_{odd}(\epsilon_r) = C_{odd}(9.6)\,(\epsilon_r/9.6)^{0.8} \tag{3.54}$$

$$C_{even}(\epsilon_r) = C_{even}(9.6)\,(\epsilon_r/9.6)^{0.9} \tag{3.55}$$

The accuracy of the above expressions is within 7 percent for the above mentioned set of parameters.

3.4.3 Steps in Width

Steps in width exist at the junction of two microstrip lines having different impedances. This type of discontinuity is encountered when designing matching transformers, couplers, filters and transitions. The configuration for step discontinuity and its equivalent circuit is shown in Figure 3.18. Results for excess capacitance C_s

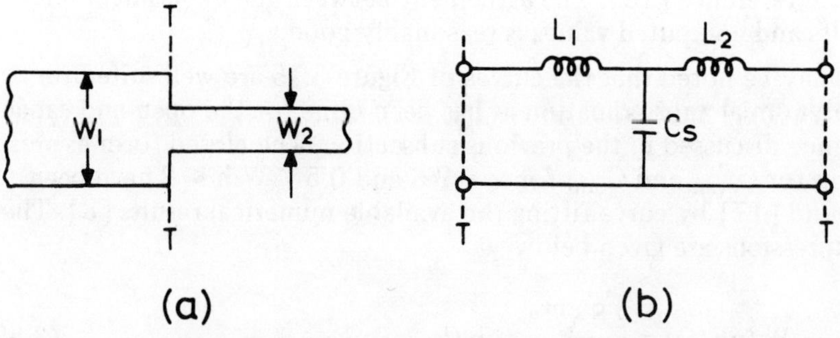

Figure 3.18 A Microstrip Step Discontinuity and the Equivalent Circuit

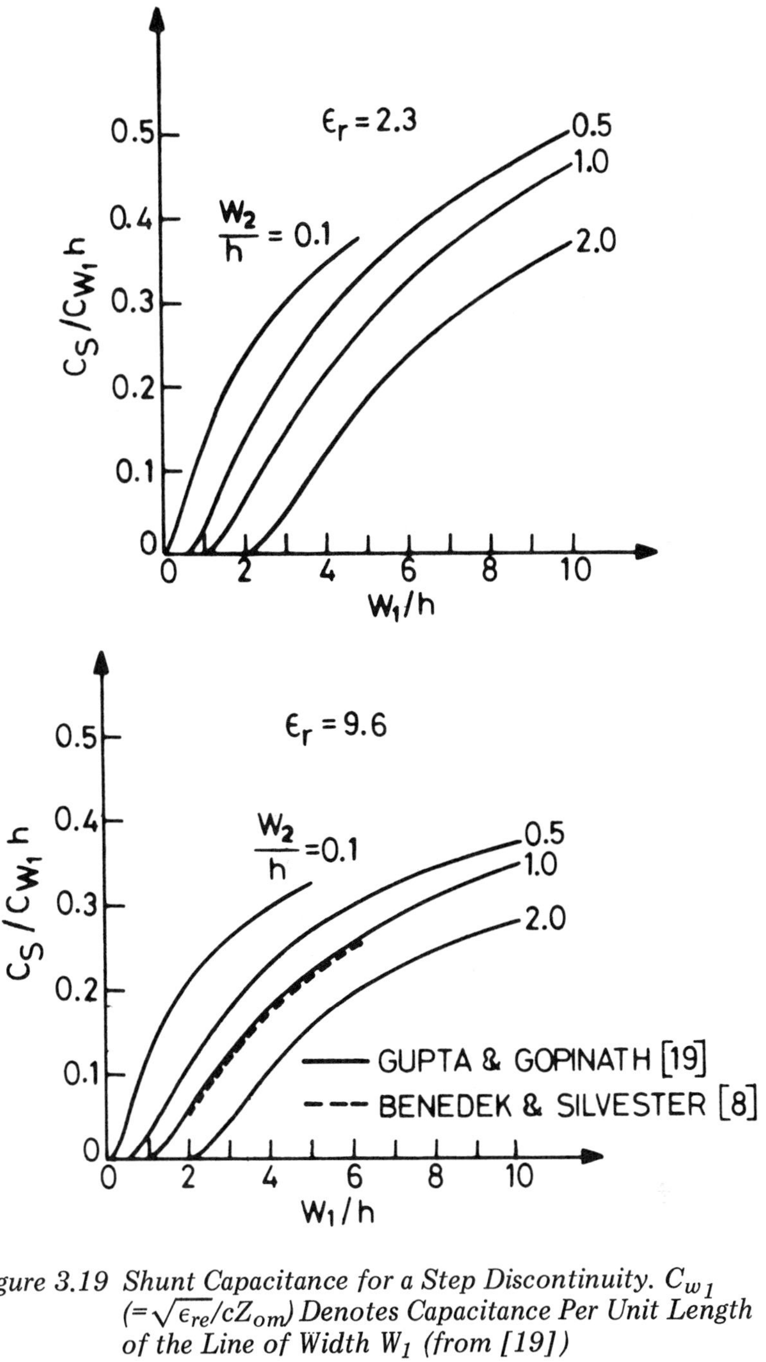

Figure 3.19 Shunt Capacitance for a Step Discontinuity. C_{w1} $(=\sqrt{\epsilon_{re}}/cZ_{om})$ *Denotes Capacitance Per Unit Length of the Line of Width* W_1 *(from [19])*

have been given by Farrar and Adams [1], Benedek and Silvester [8], and Gupta and Gopinath [19]. Data for C_s given by Gupta and Gopinath are most extensive and are presented in Figure 3.19 for ϵ_r = 2.3 and 9.6. The small dotted curve in Figure 3.19(b) corresponds to reference [8] and has been inserted for comparing the two sets of results. In terms of distributed elements, the discontinuity capacitance C_s has the effect of an increase in the wide line's length and an equal decrease in the narrow line's length. As these effects are small, the change in lengths may be approximated by $\Delta\ell_{oc}(1 - W_2/W_1)$ [16] where $\Delta\ell_{oc}$ is the open-circuit line extension calculated from Equation (3.48) for line width W_1. Measurement of step capacitance has been reported by Easter *et al.* [20]. Comparison with the results in Figure 3.19 is difficult because of insufficient information about the experimental data.

Some results for inductance associated with step discontinuity in microstrip are also available [15]. These are based on the method of quasi-static computation of inductance discussed in Section 3.3. Inductance L_s plotted in Figure 3.20 is the total of inductances L_1

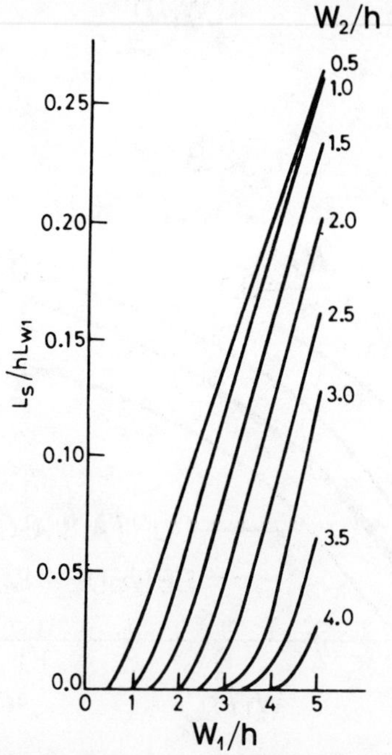

Figure 3.20 Calculated Inductance Values for a Microstrip Step Discontinuity. L_{w1} $(=\sqrt{\epsilon_{re}}\, Z_{om}/c)$ Denotes Inductance Per Unit Length of the Line of Width W_1 (from [15])

and L_2 shown in Figure 3.18 and has been normalized with respect to $(L_{wl}h)$ where L_{wl} is the inductance per unit length of microstrip of width W_1 given by

$$L_{wl} = \frac{Z_{om}\sqrt{\epsilon_{re}}}{c} \quad \text{(H/m)} \tag{3.56}$$

where Z_{om} and ϵ_{re} correspond to width W_1, and $c = 3 \times 10^8$ m/s. A comparison of theoretical and experimental results is also available [15] and is shown in Figure 3.21. The experiments were carried out

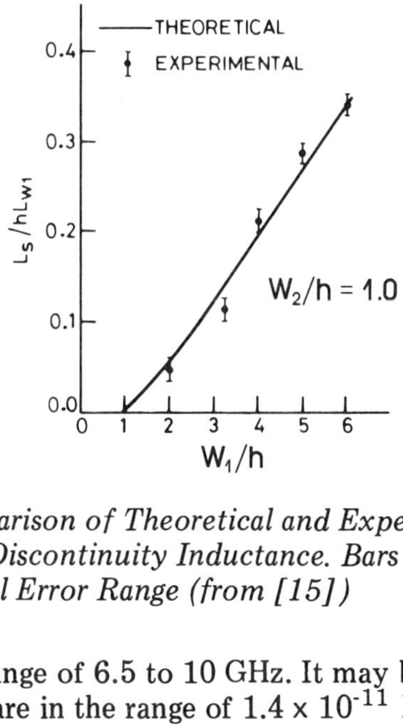

Figure 3.21 Comparison of Theoretical and Experimental Results for Step Discontinuity Inductance. Bars Indicate the Experimental Error Range (from [15])

in the frequency range of 6.5 to 10 GHz. It may be pointed out that inductance values are in the range of 1.4×10^{-11} H to 9.6×10^{-11} H.

In order to take into account the effect of discontinuity inductances in the circuit design, the total inductance L_s may be separated into L_1 and L_2 (as a first order approximation) as follows

$$L_1 = \frac{L_{w1}}{L_{w1} + L_{w2}} L_s \tag{3.57a}$$

$$L_2 = \frac{L_{w2}}{L_{w1} + L_{w2}} L_s \tag{3.57b}$$

and corresponding additional line lengths may be written as

$$\frac{\Delta \ell_1}{h} = \frac{\Delta \ell_2}{h} = \frac{L_s}{(L_{w1} + L_{w2})h} \tag{3.58}$$

The closed form expressions for C_s and L_s have been derived by curve fitting the numerical results. The expressions are given as

$$\frac{C_s}{\sqrt{W_1 W_2}} \text{ (pF/m)} = (10.1 \log \epsilon_r + 2.33) \frac{W_1}{W_2} - 12.6 \log \epsilon_r - 3.17$$

$$\text{(for } \epsilon_r \leqslant 10;\ 1.5 \leqslant W_1/W_2 \leqslant 3.5) \tag{3.59}$$

This expression yields a percentage error of less than ten percent. A more accurate expression can be written for alumina substrates ($\epsilon_r = 9.6$) as

$$\frac{C_s}{\sqrt{W_1 W_2}} \text{ (pF/m)} = 130 \log\left(\frac{W_1}{W_2}\right) - 44 \quad \text{(for } 3.5 \leqslant W_1/W_2 \leqslant 10) \tag{3.60}$$

The above relation is accurate to within 0.5 percent. The expression for inductance is given by

$$\frac{L_s}{h} \text{ (nH/m)} = 40.5 \left(\frac{W_1}{W_2} - 1.0\right) - 75 \log \frac{W_1}{W_2} + 0.2 \left(\frac{W_1}{W_2} - 1\right)^2 \tag{3.61}$$

Equation (3.61) has an error of less than 5 percent for $W_1/W_2 \leq 5$ and $W_1/h = 1.0$.

3.4.4 Bends

A microstrip bend may be formed by two lines of equal or unequal impedances. It is normally used for introducing flexibility in the layout of the circuit design. The equivalent circuit of a microstrip bend with lines of equal impedances is shown in Figure 3.22. The most common form of microstrip bend used in circuits and investigated analytically is a right-angled bend ($\phi_b = 90°$).

Silvester and Benedek [9] have computed the electrostatic value of the excess capacitance of right-angled bends; their results are shown

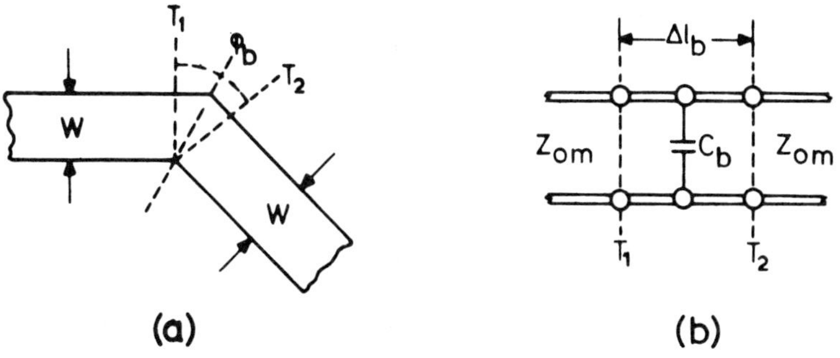

Figure 3.22 Geometry and Equivalent Circuit of a Microstrip Bend

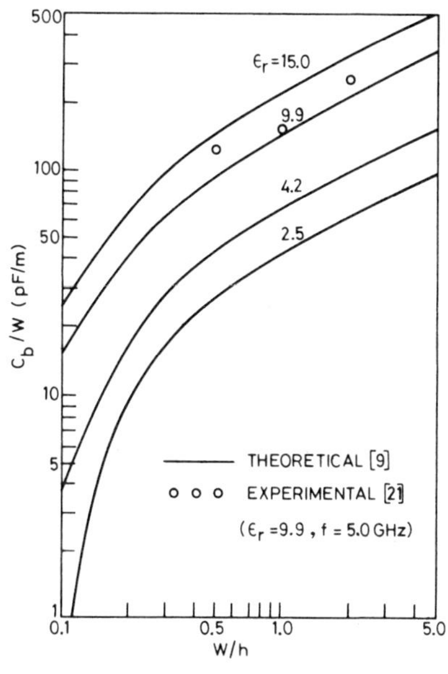

Figure 3.23 Discontinuity Capacitance of a Microstrip Right-Angled Bend (from [9])

in Figure 3.23. Experimental results given by Easter [21] are shown as three small circles in this figure. It is observed that the agreement between the theoretical and experimental results is reasonably good only for microstrips with 50 ohm impedance.

In practical circuits micrstrip bends are chamfered (see Figure 3.24) to compensate for the excess capacitance. Measurements by Easter *et al.* [20] indicate that a chamfer of approximately 72 percent as

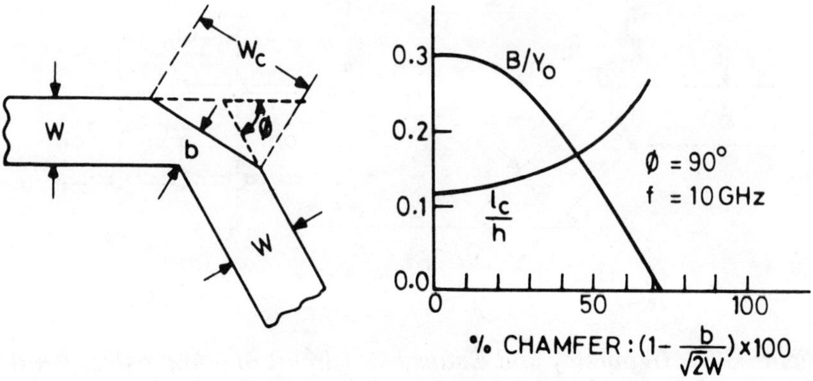

Figure 3.24 A Chamfered Bend and Variations of Shunt Susceptance and Series Equivalent Length of a Chamfered Right-Angled Bend as a Function of Percentage Chamfer (from [20])

defined in Figure 3.24 is needed for a bend in 50 ohm line on alumina substrate. This figure includes variation of normalized discontinuity susceptance (B/Y_o) as a function of percentage chamfer and shows that 72 percent chamfering will increase the length correction in the equivalent circuit to approximately 0.3 of the substrate thickness. The length of the chamfer (W_c) is approximately 1.8 W. Groll and Weidmann [22] have also found optimum length of the chamfer using TDR measurements for 50 ohm line on alumina substrate. They observed that $W_c = 1.83$ W gives VSWR less that 1.11 up to 12 GHz. Hammerstad and Bekkadal [16] have found optimum lengths of the chamfer of the 50 ohm microstrips on rexolite substrates having various bend angles ($\phi = 30°, 60°, 90°$ and $120°$). The value of W_c comes out to be about 1.8 W in all of these cases. There are no theoretical computations available for chamfered bends so far.

Inductance for right-angled bends has been computed by Thomson and Gopinath [14], and their results are shown in Figure 3.25 wherein the normalized inductance ($L_b/L_w h$) is plotted for different width-height ratios. Comparison with experimental results of Easter [21] is also shown, but the agreement is not very good.

The closed form expressions for right-angled bend discontinuities are given below [17]

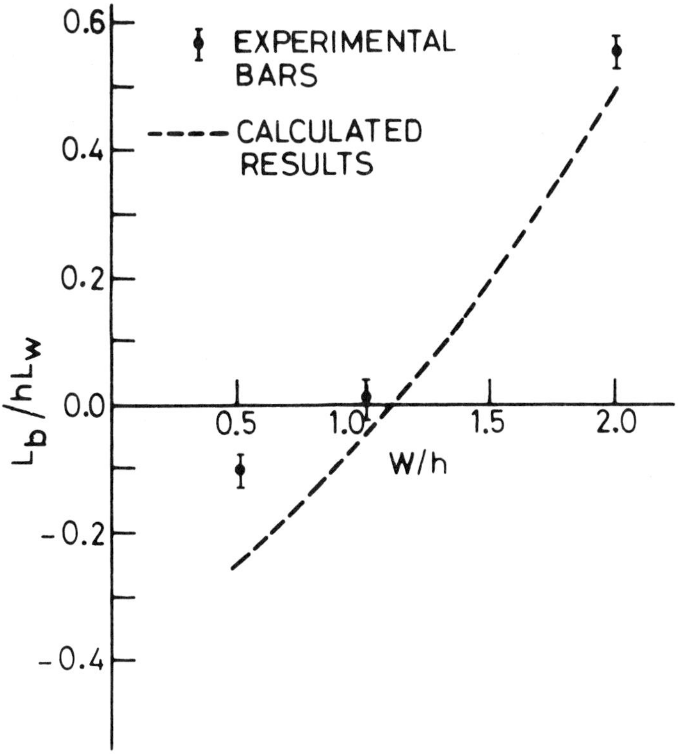

Figure 3.25 Discontinuity Inductance of a Microstrip Right-Angled Bend. Bars Indicate the Experimental Error Range (from [14])

$$\frac{C_b}{W}\ (\mathrm{pF/m}) = \begin{cases} \dfrac{(14\,\epsilon_r + 12.5)W/h - (1.83\,\epsilon_r - 2.25)}{\sqrt{W/h}} + \dfrac{0.02\,\epsilon_r}{W/h} \\ \qquad\qquad \text{for} \quad (W/h < 1) & (3.62a) \\ (9.5\,\epsilon_r + 1.25)W/h + 5.2\,\epsilon_r + 7.0 \quad (W/h \geqslant 1) & (3.62b) \end{cases}$$

$$\frac{L_b}{h}\ (\mathrm{nH/m}) = 100(4\sqrt{W/h} - 4.21) \tag{3.63}$$

Equations (3.62) are accurate to within 5 percent for $2.5 \leqslant \epsilon_r \leqslant 15$ and $0.1 \leqslant W/h \leqslant 5$. The accuracy of Equation (3.63) is about 3 percent for $0.5 \leqslant W/h \leqslant 2.0$.

3.4.5 T-junctions

The T-junction is perhaps the most important discontinuity in microstrip as it is found in most circuits such as impedance networks, stub filters and branch-line couplers. A microstrip T-junction and its equivalent circuit are shown in Figure 3.26. Discontinuity capacitance C_T

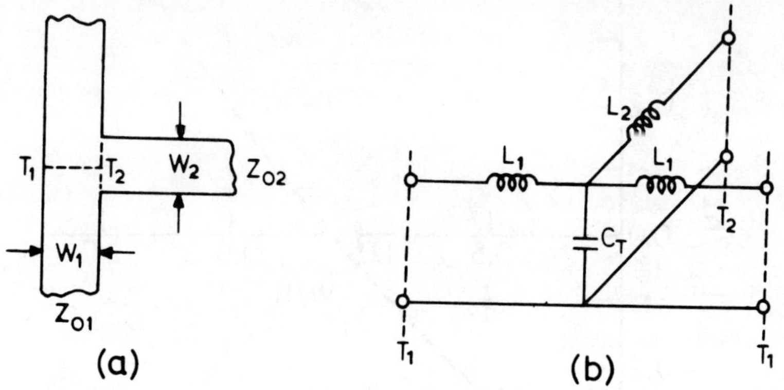

Figure 3.26 A Microstrip T-Junction and its Equivalent Circuit

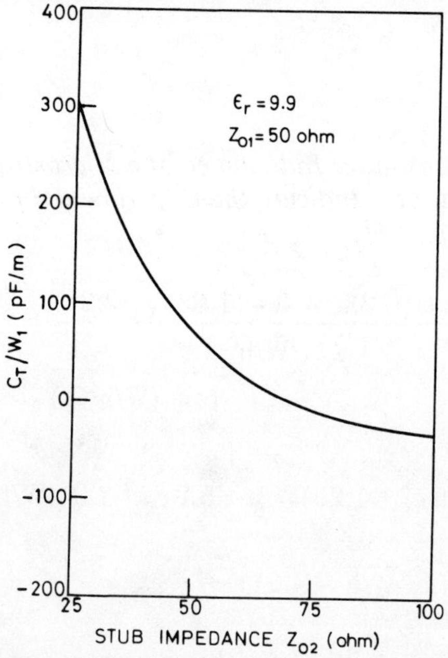

Figure 3.27 Discontinuity Capacitance of a Microstrip T-Junction (from [9])

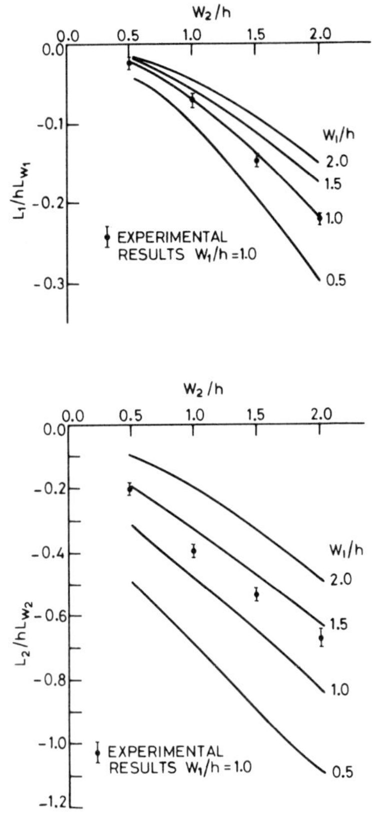

Figure 3.28 Discontinuity Inductances of a Microstrip T-Junction (from [14])

for this structure has been calculated by Silvester and Benedek [9]. Their results are shown in Figure 3.27. Capacitances shown in this figure are for per unit main-line width. Inductance calculation for T-junctions have been carried out by Thomson and Gopinath [14]. Their results are shown in Figure 3.28. Comparison with the experimental results of Easter [21] is also shown. The agreement between the experimental and theoretical results for L_2 is not as good as for L_1.

In the design of stubs, the inductance L_2 plays a significant role in determining stub length, while for branch line couplers and switches both L_1 and L_2 are equally important. If T-junction effects are not considered, the center frequency of a branch-line coupler deviates approximately 5 percent [23] from the calculated one. Thus there

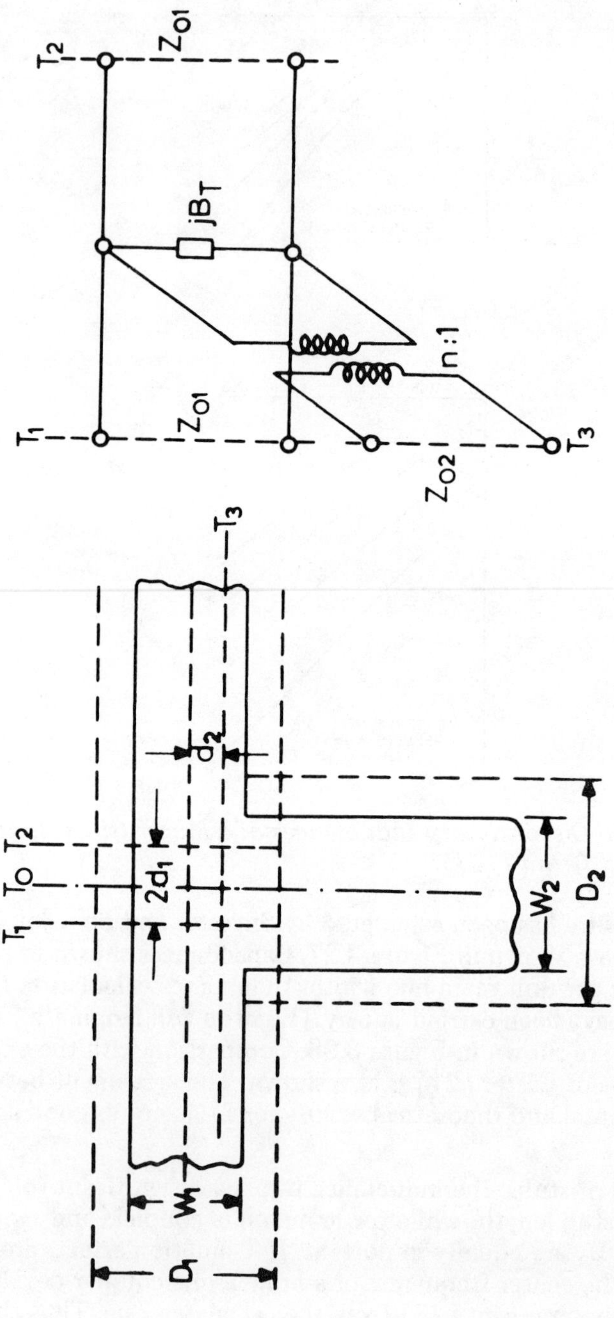

Figure 3.29 T-Junction and its Equivalent Circuit as Considered for Equations (3.64-3.68)

is considerable interest in deriving closed form expressions for its equivalent circuits. The following recommendation of Hammerstad and Bekkadal [16] appears to be of most practical use. Their notations are shown in Figure 3.29.

$$D_1 = 120\ \pi h/Z^a_{o1} \quad , \quad D_2 = 120\ \pi h/Z^a_{o2} \tag{3.64}$$

$$n = \frac{\sin\left(\frac{\pi}{2}\frac{2D_1}{\lambda_m}\frac{Z_{o1}}{Z_{o2}}\right)}{\frac{\pi}{2}\frac{2D_1}{\lambda_m}\frac{Z_{o1}}{Z_{o2}}} \tag{3.65}$$

$$\frac{d_1}{D_2} = 0.05\frac{Z_{o1}}{Z_{o2}}\,n^2 \tag{3.66}$$

$$\frac{d_2}{D_1} = \frac{1}{2} - 0.16\left[1 + (2D_1/\lambda_m)^2 - 2\,\ln\left(\frac{Z_{o1}}{Z_{o2}}\right)\right]\frac{Z_{o1}}{Z_{o2}} \tag{3.67}$$

$$\frac{B_T\lambda_m}{Y_{o1}D_1} = \begin{cases} -(1-2D_1/\lambda_m)\,Z_{o1}/Z_{o2}\ , & Z_{o1}/Z_{o2} \leqslant 0.5 \\ (1-2D_1/\lambda_m)\,(3\frac{Z_{o1}}{Z_{o2}} - 2)\ , & Z_{o1}/Z_{o2} \geqslant 0.5 \end{cases} \tag{3.68}$$

It has been pointed out [16] that Equations (3.64 through 3.68) give good results except for $Z_{o1}/Z_{o2} > 2$ where the calculated values of d_2/D_1 are too high. In this range a better value for d_2 is obtained by replacing Z_{o1}/Z_{o2} with Z_{o2}/Z_{o1}.

The shift in the reference planes of T-junction discontinuities can be compensated by adjusting the lengths of the three microstrip lines forming the junction. The effect of shunt susceptance can be compensated by changing microstrip widths near the junction as shown in Figure 3.30. The lengths θ_1, θ_2 and the characteristic impedances (Z_{m1}, Z_{m2}) of the modified portions near the junction can be derived from the values of discontinuity reactances [24].

The closed form expressions for the discontinuity reactances of the equivalent circuit shown in Figure 3.26(b) with a main line impedance of 50 ohm and for $\epsilon_r = 9.9$ have also been derived [17] as follows

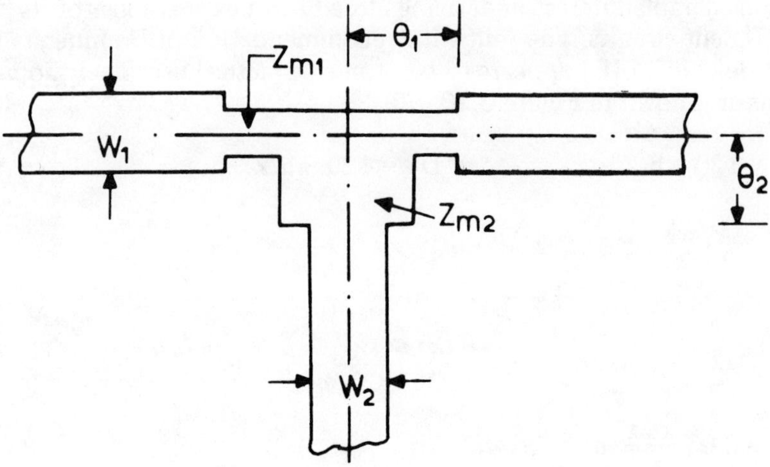

Figure 3.30 A T-Junction With Compensation for Junction Discontinuity Reactances

$$\frac{C_T}{W_1}\,(\mathrm{pF/m}) = \frac{100}{\tanh\,(0.0072\,Z_o)} + 0.64\,Z_o - 261 \quad (25 \leqslant Z_o \leqslant 100) \tag{3.69}$$

where Z_o is the characteristic impedance of the stub.

$$\frac{L_1}{h}\,(\mathrm{nH/m}) = -\frac{W_2}{h}\left\{\frac{W_2}{h}\left(-0.016\,\frac{W_1}{h} + 0.064\right) + \frac{0.016}{W_1/h}\right\}L_{w1}$$

$$(0.5 \leqslant (W_1/h,\ W_2/h) \leqslant 2.0) \tag{3.70}$$

$$\frac{L_2}{h}\,(\mathrm{nH/m}) = \left\{\left(0.12\,\frac{W_1}{h} - 0.47\right)\frac{W_2}{h} + 0.195\,\frac{W_1}{h} - 0.357 + 0.0283\,\sin\left(\pi\,\frac{W_1}{h} - 0.75\,\pi\right)\right\}L_{w2} \tag{3.71}$$

$$(1 \leqslant W_1/h \leqslant 2.0;\ 0.5 \leqslant W_2/h \leqslant 2)$$

where L_W is the inductance per unit length for a microstrip of width W. The above equations have an error of less than 5 percent.

3.4.6 Cross Junctions

One of the most common applications of a cross junction is the realization of low impedance stubs. When a low impedance stub has a strip width large enough to sustain transverse resonance modes, one of the possible solutions is to employ two stubs in parallel connected on either side of the main line. The impedance of each of the equivalent stubs is equal to twice the impedance of the simulated stub.

The geometry of a microstrip cross junction and its equivalent circuit are shown in Figure 3.31. Capacitance C_+ has been calculated

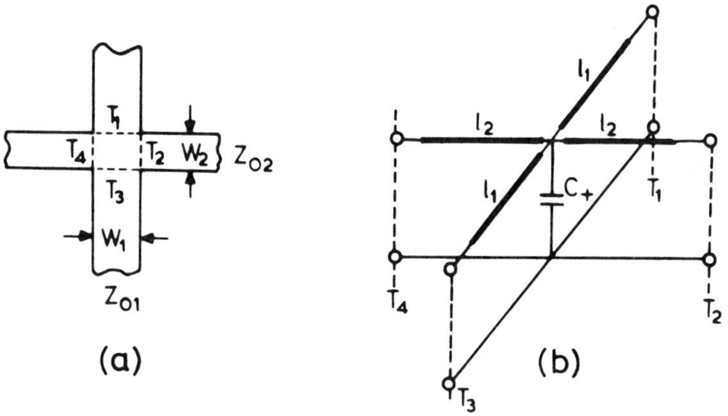

Figure 3.31 Geometry and Equivalent Circuit of a Microstrip Cross Junction

by Silvester and Benedek [9] and their results are shown in Figure 3.32. Inductances associated with a cross junction have been computed by Gopinath *et al.* [15] but are expressed in terms of a somewhat different equivalent circuit (shown in Figure 3.33). Inductance results are shown in Figures 3.34(a) and (b). Figure 3.34(a) presents calculated values of L_1 normalized to $L_{w1}h$ of the cross junction for different W_1/h and W_2/h. This same set of curves is to be used for estimating normalized L_2 by interchanging W_1 and W_2. Calculated values of L_3 normalized to $L_{w1}h$ are shown in Figure 3.34(b). Only one experimental point due to Easter [21] is available for comparison and is indicated in these figures. The agreement is good for L_1 and L_2, but not for L_3.

The closed form expressions for cross-junction discontinuities have been derived [17] by curve fitting the available numerical results for capacitances and inductances for $\epsilon_r = 9.9$. The expressions are accurate to within 5 percent and are given below:

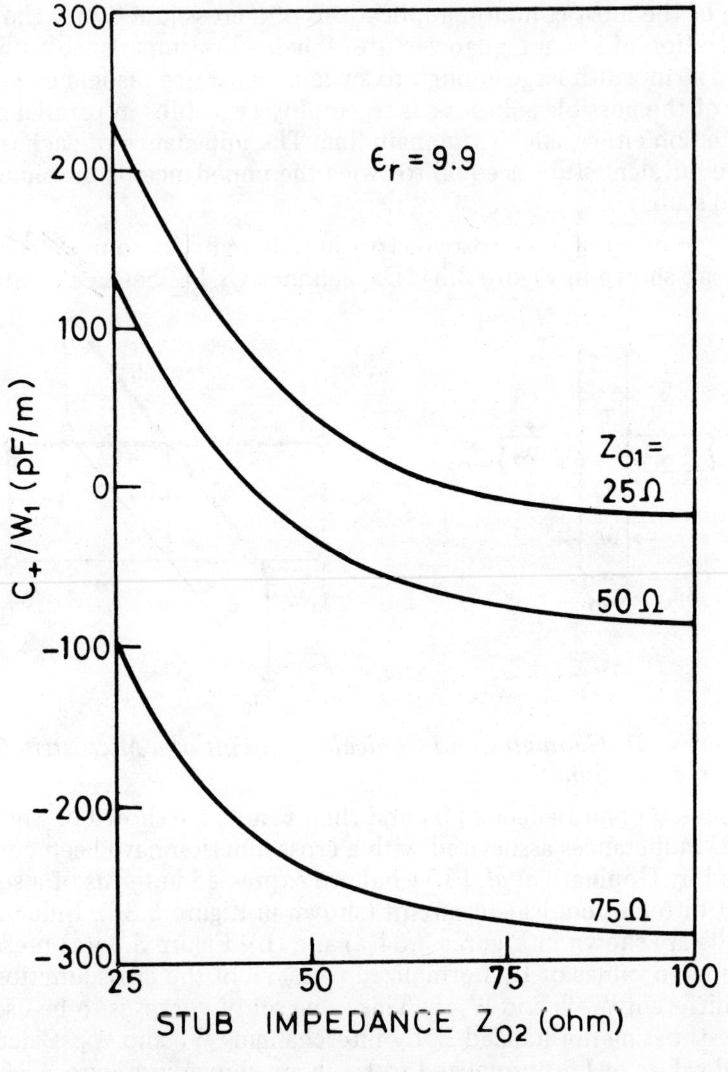

Figure 3.32 Discontinuity Capacitance of a Microstrip Cross Junction (from [9])

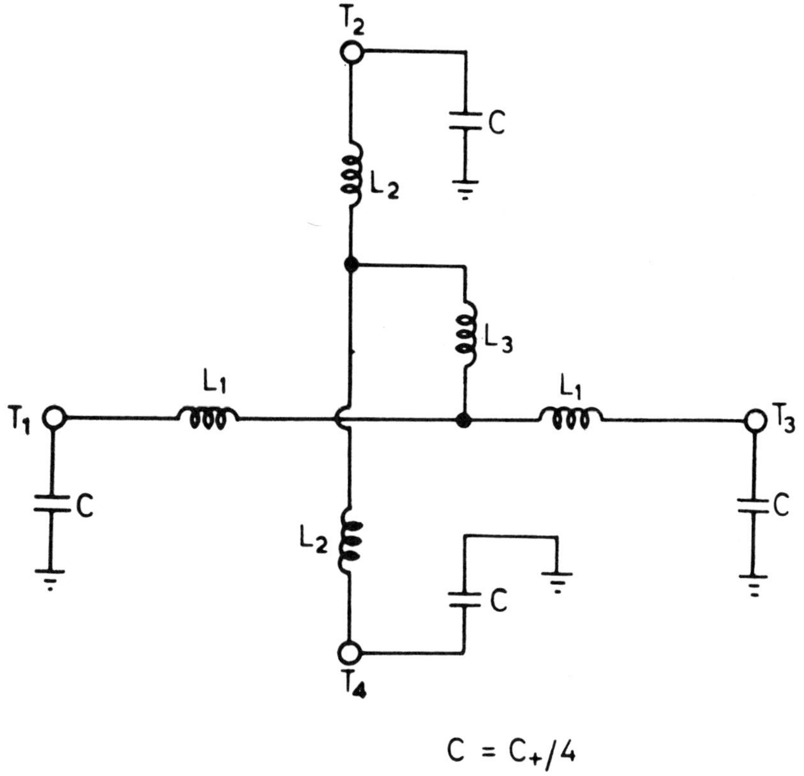

Figure 3.33 An Equivalent Circuit for a Microstrip Cross Junction Using Lumped Inductors (from [15])

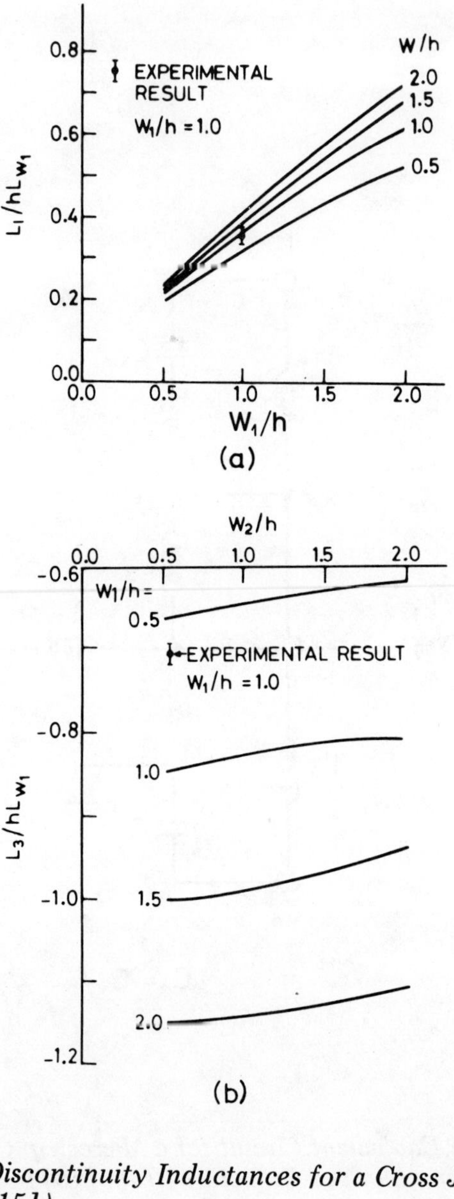

Figure 3.34 Discontinuity Inductances for a Cross Junction (from [15])

$$\frac{C_+}{W_1}\,(\text{pF/m}) = \left[\log\frac{W_1}{h}\left\{86.6\,\frac{W_2}{h} - 30.9\left(\frac{W_2}{h}\right)^{1/2} + 367\right\} + \left(\frac{W_2}{h}\right)^3 + 74\,\frac{W_2}{h} + 130\right]\left(\frac{W_1}{h}\right)^{-1/3} - 240 + \frac{2}{W_2/h} - 1.5\,\frac{W_1}{h}\left(1 - \frac{W_2}{h}\right) \tag{3.72}$$

$$(0.3 \leqslant W_1/h \leqslant 3.0 \text{ and } 0.1 < W_2/h \leqslant 3.0)$$

$$\frac{L_1}{h}\,(\text{nH/m}) = \left\{\frac{W_1}{h}\left[165.6\,\frac{W_2}{h} + 31.2\sqrt{\frac{W_2}{h}} - 11.8\left(\frac{W_2}{h}\right)^2\right] - 32\,\frac{W_2}{h} + 3\right\}\left(\frac{W_1}{h}\right)^{-3/2} \tag{3.73}$$

$$-\frac{L_3}{h}\,(\text{nH/m}) = 337.5 + \left(1 + \frac{7}{W_1/h}\right)\frac{1}{W_2/h} - 5\,\frac{W_2}{h}\cos\left[\frac{\pi}{2}\left(1.5 - \frac{W_1}{h}\right)\right]$$

$$(0.5 \leqslant (W_1/h,\ W_2/h) \leqslant 2.0) \tag{3.74}$$

The unsymmetric cross junction has been studied [25] experimentally and compared with the T-junction. This comparison indicates that the T-junction data may be used as a first step to estimate the properties of the cross junction.

The discussion on microstrip discontinuities will be continued in Chapter 4. Fullwave analyses for discontinuities and the techniques for experimental measurements of discontinuity parameters will also be discussed.

REFERENCES

[1] Farrar, A. and A.T. Adams, "Matrix Methods for Microstrip three-dimensional Problems," *IEEE Trans. Vol. MTT-20*, 1972, pp. 497-504.

[2] Farrar, A. and A.T. Adams, "Computation of Static Capacitance Data for Single, Double and Triple Microstrip Line," *1970 IEEE - GMTT Int. Microwave Symp. Digest*, pp. 257-261.

[3] Farrar, A. and A.T. Adams, "Computation of Lumped Microstrip Capacities by Matrix Methods: Rectangular Sections and End Effect," *IEEE Trans. Vol. MTT-19*, 1971, pp. 495-497. Also see correction *IEEE Trans. Vol. MTT-20*, 1972, p. 294.

[4] Maeda, M., "An Analysis of Gap in Microstrip Transmission Lines," *IEEE Trans., Vol. MTT-20*, 1972, pp. 390-396.

[5] Itoh, T., R. Mittra, and R.D. Ward, "A New Method for Solving Discontinuity Problems in Microstrip Lines," *1972 IEEE - GMTT Int. Microwave Symp. Digest*, pp. 68-70.

[6] Itoh, T., R. Mittra and R.D. Ward, "A Method for Computing Edge Capacitance of Finite and Semi-finite Microstrip Lines," *IEEE Trans., Vol. MTT-20*, 1972, pp. 847-849.

[7] Silvester, P. and P. Benedek, "Equivalent Capacitance of Microstrip Open Circuits, " *IEEE Trans., Vol. MTT-20*, 1972, pp. 511-516.

[8] Benedek, P. and P. Silvester, "Equivalent Capacitance for Microstrip Gaps and Steps, " *IEEE Trans., Vol. MTT-20*, 1972, pp. 729-733..

[9] Silvester, P. and P. Benedek, "Microstrip Discontinuity Capacitances for Right-angle Bends, T-junctions and Crossings," *IEEE Trans., Vol. MTT-21*, 1973, pp. 341-346. Also see correction *IEEE Trans., Vol. MTT-23*, 1975, p. 456.

[10] Horton, R., "The Electrical Characterization of a right-angled Bend in Microstrip Line," *IEEE Trans., Vol. MTT-21*, 1973, pp. 427-429.

[11] Horton, R., "Equivalent Representation of an Abrupt Impedance Step in Microstrip Line," *IEEE Trans., Vol. MTT-21*, 1973, pp. 562-564.

[12] Collin, R.E., *Field Theory of Guided Waves*, New York: McGraw-Hill, 1960, p. 148.

[13] Yamashita, E., "Variational Method for the Analysis of Microstrip-like Transmission Lines," *IEEE Trans., Vol. MTT-16*, 1968, pp. 529-535.

[14] Thompson, A.F. and A. Gopinath, "Calculation of Microstrip Discontinuity Inductances," *IEEE Trans., Vol. MTT-23*, 1975, pp. 648-655.

[15] Gopinath, A. *et al.*, "Equivalent Circuit Parameters of Microstrip Step Change in Width and Cross Junctions," *IEEE Trans., Vol. MTT-24*, 1976, pp. 142-144.

[16] Hammerstad, E.O. and F. Bekkadal, *Microstrip Handbook*, ELAB report STF 44 A74169, The University of Trondheim, The Norwegian Institute of Technology, 1975.

[17] Garg, Ramesh and I.J. Bahl, "Microstrip Discontinuities," *Int. J. Electronics*, Vol. 45, July, 1978.

[18] *The Microwave Engineer's Handbook and Buyers Guide*, Dedham, MA: Horizon House, 1969, p. 72.

[19] Gupta, C. and A. Gopinath, "Equivalent Circuit Capacitance of Microstrip Step Change in Width, " *IEEE Trans., Vol. MTT-25*, 1977, pp. 819-822.

[20] Easter, B., *et al.*, "Resonant Techniques for the Accurate Measurement of Microstrip Properties and Equivalent Circuits," *Proc. 1973, European Microwave Conf.*, paper B. 7.5.

[21] Easter, B., "The Equivalent Circuit of some Microstrip Discontinuities," *IEEE Trans., Vol. MTT-23*, 1975, pp. 655-660.

[22] Groll, H. and W. Weidmann, "Measurement of Equivalent Circuit Elements of Microstrip Discontinuities by a Resonant Method," *NTZ, Vol. 28*, 1975, pp. 74-77.

[23] Leighton Jr., W.H. and A.G. Milnes, "Junction Reactance and Dimensional Tolerance Effects on X-band 3-dB Directional Coupler," *IEEE Trans., Vol. MTT-19*, 1971, pp. 818-824.

[24] Dydyk, M., "Master the T-junction and Sharpen Your MIC Designs," *Microwaves, Vol. 16*, May 1977, pp. 184-186.

[25] Akello, R.J., *et al.*, "Equivalent Circuit of the Asymmetric Cross Over Junction," *Electron. Lett. Vol. 13*, 1977, pp. 117-118.

Chapter 4 Microstrip Discontinuities II : Fullwave Analysis and Measurements

Quasi-static characterization of capacitances and inductances associated with microstrip discontinuities has been discussed earlier in Chapter 3. These results are valid, with sufficient accuracy, only up to few gigahertz. For a complete characterization of discontinuities, it is required to determine frequency dependence of various parameters. This information is obtained from fullwave analysis which is discussed in this chapter. Techniques for the measurement of microstrip discontinuities are also included.

4.1 FULLWAVE ANALYSIS

Fullwave analysis of microstrip discontinuities has been carried out using Galerkin's method in FTD [1] and by using the planar waveguide model [2,3]. These methods are discussed in the following sections.

4.1.1 Galerkin's Method in FTD

Galerkin's method in FTD has been used for fullwave analysis of microstrip open-ends and gaps. Characterization of these two discontinuities can be carried out by analyzing suitably designed linear resonators. For open-end, one can consider a section of microstrip with open-ends on each side, as shown in Figure 4.1. By carrying out a fullwave analysis for the resonance frequency of this structure, one can obtain the equivalent line length contributed by the open-end. The extent of the substrate can be finite in either one or both of the dimensions x and z. In the analysis reported in reference [1] the substrate is considered to be infinite along z and finite along the x-direction. In the x-direciton two conducting planes (2L apart) are placed symmetrically with respect to the microstrip. A cover plate is located at $y = H$. Analysis of such a structure in

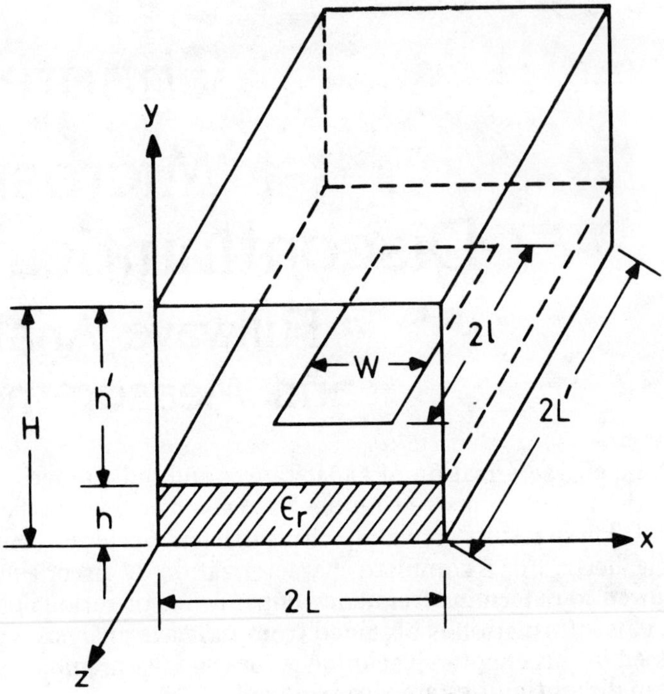

Figure 4.1 Geometry for Analysis of Microstrip Open-Ends and Gaps

FTD requires a Fourier transform along the z-direction and a finite Fourier transform along x.

Details of the Galerkin's method in FTD have been discussed earlier in Chapter 2. The choice of the basis functions for currents on the strip is important for the numerical efficiency of the method. For the dominant mode of resonance, the following forms for J_z and J_x are suitable.

$$J_z(x,z) = J_1(x)\, J_2(z) \tag{4.1}$$

$$J_x(x,z) = J_3(x)\, J_4(z) \tag{4.2}$$

where

$$J_1(x) = \begin{cases} \dfrac{1}{W}\left[1 + \left|\dfrac{2x}{W}\right|^3\right] & |x| \leqslant W/2 \\ 0 & \text{elsewhere} \end{cases} \tag{4.3a}$$

$$J_2(z) = \begin{cases} \dfrac{1}{\ell} \cos\left(\dfrac{\pi z}{2\ell}\right) & |z| \leqslant \ell \\ 0 & \text{elsewhere} \end{cases} \tag{4.3b}$$

$$J_3(x) = \begin{cases} \dfrac{2}{W} \sin\left(\dfrac{2\pi x}{W}\right) & |x| \leqslant W/2 \\ 0 & \text{elsewhere} \end{cases} \tag{4.3c}$$

$$J_4(z) = \begin{cases} \dfrac{z}{2\ell^2} & |z| \leqslant \ell \\ 0 & \text{elsewhere} \end{cases} \tag{4.3d}$$

After performing various steps for Galerkin's method in FTD discussed in Seciton 2.3.3, a dispersion relation for the microstrip resonator is developed. This dispersion relation is solved for the resonant frequency. The microstrip open-end and gap discontinuities can be characterized by calculating the effective increase in length, $\Delta\ell$, of suitably designed microstrip resonators. For resonance one can write

$$2(\ell + \Delta\ell) = \lambda_m/2 \tag{4.4}$$

where $\lambda_m = \lambda_o/\sqrt{\epsilon_{re}} = c/(\sqrt{\epsilon_{re}}\ f_{res})$.

Open-end

The effective increase in length $2\Delta\ell_{oc}$ for a microstrip resonator is determined from the method described above. From $\Delta\ell_{oc}$ one can find open-end discontinuity capacitance C_{oc} by using Equation (3.48). The frequency dependent behavior of C_{oc} can be found by calculating resonant frequencies of microstrip resonators of different lengths. However, adequate results for open-end capacitance calculations (based on this method) are not available.

It may be pointed out that for frequencies up to about 10 GHz the quasi-static approach gives reasonably reliable results. At 8 GHz, for $h = 0.66$ mm, $W/h = 1.0$ and $\epsilon_r = 9.8$, the measured value of $\Delta\ell_{oc}$ is 0.021 ± 0.001 mm [4], whereas corresponding quasi-static value of $\Delta\ell_{oc}$ calculated using Equation (3.49) is 0.0206 mm.

Gap

Fullwave analysis of a gap can also be carried out by using Galerkin's method in FTD. In this case, one considers two types of resonators. First, an analysis is carried out with conducting planes (electric walls) at z = 0 and z = 2L′. The latter dimension is chosen such that (2L′-2ℓ) is equal to gap spacing. A second computation is carried out for magnetic walls at z = 0 and z = 2L′. For both of these computations, finite Fourier transforms are used along the x and z directions. Equivalent lengths $\Delta\ell_e$ and $\Delta\ell_m$ for electric and magnetic walls, respectively, are determined from the respective resonance frequencies of resonators. From $\Delta\ell_e$ and $\Delta\ell_m$ two equivalent capacitances C_e and C_m are calculated. These capacitances are related to the discontinuity capacitances of pi equivalent circuits of a gap (Figure 3.7a) by the following equations.

$$C_g = (C_e - C_m)/2 \tag{4.5a}$$

$$C_p = C_m \tag{4.5b}$$

4.1.2 Analysis Using Planar Waveguide Model

The frequency dependent behavior of microstrip discontinuities can also be described in terms of scattering parameters. A general method of evaluating these parameters is by matching the fields at the discontinuity interface. The planar waveguide model [2,3] for the microstrip discussed in Section 1.3 is a very powerful technique for this type of analysis. Steps in width, T-junctions, bends and cross junctions have been analyzed using this method and are discussed in this section. The equivalent circuits of these discontinuities can be obtained by using the derived scattering parameters and the theory of linear networks.

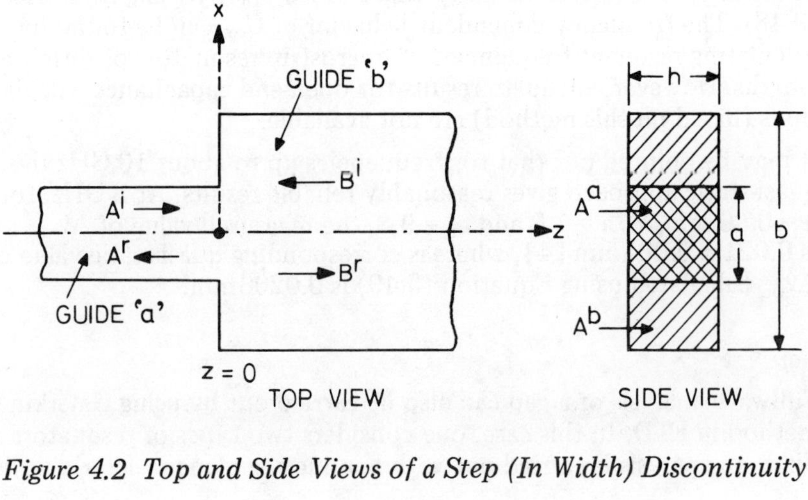

Figure 4.2 Top and Side Views of a Step (In Width) Discontinuity

Step in Width [5]

The planar waveguide model of a step discontinuity is shown in Figure 4.2. Dimensions a and b are widths of planar waveguides corresponding to the microstrip lines "a" and "b" respectively. The cross sectional areas of these guides are denoted by $A^a (= axh)$ and $A^b (= bxh)$.

Since the height of the substrate, h, is much less than the wavelength in the microstrip, the fields are uniform along the y-direction. Under this condition only TEM and TE_{mo} modes can be excited in the discontinuity. (TM_{mn} modes do not exist because a small value of the substrate height requires n = 0 whereas the lowest value of n for TM modes is unity.) For TE_{mo} modes, the transverse fields in the planar waveguide model can be expressed in terms of orthogonal series expansion

$$E_t = \sum_{m=o}^{\infty} U_{mo} \left\{ \hat{z} \times \nabla_t \, \psi_{mo}(x,y) \right\} \qquad (4.6)$$

$$H_t = \sum_{m=o}^{\infty} I_{mo} \left\{ -\nabla_t \, \psi_{mo}(x,y) \right\} \qquad (4.7)$$

where U_{mo} and I_{mo} are the expansion coefficients and ψ_{mo} are the scalar potentials for TE modes. The unit vector along the z-axis is denoted by $\hat{z}$ and m = o corresponds to the dominant mode (TEM). The symbol ∇_t designates the transverse component of the gradient.

In the discontinuity plane (z = o) the following boundary and interface conditions must be satisfied:

$$H_t^b = 0 \qquad \text{in region } (A^b - A^a) \qquad (4.8a)$$

$$H_t^a = H_t^b \qquad \text{in region } A^a \qquad (4.8b)$$

$$E_t^a = E_t^b \qquad \text{in region } A^a \qquad (4.8c)$$

It can be shown that the conditions given by Equation (4.8) can only be satisfied if the transverse magnetic field of guide "a" is expanded in terms of the modes of guide "b". While expanding the magnetic field H_t^a in terms of the modes of guide "b", the expansion coefficients I^b are chosen in such a way that $H_t^b = 0$ in region $A^b - A^a$ and will be equal to H_t^a in the discontinuity plane. On the other hand, no special boundary condition exists for the transverse electric field in the region $A^b - A^a$, so that the electric field E_t^b in the discontinuity cross-section can be expanded in terms of the modes of guide "a".

Multiplying Equation (4.8c) by $(\hat{z} \times \nabla_t \psi^a_{Mo})$ for various values of M(= 0,1,2. . .) and integrating over the aperture A^a leads to the equation

$$U^a_{Mo} = \iint_{A^a} E^b_t \cdot (\hat{z} \times \nabla_t \psi^a_{Mo})\, dA \tag{4.9}$$

Due to the orthogonality property of the employed functions only coefficients U^a_{Mo} will be non-zero. Similarly the following expression is found for the expansion coefficients I^b:

$$I^b_{Po} = \iint_{A^a} H^a_t (-\nabla_t \psi^b_{Po})\, dA \tag{4.10}$$

Substituting the expansions of E^b_t and H^a_t from Equations (4.6) and (4.7), respectively, one gets the following expressions for U^a_{Mo} and I^b_{Po}

$$U^a_{Mo} = \sum_{p=0}^{\infty} U^b_{po} K_{(Mo)(po)} \tag{4.11}$$

$$I^b_{Po} = \sum_{m=0}^{\infty} I^a_{mo} K_{(mo)(Po)} \tag{4.12}$$

where M,m and P,p correspond to the modes in guide "a and "b" respectively. K's are called the coupling integrals, and the evaluation of these integrals gives information about the degree of interaction between the modes in the two guides. The coupling integrals are given by

$$K = K_{(Mo)(po)} = \iint_{A^a} (\hat{z} \times \nabla_t \psi^b_{po}) \cdot (\hat{z} \times \nabla_t \psi^a_{Mo})\, dA \tag{4.13a}$$

$$K^T = K_{(mo)(Po)} = \iint_{A^a} (\nabla_t \psi^a_{mo}) \cdot (\nabla_t \psi^b_{Po})\, dA \tag{4.13b}$$

The expansion coefficients, U and I can be replaced by the normal modes coefficients A^i, A^r and B^i, B^r (see Figure 4.2). The resulting equations are:

$$\sqrt{Z^a_{Mo}}\,\left(A^i_{Mo} + A^r_{Mo}\right) = \sum_{p=0}^{\infty} \sqrt{Z^b_{po}}\; K_{(Mo)\,(po)} \left(B^i_{po} + B^r_{po}\right) \tag{4.14a}$$

$$\sqrt{Y^b_{Po}}\left(B^i_{Po} - B^r_{Po}\right) = \sum_{m=o}^{\infty} \sqrt{Y^a_{mo}}\; K_{(mo)(Po)} \left(A^i_{mo} - A^r_{mo}\right) \tag{4.14b}$$

where m,M,p,P = 0,1,2. . . , and Z(= 1/Y) is the wave impedance for TE mode given by

$$Z = \frac{\omega\mu}{\beta_z}$$

Here β_z is the propagation constant along the z-axis. For simplicity, Equations (4.14) may be written as

$$\sqrt{Z^a}\;(A^i + A^r) = \sqrt{Z^b}\;K(B^i + B^r) \tag{4.15a}$$

$$\sqrt{Y^b}\;(B^i - B^r) = \sqrt{Y^a}\;K^T(A^i - A^r) \tag{4.15b}$$

The incident and the reflected modes may be related by an S-matrix as

$$\begin{bmatrix} A^r \\ B^r \end{bmatrix} = \begin{bmatrix} S \end{bmatrix} \begin{bmatrix} A^i \\ B^i \end{bmatrix} \tag{4.16}$$

By knowing K, K^T, Z^a and Z^b one can calculate the S-parameters of the step discontinuity.

Results and equivalent circuit

Numerical results of scattering parameters of a step discontinuity have been reported by Kompa [5]. Typical results for frequency dependent scattering matrix coefficients are shown in Figure 4.3. The incident mode considered here is the dominant TEM mode while only even modes with m = 0,2,4; are assumed to be excited by the discontinuity. Figure 4.3 shows that, at frequencies well below the cut-off frequency of the first higher-order mode (m = 2), the transmission and reflection coefficients are fairly constant. At the cut-off frequency of the TE_{20} mode (f_{c1}) the incident TEM mode is rejected and no transmission is possible. Assuming the step to be lossless, the reflection coefficient becomes equal to unity. For frequencies greater than the cut-off frequency, a part of the power is transmitted by the TE_{20} mode due to mode conversion, so that the transmission coefficient S_{21} for the dominant mode is always smaller than that for f = 0.

The equivalent circuit of a step discontinuity is determined from

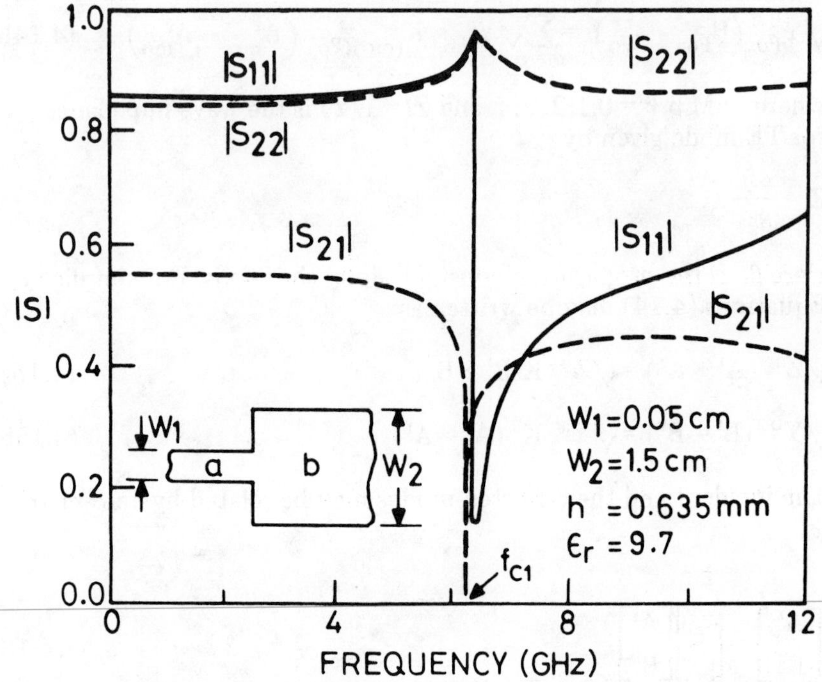

Figure 4.3 Computed Scattering Coefficients for a Step Discontinuity as a Function of Frequency (from [5])

the known S-matrix by converting it into the Y-matrix. The Y-matrix elements y_{ik}, which are normalized with respect to the characteristic admittance of guide "a", can be obtained from the following relation

$$Y = (\bar{I} + S)^{-1} (\bar{I} - S) \tag{4.17}$$

where $\bar{I}$ is the identity matrix. The equivalent circuit is shown in Figure 4.4(a). Ports 1-1′ and 2-2′ refer to the TEM mode, while the port 3-3′ corresponds to the first higher order mode. The characteristic impedance Z_{o3} of the imaginary line is defined by the axial power flow of the first higher order mode in guide "b", i.e.

$$Z_{o3} = \frac{h^2 \, |E_{max}|^2}{2 \, P_{po}} \tag{4.18}$$

where P_{po} is the axial power flowing in the (po) mode.

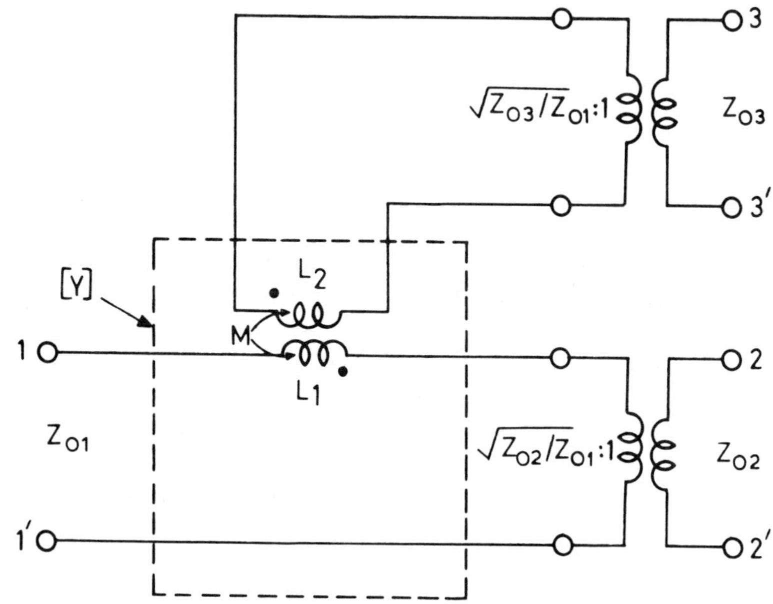

Figure 4.4(a) Frequency Dependent Equivalent Circuit for a Step Discontinuity

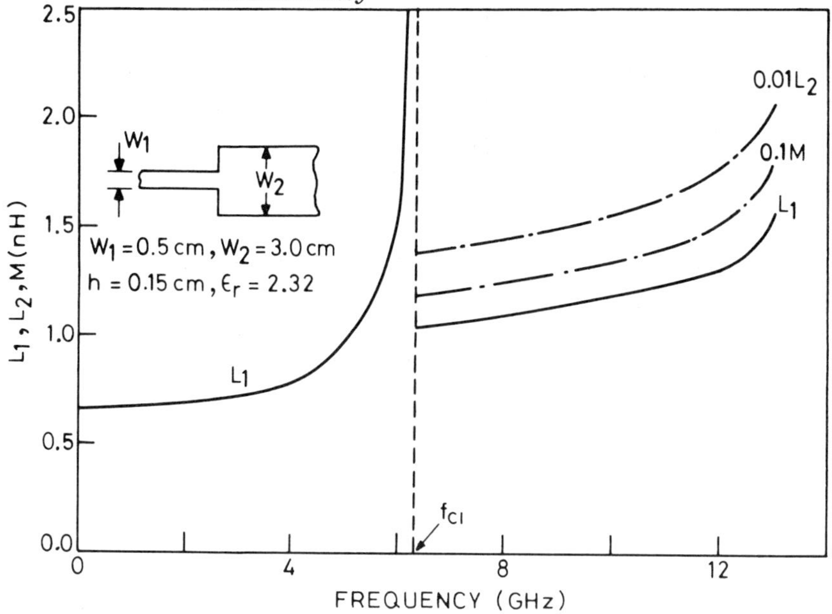

Figure 4.4(b) Variations of Equivalent Circuit Parameters of a Step Discontinuity With Frequency (from [5])

Figure 4.4(b) shows computed results for the equivalent circuit parameters. It can be seen that under single mode propagation conditions, the discontinuity can be represented by a series inductance only.

T-junction [6]

The fullwave analysis of a T-junction using the planar waveguide model has been reported by Mehran [6]. The other two discontinuities (the right-angled bend and the cross junction) can be considered in terms of the T-junction by making use of the symmetry considerations. Therefore the T-junction will be considered in detail for formulating the boundary value problem.

T-junction geometry (shown in Figure 4.5) is sub-divided into regions "a" and "b" wherein transverse fields are expressed in terms

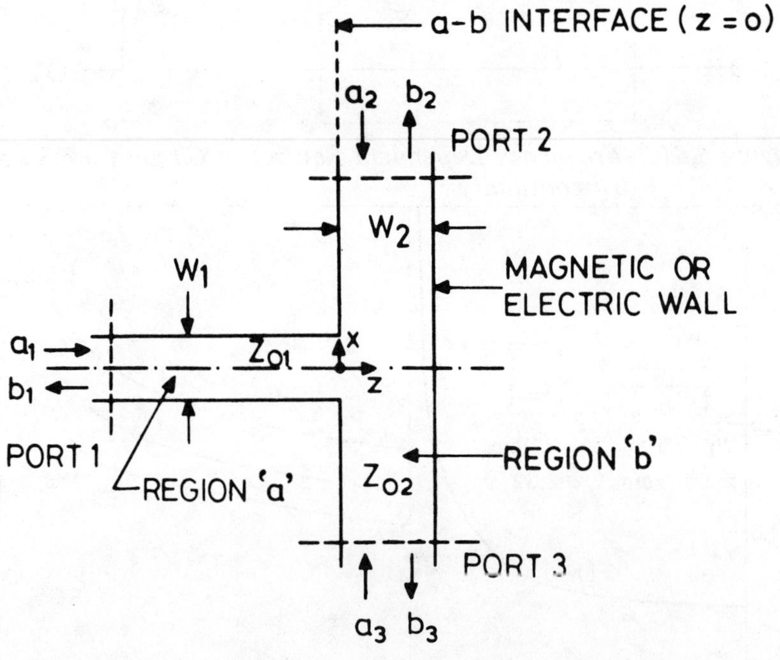

Figure 4.5 Configuration for Analysis of a T-Junction

of orthogonal series expansion. Fields are matched at the discontinuity interface z = 0 which results in an infinite system of linear equations. The wave amplitudes in region "a", for arbitrary excitation, can be calculated by truncating the system of linear equations.

In order to obtain the scattering parameters of the T-junction, the wave amplitudes of the transmitted waves in region "b" are evaluated.

The height of the substrate, h, is again much less than the wavelength in the microstrip, and the magnetic field does not have a component in the y-direction. Therefore, as was the case for step discontinuity, the description of the total field is complete in terms of an expansion using TE_{mo} modes only (m = 0 corresponds to TEM-mode).

In region "a", the transverse field components may be written in terms of the series of scalar potentials used in Equations (4.6) and (4.7) as

$$E_t^a = U_{oo} \nabla_t \psi_{oo}^a + \sum_{m=1}^{\infty} U_{mo} (\hat{z} \times \nabla_t \psi_{mo}^a) \tag{4.19}$$

$$H_t^a = I_{oo} (\hat{z} \times \nabla_t \psi_{oo}^a) + \sum_{m=1}^{\infty} I_{mo} (-\nabla_t \psi_{mo}^a) \tag{4.20}$$

These field components satisfy the boundary conditions on the guide walls. ψ_{oo}^a represents the scalar potential for the TEM mode and is given by

$$\psi_{oo}^a = \frac{1}{\sqrt{W_1 h}} \cdot y \tag{4.21a}$$

The scalar potentials ψ_{mo}^a (which are also known as orthonormalized vector mode functions of guide "a") are given by

$$\psi_{mo}^a = \frac{1}{m\pi} \sqrt{\frac{2W_1}{h}} \sin\left\{\frac{m\pi}{W_1}\left(x + \frac{W_1}{2}\right)\right\} \qquad m \neq 0 \tag{4.21b}$$

Further, the expansion coefficients U_{mo} and I_{mo} for field components E_t^a and H_t^a, respectively, are related to wave amplitudes $a_{1(mo)}$ and $b_{1(mo)}$ by

$$\sqrt{Y_{mo}^a}\; U_{mo} = a_{1(mo)} \exp(-j\beta_z^a z) + b_{1(mo)} \exp(j\beta_z^a z) \tag{4.22}$$

$$\sqrt{Z_{mo}^a}\; I_{mo} = a_{1(mo)} \exp(-j\beta_z^a z) - b_{1(mo)} \exp(j\beta_z^a z) \tag{4.23}$$

where Z^a_{mo} and Y^a_{mo} are wave impedances and admittances, respectively, for TE modes in region "a" and are given by

$$Z^a_{mo} = \frac{1}{Y^a_{mo}} = \frac{\omega\mu}{\beta^a_z} \tag{4.24}$$

where β^a_z is the propagation constant along the z-axis in region "a". Fields in region "b" also may be expanded by writing relations analogous to Equations (4.19) and (4.20). However, by using an expansion of this type, matching the fields at the interface cannot be achieved because the functions ψ^b_{mo} of guide "b" will vanish in the z = 0 plane. Hence an additional continuous spectrum is taken into account in region "b". This yields

$$E^b_t = E^{eb}_t + \int_{-\infty}^{\infty} F(\beta^b_x) \sqrt{\frac{\omega\mu}{\beta^b_z}} \left\{ \begin{matrix} \cos[\beta^b_z (z - W_2)] \\ \\ \sin[\beta^b_z (z - W_2)] \end{matrix} \right\} \left[\hat{z} \times \nabla_t \psi^b(\beta_x) \right] d \tag{4.25}$$

$$H^b_t = H^{eb}_t + j \int_{-\infty}^{\infty} F(\beta^b_x) \sqrt{\frac{\beta^b_z}{\omega\mu}} \left\{ \begin{matrix} \sin[\beta^b_z (z - W_2)] \\ \\ -\cos[\beta^b_z (z - W_2)] \end{matrix} \right\} \left[\nabla_t \psi^b(\beta_x) \right] d\beta^b_x \tag{4.26}$$

where β^b_x is the propagation constant in x-direction in region "b". The superscript e denotes a set of discrete incident modes, and $F(\beta^b_x)$ is a weighting function to be determined. The function $\psi^b(\beta_x)$ is defined by

$$\psi^b(\beta_x) = \frac{\exp(j\beta^b_x x)}{\beta^b_x \sqrt{h}} \tag{4.27}$$

In Equations (4.25) and (4.26), and also in equations appearing later in this section, the upper functions are used if a T-junction with a magnetic side wall opposite to guide "a" is analyzed. For an electric wall, the lower functions are valid. The latter configuration is useful for extending the results for T-junction discontinuity to the case of cross junctions.

The boundary condition which must be fulfilled by the transverse field components given by Equations (4.19), (4.20) and Equations (4.25), (4.26) is the continuity relation at the interface z = 0 plane. However, the unknown weighting function $F(\beta_x^b)$ may be derived first. This is done by choosing the magnetic field components at the interface a–b in the following way

$$H_t^b(z=0) = \begin{cases} H_t^a(z=0) & \text{for } W_1/2 \geqslant x \geqslant -W_1/2 \\ 0 & \text{for } W_1/2 \leqslant x \leqslant -W_1/2 \end{cases} \tag{4.28}$$

When Equation (4.28) is multiplied by $\nabla_t\, \psi^{b*}(\beta_x)$ and integrated with respect to y from 0 to h, the weighting function $F(\beta_x^b)$ is obtained through the orthogonality of the employed functions. This results in

$$F(\beta_x^b) = \frac{j\sqrt{\omega\mu/\beta_z^b}}{2\pi \begin{Bmatrix} \sin \beta_z^b W_2 \\ \cos \beta_z^b W_2 \end{Bmatrix}} \int_{-W_1/2}^{W_1/2} \int_{o}^{h} H_t^a(z=0) \left\{ \nabla_t\, \psi^{b*}(\beta_x) \right\} dxdy \tag{4.29}$$

where the asterisk * denotes the complex conjugate.

Finally, expressions for E_t^a and E_t^b, Equations (4.19) and (4.25), at the interface a–b are equated. The resulting equation is solved by projecting the series in Equations (4.19) and (4.25) into the function space spanned by the elements $\{\nabla_t \psi^{b*}(\beta_x)\}$. The integration is performed with respect to the strip $-\infty \leqslant x \leqslant \infty$, $0 \leqslant y \leqslant h$. This procedure results in an infinite system of linear equations. The wave amplitudes $a_{1\,(mo)}$ and $b_{1(mo)}$ of region "a" for arbitrary excitation can be calculated from truncating the infinite system of linear equations. Thus the field component $H_t^a(z=0)$ is known and Equation (4.29) yields the weighting function $F(\beta_x^b)$.

In order to obtain the scattering parameters of the T-junction, the wave amplitude of the transmitted wave in region "b" is calculated. It is known that the integral representation of E_t^b has to decompose into the discrete modes of waveguide "b" for $|x| \geqslant W_1/2$. This decomposition is achieved by inserting the known function $F(\beta_x^b)$ in

Equation (4.25) and evaluating the resulting integral. The field amplitudes then can be recognized as the coefficients of the constituent modal terms.

For TE_{mo} modes the expansion coefficients for guide "a" are related by the following equation

$$U_{Mo} = \frac{-j\omega\mu}{\beta^b_{z(Mo)}} \left\{ \begin{array}{l} \cot(\beta^b_{z(Mo)} W_2) \\ -\tan(\beta^b_{z(Mo)} W_2) \end{array} \right\} I_{Mo} +$$

$$\sum_{m=o}^{\infty} \sum_{p=o}^{\infty} \frac{j\omega\mu \left\{ \begin{array}{c} \epsilon_{op} \\ 2 \end{array} \right\} \sqrt{\epsilon_{om}\, \epsilon_{oM}} \exp(-j\beta^b_x W_1/2)}{W_1 W_2 \left\{ [\beta^b_{x(po)}]^2 - \left(\frac{m\pi}{W_1}\right)^2 \right\}} \cdot H(M, \beta^b_x) I_{mo} + R_{Mo} \tag{4.30a}$$

$$\text{with } \epsilon_{oi} = \left\{ \begin{array}{ll} 2 & \text{for } i \neq 0 \\ 1 & \text{for } i = 0 \end{array} \right.$$

$$H(M, \beta^b_x) = \left\{ \begin{array}{ll} \dfrac{2\beta^b_{x(po)} \sin(\beta^b_{x(po)} W_1/2)}{(\beta^b_{x(po)})^2 - (M\pi/W_1)^2} & \text{for } \dfrac{M\pi}{W_1} \neq \beta^b_{x(po)} \\ \tfrac{1}{2} W_1 \cos\dfrac{M\pi}{2} & \text{for } \dfrac{M\pi}{W_1} = \beta^b_{x(po)} \end{array} \right. \tag{4.30b}$$

$$R_{Mo} = \left\{ \begin{array}{ll} \displaystyle\int_o^h \int_{-W_1/2}^{W_1/2} E^{eb}_t(z{=}0)\,(\hat{z} \times \nabla_t \psi^a_{Mo})\, dx\, dy & \text{for } M \neq 0 \\ \displaystyle\int_o^h \int_{-W_1/2}^{W_1/2} E^{eb}_t(z{=}0)\,(\hat{z} \times \nabla_t \psi^a_{oo})\, dx\, dy & \text{for } M = 0 \end{array} \right. \tag{4.30c}$$

where M = 0, 2, 4 . . . and M and p denote modes present in regions "a" and "b", respectively. Since the amplitudes of the incident waves are known, the amplitudes of the reflected waves in region "a" can be computed from Equations (4.22), (4.23) and (4.30). The amplitudes of the waves transmitted into region "b" can also be calculated. For the waves transmitted in region "b", the amplitudes are described by

$$b_{2(po)} = \exp[-j\beta^b_{x(po)} W_1] \begin{Bmatrix} 1 \\ 0 \end{Bmatrix} a_{3(po)} + \sum_{m=0}^{\infty} I_{mo} \cdot$$

$$\frac{\omega\mu(-1)^p \begin{Bmatrix} \sqrt{\epsilon_{op}\,\epsilon_{om}} \\ \sqrt{2\epsilon_{om}} \end{Bmatrix} \sin[\beta^b_{x(po)} W_1/2]}{\sqrt{W_1 W_2}\,\sqrt{Z^b_{po}} \left[\left(\beta^b_{x(po)}\right)^2 - \left(\frac{m\pi}{W_1}\right)^2 \right]} \exp[-j\beta^b_{x(po)} W_1/2]$$

(4.31a)

and

$$b_{3(po)} = \exp[-j\beta^b_{x(po)} W_1] \begin{Bmatrix} 1 \\ 0 \end{Bmatrix} a_{2(po)} + \sum_{m=0}^{\infty} I_{mo} \cdot$$

$$\frac{\omega\mu(-1)^p \begin{Bmatrix} \sqrt{\epsilon_{op}\,\epsilon_{om}} \\ \sqrt{2\epsilon_{om}} \end{Bmatrix} \sin[\beta^b_{x(po)} W_1/2]}{\sqrt{W_1 W_2}\,\sqrt{Z^b_{po}} \left[\left(\beta^b_{x(po)}\right)^2 - \left(\frac{m\pi}{W_1}\right)^2 \right]} \exp[j\beta^b_{x(po)} W_1/2]$$

(4.31b)

with $p = 0, 1, 2, \ldots, m = 0, 2, 4, \ldots$.

In the above equations also, the upper functions are used when a T-junction is analyzed with a magnetic side wall opposite to guide "a". For an electric wall, the lower functions are valid.

For odd values of m and M, the expression $\sin[\beta^b_{x(po)} W_1/2]$ in Equations (4.30) and (4.31) must be replaced by $-j\cos[\beta^b_{x(po)} W_1/2]$. Using Equations (4.30) and (4.31), scattering parameters of the T-junction can be calculated.

Results and Equivalent Circuit

Numerical results for scattering parameters have been reported by Mehran [6]. If the incident wave is the dominant TEM mode, at least four modes should be considered in region "b" and at least two modes in region "a" when the transmission coefficient is to be calculated with an accuracy of 1 percent. The two modes in region "a" describe the total field and account for the reflected wave also.

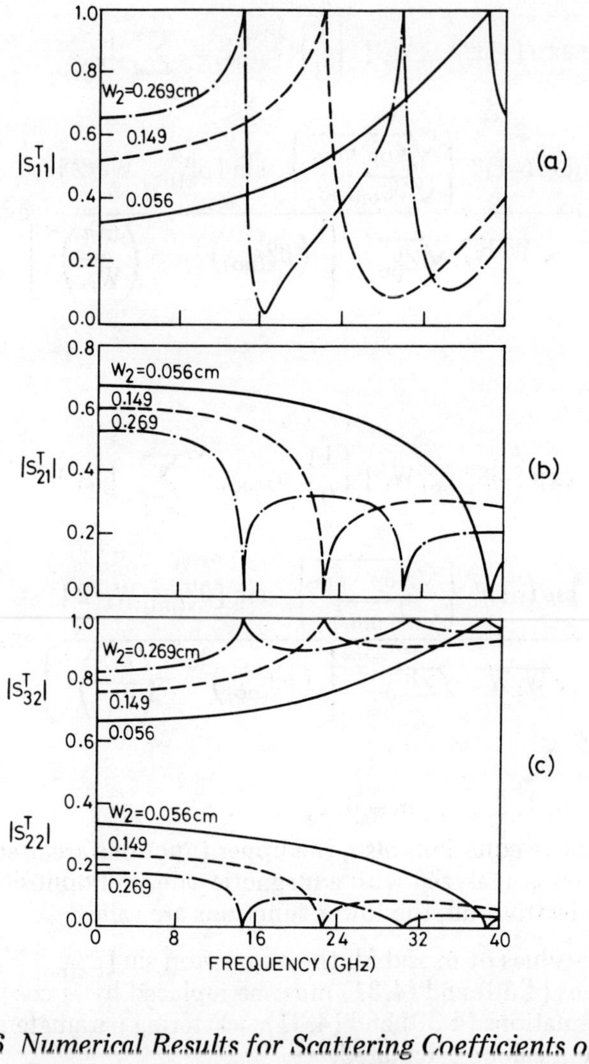

Figure 4.6 Numerical Results for Scattering Coefficients of a T-Junction ($\epsilon_r = 9.7$, $h = 0.0635$ cm, $W_1 = 0.056$ cm) (from [6])

Typical results for frequency dependent scattering matrix coefficients for a T-junction are shown in Figure 4.6. We note that $|S_{11}^T|$, and therefore the power reflected by the T-junction discontinuity at $z = 0$ increases with frequency in the range $0 \leqslant f \leqslant f_{c1}$, where f_{c1} is the cut-off frequency of the first higher order (TE_{10}) mode in region "b". Correspondingly the power transmitted into region "b" decreases with frequency (Figure 4.6(b)). For frequencies greater than f_{c1}, a part of the power is transmitted by the TE_{10} mode, so that the transmission coefficient $|S_{21}^T|$ for the TEM mode is always smaller than that for f = 0. Figure 4.6(c) indicates that, if the TEM mode is incident at port 2, the power reflected into guide "b" decreases with increasing frequency. Also the power transmitted into guide "a" decreases whereas the power transmitted into port 3 behaves in the opposite sense. It may be pointed out that the information contained in Figure 4.6 provides S-parameters for the TEM-mode since the incident power has been assumed to propagate in the dominant TEM-mode. For frequencies greater than f_{c1} (cut-off for the TE_{10}-mode) a part of power is transmitted in the TE_{10} mode also. Therefore, S-parameters for the TEM-mode do not describe the circuit completely for frequencies greater than f_{c1}.

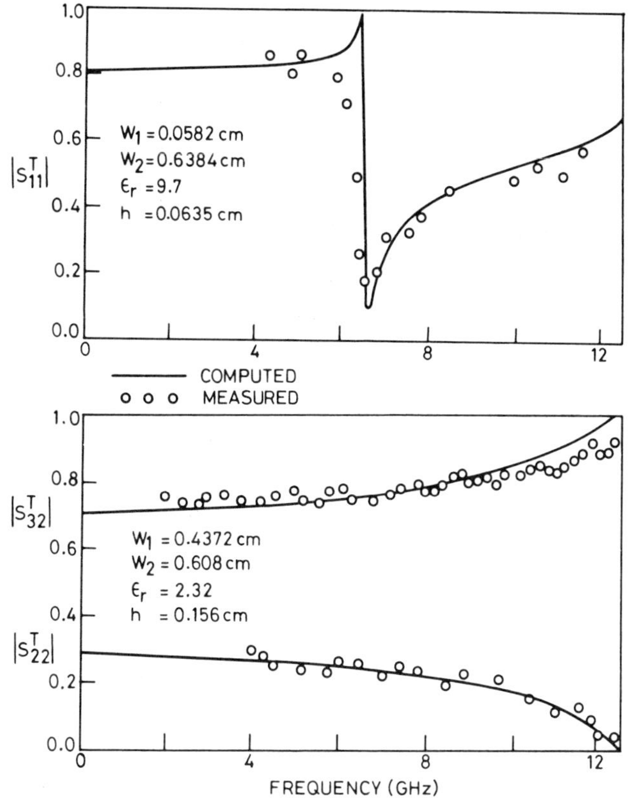

Figure 4.7 Comparison of Computed Results of Fullwave Theory for a T-Junction With Experimental Results (from [6])

A comparison between theoretical and experimental results is shown in Figure 4.7. Small circles show the experimental points. Discrepancies near cut-off frequencies of higher order modes in microstrip of width W_2 are attributed to the radiation effects.

The frequency dependent equivalent circuit of a discontinuity can be derived from the scattering parameters. The equivalent circuits of a T-junction with a magnetic wall and an electric wall at $z = W_2$ can be represented as shown in Figures 4.8(a) and 4.8(b), respectively.

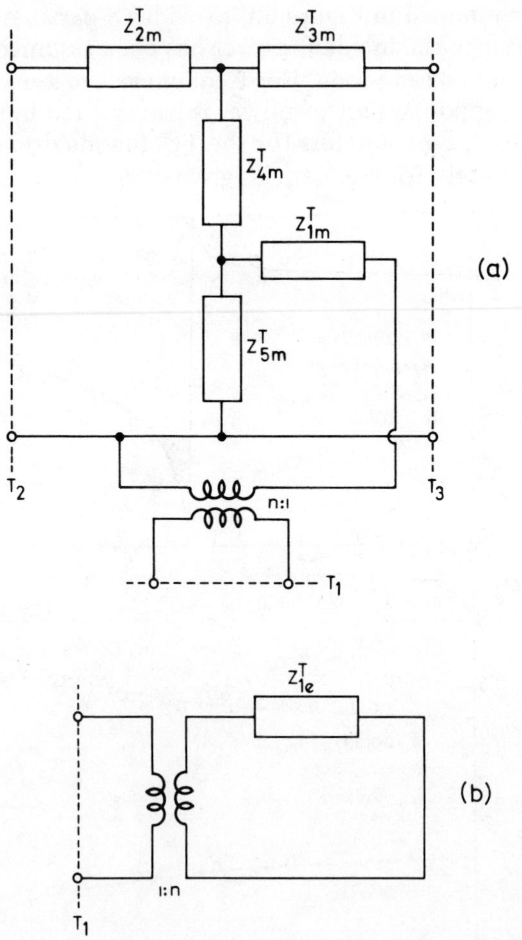

Figure 4.8 Frequency-Dependent Equivalent Circuit for Microstrip T-Junction (a) With Magnetic Wall and (b) With Electric Wall (from [7])

The impedances Z_{im}^{T} of the equivalent circuit elements can be determined using the relation between the short-circuit admittance matrix and the scattering matrix. These impedances may be written in terms of S-parameters as [7]

$$Z_{1m}^{T} = \frac{n\left[(1-S_{22}^{T} + S_{32}^{T})\left\{2S_{12}^{T}(nS_{12}^{T}-1) + n(1+S_{11}^{T})(1-S_{22}^{T}-S_{23}^{T})\right\}\right]}{D^{T}}$$

$$Z_{3m}^{T} = Z_{2m}^{T} = \frac{(1+S_{22}^{T}-S_{23}^{T})\left[(1-S_{11}^{T})(1-S_{22}^{T}-S_{23}^{T}) - 2(S_{12}^{T})^{2}\right]}{D^{T}}$$

$$Z_{4m}^{T} = 2\,\frac{(S_{12}^{T})^{2} - 2n\,S_{12}^{T}(1-S_{22}^{T} + S_{23}^{T}) + S_{23}^{T}(1-S_{11}^{T})}{D^{T}}$$

$$Z_{5m}^{T} = \frac{2n\,S_{12}^{T}(1-S_{22}^{T} + S_{23}^{T})}{D^{T}} \qquad (4.32)$$

where

$$D^{T} = (1-S_{22}^{T} + S_{23}^{T})\left[(1-S_{11}^{T})(1-S_{22}^{T}-S_{23}^{T}) - 2(S_{12}^{T})^{2}\right]$$

$$n^{2} = Z_{01}/Z_{02}$$

In the above equation, the subscript m denotes a magnetic wall. The impedances Z_{im}^{T} are normalized with respect to Z_{02}. For frequencies lower than the cut-off frequency of the first-higher order mode all elements of the equivalent circuit are reactances (capacitive or inductive). The reactance representation of the equivalent circuit is shown in Figure 4.9(a). For a typical set of T-junction parameters the variations of reactances with frequency are shown in Figure 4.9(b). This figure shows that except for C_{4T} other capacitances and inductances of the equivalent circuit do not vary much with frequency up to about 10 GHz.

For a T-junction with electric wall, Z_{1e}^{T} is given by expression for Z_{1m}^{T} when S-parameters corresponding to a T-junction with electric wall (Figure 4.5) are used.

Right-angled Bend and Cross Junction [6]

Scattering parameters for right-angled bends and cross junctions can be derived from those for the T-junction. This is achieved by an even and odd mode excitation at the opposite ports (ports 2 and 3 in Figure 4.5). Right-angled bends and cross junctions are discussed in the following paragraphs.

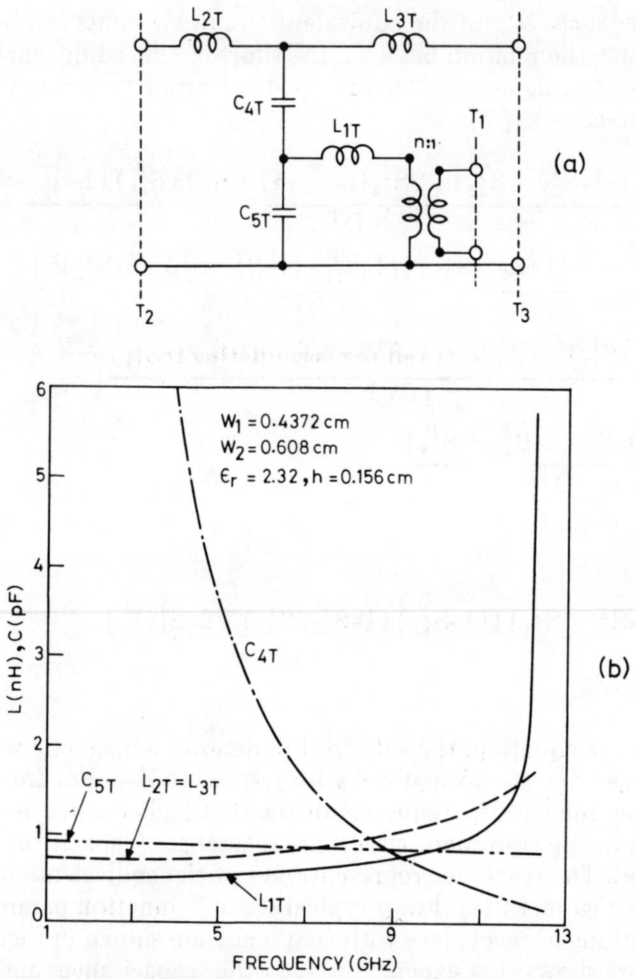

Figure 4.9 (a) Microstrip T-Junction Discontinuity Capacitances and Inductances

(b) Variations of Equivalent Circuit Parameters With Frequency (from [7])

The scattering parameters of a right-angled bend can be arrived at from the analysis of a T-junction with a magnetic wall at $z = W_2$. When the T-junction is excited symmetrically at ports 2 and 3 ($a_2 = a_3 = v_2$ as shown in Figure 4.10), the symmetry plane $x = 0$ (which bisects the T-junction into two identical right-angled bends) can be

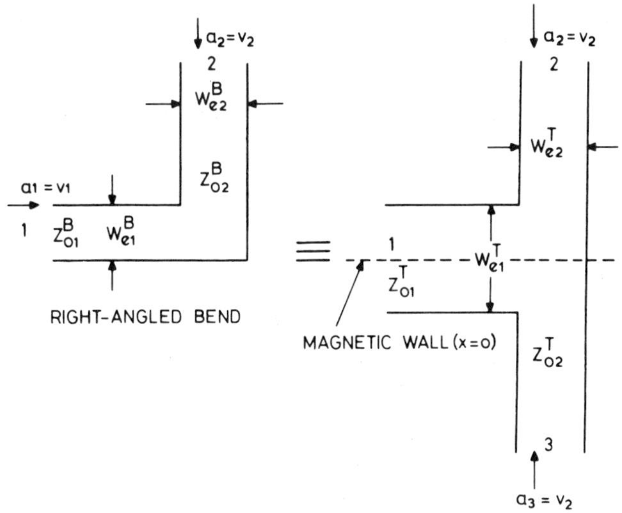

Figure 4.10 Derivation of Right-Angled Bend from Symmetrically Excited T-Junction

replaced by a magnetic wall. Using the symmetry and reciprocity properties of the structure, the relationship between the scattering parameters of the T-junction and the bend may be written as

$$
\begin{aligned}
S_{12}^B &= \sqrt{2}\, S_{12m}^T \\
S_{21}^B &= \sqrt{2}\, S_{21m}^T \\
S_{11}^B &= S_{11m}^T \\
S_{22}^B &= S_{23m}^T + S_{22m}^T
\end{aligned}
\tag{4.33}
$$

The superscripts B and T denote the bend and the T-junction, respectively. The subscript m indicates a T-junction with a magnetic wall at $z = W_2$. Equations (4.33) constitute a correspondence between a right-angled bend and a T-junction whose W_1 is chosen such that

$$Z_{01}^T = Z_{01}^B/2$$

or

$$W_{e1}^T(f) = 2W_{e1}^B(f) \tag{4.34}$$

S-parameters of a cross junction are calculated in the following manner. Any arbitrary excitation v at port 1 can be considered as superposition of a symmetric ($a_1 = v/2$, $a_3 = v/2$) excitation and an antisymmetric excitation ($a_1 = v/2$, $a_3 = -v/2$) at ports 1 and 3. This situation is shown in Figure 4.11. The cross junction with symmetric

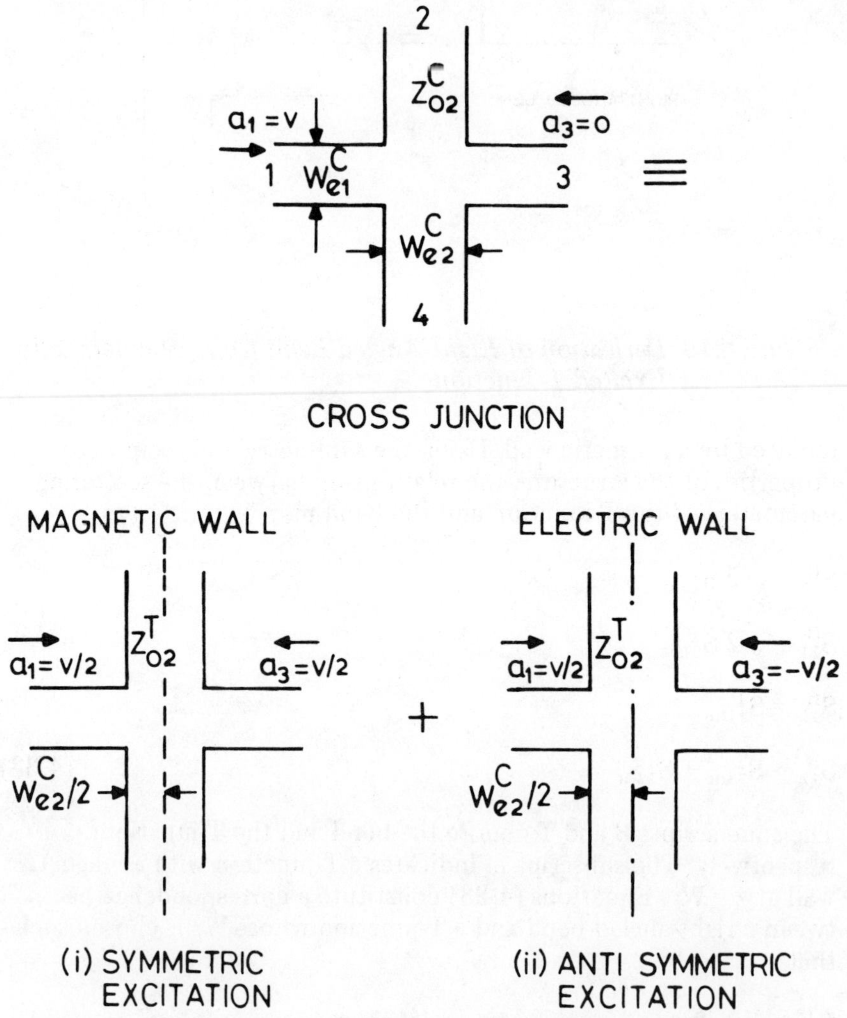

Figure 4.11 Derivation of Cross Junction from Superposition of Symmetrically and Antisymmetrically Excited T-Junctions

excitation is a combination of two T-junctions with magnetic walls placed back to back. Similarly, for antisymmetric excitation, a cross junction corresponds to two T-junctions with an electric wall as shown in Figure 4.11. These T-junctions have the effective width of the through arm equal to $W_{e2}^C/2$. The above considerations allow us to write S-parameters of a cross junction as

$$S_{11}^C = (S_{11m}^T + S_{11e}^T)/2$$

$$S_{13}^C = (S_{11m}^T - S_{11e}^T)/2$$

$$S_{12}^C = (1/\sqrt{2})\, S_{12m}^T ;\; S_{22}^C = S_{22m}^T ;\; S_{24}^C = S_{23m}^T \qquad (4.35)$$

The effective width of the T-junction has to be determined so that

$$Z_{02}^C = Z_{02}^T/2 \;\text{ or }\; W_{e2}^C(f) = 2\, W_{e2}^T(f) \qquad (4.36)$$

The superscript C denotes cross junction.

Results and Equivalent Circuit

S-parameters for right-angled bends are calculated using Equations (4.33) and (4.34). For cross junctions, Equations (4.35) and (4.36) are used. The equivalent circuits for these discontinuities are derived from the equivalent circuit impedances Z_{im}^T of the T-junction.

The frequency dependent equivalent circuit of the right-angled bend, based on the conversion procedure from the T-junction (with magnetic wall at $z = W_2$) to the right-angled bend discussed above is shown in Figure 4.12(a). The equivalent circuit element impedances are obtained from the following relations

$$Z_1^B = Z_{2m}^T + 2Z_{4m}^T$$

$$Z_2^B = 2Z_{5m}^T$$

$$Z_3^B = 2Z_{1m}^T \qquad (4.37)$$

The superscript B denotes a right-angled bend while subscript m denotes a magnetic wall. The variations of capacitive and inductive components of an equivalent circuit (shown in Figure 4.12(b)) with frequency are shown in Figure 4.12(c). This figure shows that the capacitive and inductive values are almost constant up to 10 GHz.

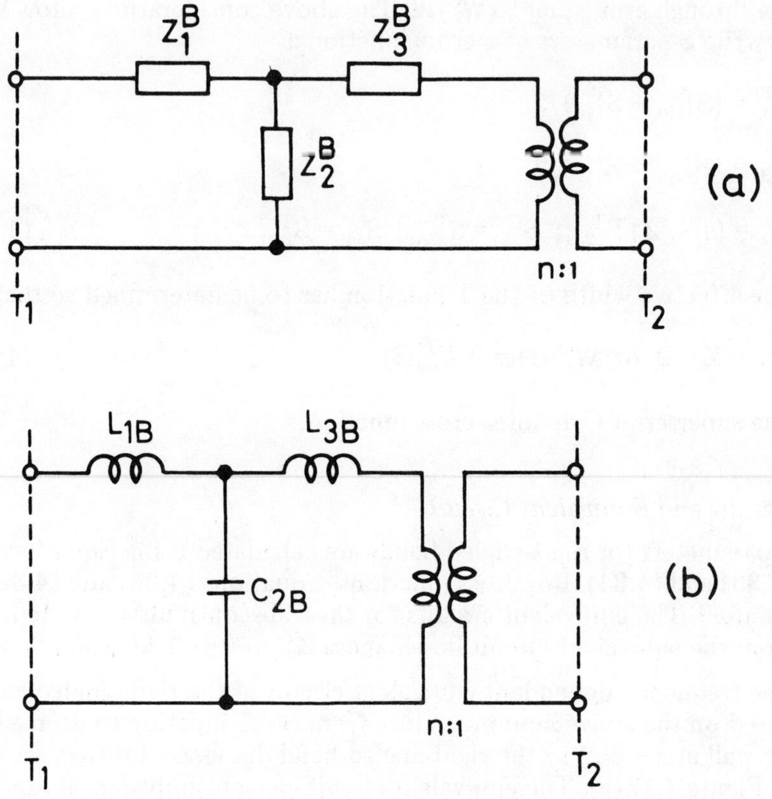

Figure 4.12(a) and (b) Equivalent Circuits of a Right-Angled Bend Based on Fullwave Analysis (from [7])

The frequency dependent equivalent circuit of the cross junction, based on the conversion procedure from the T-junctions (with magnetic and electric walls at $z = W_2/2$) is shown in Figure 4.13(a). The following relations between the elements of the equivalent circuit of the T-junction and the cross junction can be written

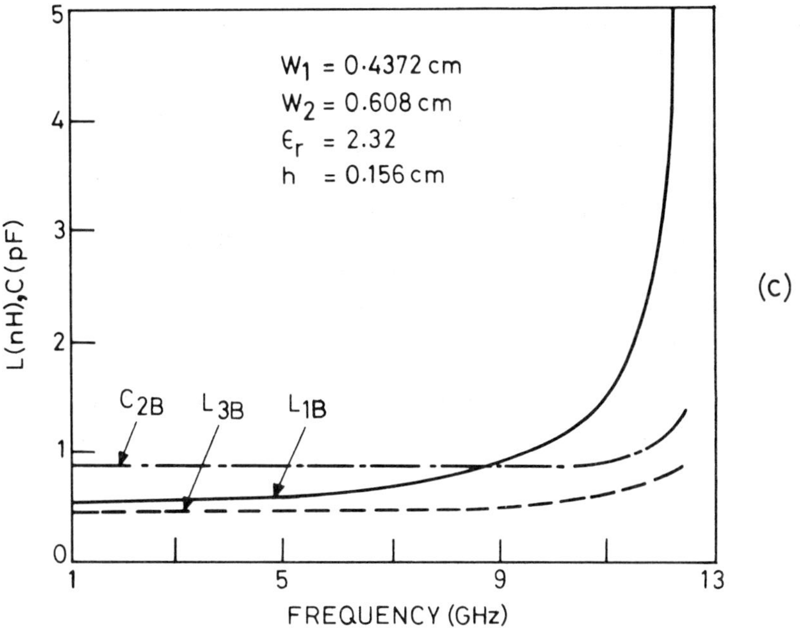

Figure 4.12(c) Variations of Computed Results for Capacitance and Inductances as a Function of Frequency (from [7])

$$Z_1^C = 2\, Z_{1e}^T$$

$$Z_2^C = Z_{2m}^T$$

$$Z_3^C = Z_{4m}^T(Z_{1m}^T - Z_{1e}^T) \left\{ \frac{1}{Z_{4m}^T} + \frac{1}{Z_{1m}^T - Z_{1e}^T} + \frac{1}{Z_{5m}^T} \right\}$$

$$Z_4^C = Z_{5m}^T \cdot Z_3^C / Z_{4m}^T$$

$$Z_5^C = Z_{5m}^T \cdot Z_3^C / (Z_{1m}^T - Z_{1e}^T) \tag{4.38}$$

with superscript C denoting the cross junction. The subscript e indicates electric wall at $z = W_2/2$ opposite to guide "a" of the T-junction. The equivalent circuit in terms of capacitances and inductances, based on the results of Equation (4.38), is shown in Figure 4.13(b). The variations of these components with frequency are shown in Figure 4.13(c). In this case also, the variation of inductances with frequency is small up to 10 GHz.

The planar waveguide model of microstrip can also be used for analyzing more general unsymmetrical discontinuities [8]. An example of an unsymmetrical crossing is shown in Figure 4.14(a). The microstrip lines are replaced by the equivalent planar waveguides and the connecting field region is treated as a rectangular disc resonator. The fields of the rectangular disc resonator can also be approximated by a magnetic wall model. The magnetic fields of the regions are matched in the subareas A_i ($i = 1, 2, 3, 4$), all other boundaries being magnetic walls. By superposition of the fields of the four subproblems and matching the electric fields in the areas A_i, the scattering matrix of the discontinuity can be calculated, taking into account the influence of dispersion effects and higher order modes. Figure 4.14(b) shows some other types of discontinuities that can be analysed using this method.

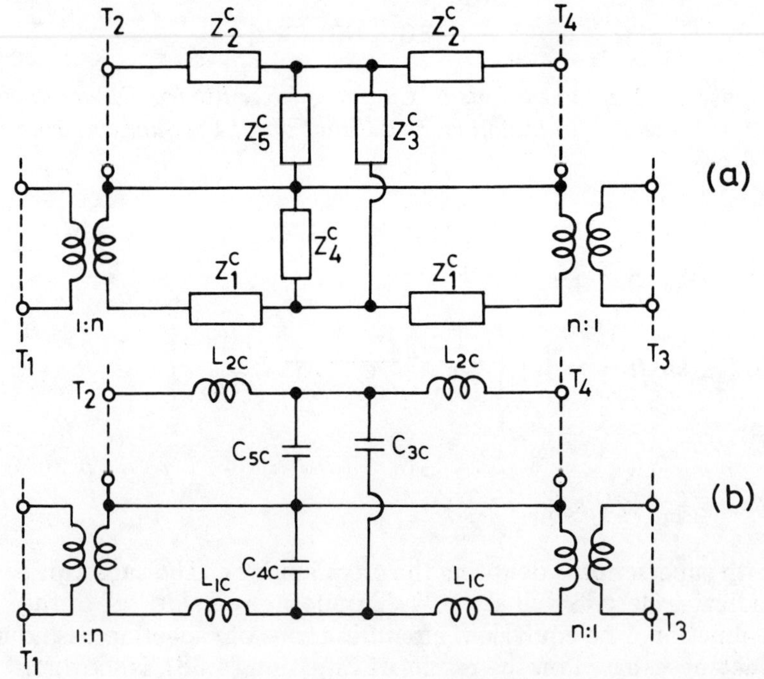

Figure 4.13(a) and (b) Frequency Dependent Equivalent Circuits of a Cross Junction (from [7])

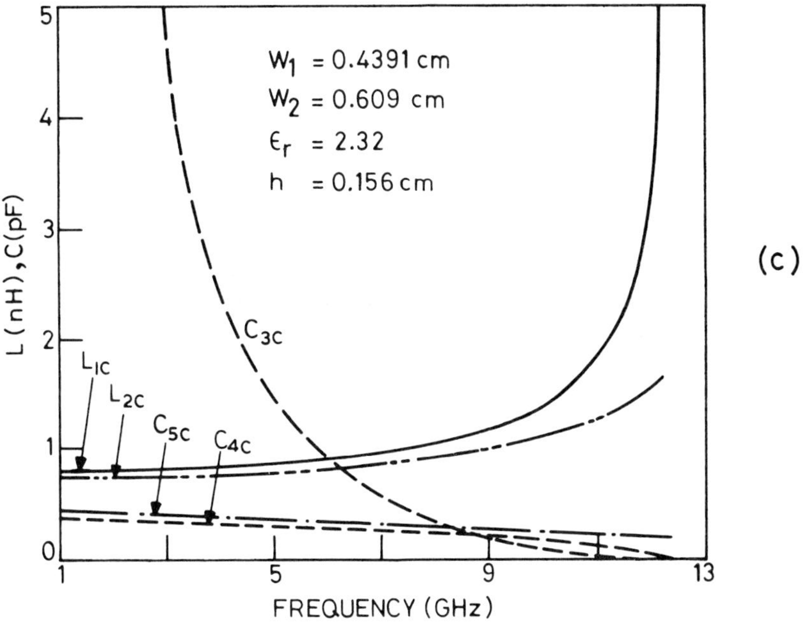

Figure 4.13(c) Discontinuity Capacitances and Inductances as a Function of Frequency (from [7])

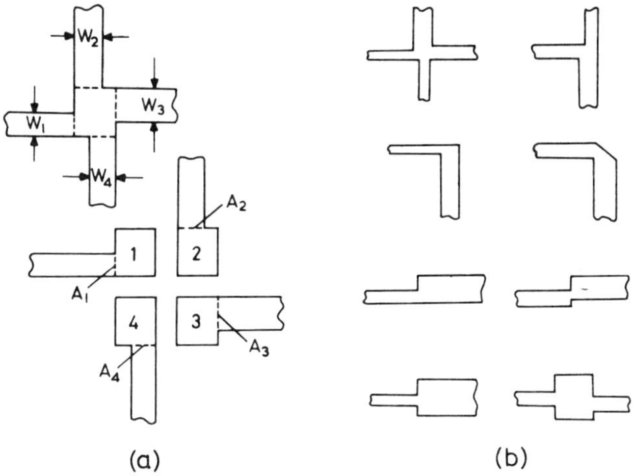

Figure 4.14(a) Configuration for Calculation of Dynamic Properties of an Unsymmetric Cross Junction
(b) Other Types of Discontinuities That Could Be Analyzed by Parallel Plate Waveguide Model

4.2 DISCONTINUITY MEASUREMENTS

Since detailed and reliably accurate data for various microstrip discontinuities are not available, it becomes necessary to carry out measurements of specific discontinuities so that their influence may be incorporated into microstrip circuit design.

Methods for accurate measurement of microstrip discontinuities are based on the technique of incorporating discontinuities in microstrip resonators and measuring the change in resonance frequency. Since these resonators are coupled very loosely to the test equipment, the measurements are not affected by the uncertain characteristics of coaxial to microstrip transitions. Both the linear and the ring resonators have been used for discontinuity measurements. Use of these resonators for measuring the phase velocity in microstrip has been discussed in Chapter 1 (Section1.4.3). Measurements of discontinuities using these resonators are discussed in this section.

4.2.1 Linear Resonator Method

This method [4, 10, 11] uses a linear microstrip resonator which incorporates the discontinuity to be tested and is lightly coupled to the measuring instrumentation through a microstrip gap. The linear resonator is obtained by a $n\lambda_m/2$ length of a microstrip section open at the two ends. Thus the microstrip open-end and the microstrip gap constitute essential parts of this measuring arrangement and have to be calibrated before measurements on any other discontinuity may be carried out.

To minimize significant effects due to the change in substrate properties and the fabrication, it is necessary to measure the effective dielectric constant ϵ_{re} for each circuit, either by adding a linear resonator alongside each test configuration, or by etching the test configuration to a suitable form and making a second measurement of the resonant frequency. Careful use of the latter strategy realizes the advantages of a substitutional method and will be illustrated in the method for characterization of microstrip gap discussed in the following paragraph.

Open-ends and Gaps

An arrangement for characterization of the open-end and the gap is shown in Figure 4.15(a). The length ℓ is chosen so that the effective length of this section at the frequency of measurement is $n\lambda_m/2$, where n is an integer and λ_m the microstrip wavelength. The length ℓ' should have an effective length of $\lambda_m/4$. The free space wavelength

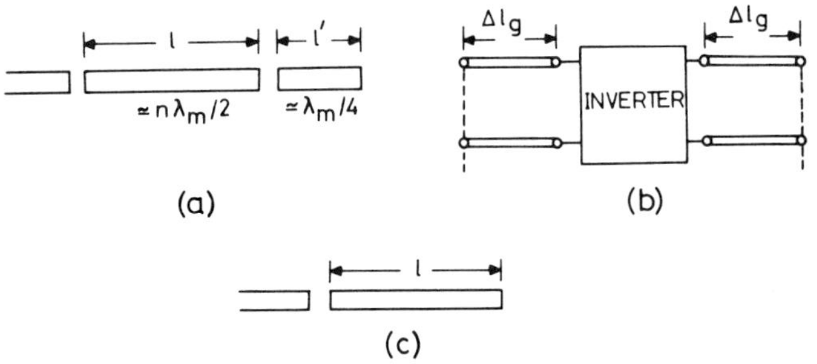

Figure 4.15 An Arrangement for Experimental Characterization of an Open-End and a Gap

for the resonance of the structure, shown in Figure 4.15(a), is then given by

$$(\ell + 2\Delta\ell_g) = \frac{n}{2}\,\frac{\lambda_o}{\sqrt{\epsilon_{re}}} \tag{4.39}$$

where $\Delta\ell_g$ is the extra length contributed by the microstrip gap. The equivalent circuit used for the gap as shown in Figure 3.15(b) may be represented by an alternate arrangement as shown in Figure 4.15(b). The gap capacitance C_g is represented by an inverter. The next step involves selective etching of length ℓ'. The resonance wavelength is measured again after ℓ' is removed (Figure 4.15(c)). Equation (4.39) can now be modified as

$$(\ell + \Delta\ell_{oc} + \Delta\ell_g) = \frac{n}{2}\,\frac{\lambda_o}{\sqrt{\epsilon_{re}}} \tag{4.40}$$

where $\Delta\ell_{oc}$ is the equivalent line length associated with an open-end. There are three unknowns appearing in Equations (4.39) and (4.40), namely, $\Delta\ell_g$, $\Delta\ell_{oc}$ and ϵ_{re}. So an additional measurement is required. If two values of ℓ are chosen to give resonance with different n close to the normal frequency of measurement, then one measurement with ℓ' present, together with two measurements with the extra section ℓ' removed, are sufficient to give ϵ_{re}, $\Delta\ell_{oc}$ and $\Delta\ell_g$. Suitable choice of resonant mode, n, and length ℓ has to be made such that various resonant frequencies are close together and ϵ_{re} can be taken as constant over the frequency range.

It has been mentioned [4] that this method has an experimental uncertainty of ± 10 μm, which is largely attributable to substrate variations. This uncertainty corresponds to about ± 0.005 Y_o at 10 GHz.

Right-angled Bends and Steps in Width

Variations of the procedure described above may be used for other discontinuities also. The arrangement for characterization of a right-angled bend [4, 11] and its equivalent circuit are shown in Figure 4.16. Two resonators of different lengths are needed to determine

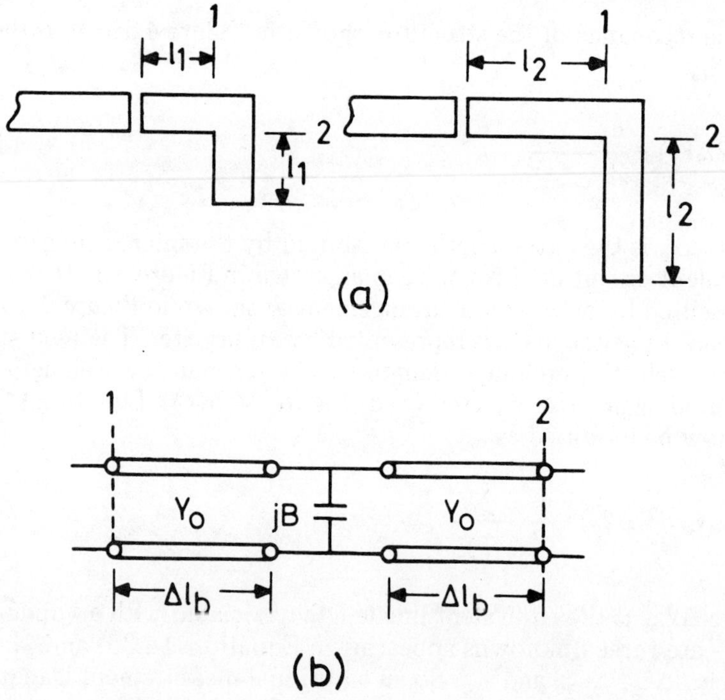

Figure 4.16(a) An Arrangement for Experimental Characterization of a Right-Angled Bend

(b) Equivalent Circuit of the Right-Angled Bend

two unknowns (B and $\Delta\ell_b$) in the equivalent circuit. These resonators will either have a voltage minimum or a voltage maximum at the corner, according to whether the effective overall length $(2\ell_1 + 2\Delta\ell_b + \Delta\ell_{oc} + \Delta\ell_g)$ or $(2\ell_2 + 2\Delta\ell_b + \Delta\ell_{oc} + \Delta\ell_g)$ at resonance is an odd or an even number of half wavelengths. For example, in the case of a half wave resonator, there will be a voltage minimum at the corner of the bend and the effective increase in length will be $2\Delta\ell_b$. On the other hand, for a fullwave resonator the presence of a voltage maximum at the corner will cause the shunt susceptance B to increase the effective length of the fullwave resonator by an amount $(\lambda_m/\pi) \cdot \tan^{-1}(B/2Y_o)$. The relation for resonance frequency may now be written as

$$\ell_2 + \Delta\ell_b + \frac{\Delta\ell_{oc} + \Delta\ell_g}{2} + \frac{\lambda_m}{2\pi} \tan^{-1}\left(\frac{B}{2Y_o}\right) = (2n+1)\frac{\lambda_m}{2} \qquad (4.41)$$

Thus the series and the shunt components of the equivalent circuit can be separated. As ϵ_{re}, $\Delta\ell_{oc}$ and $\Delta\ell_g$ are known from previous measurement, the parameters of the equivalent circuit shown in Figure 4.16(b) may be determined from the two frequencies of resonance.

A similar arrangement can be used for determing equivalent circuit parameters of a step discontinuity. The circuit arrangement is shown in Figure 4.17. Two resonators are used. Their lengths are adjusted so

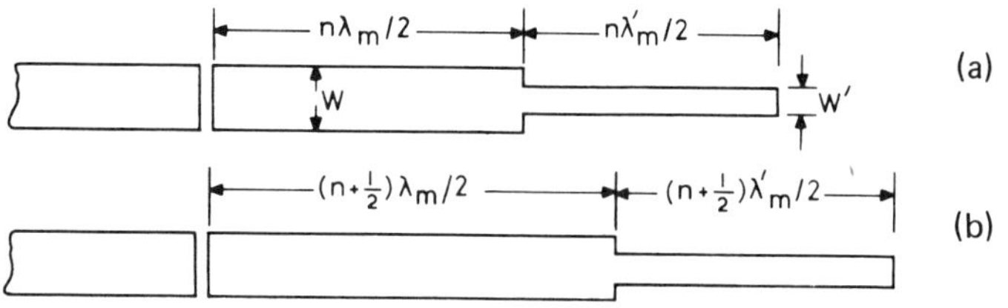

Figure 4.17 Circuit Lay-Out for Measuring Equivalent Circuit of a Step Discontinuity

that in one case (a) we have a voltage maximum at the step; while in the other case (b) we have voltage minimum at the step. Note that microstrip wavelengths λ_m and λ'_m correspond to microstrip lines of width W and W′, respectively, and will not be equal. Also in this case, we need the previous characterization of ϵ_{re}, $\Delta\ell_{oc}$ and $\Delta\ell_g$ for two widths W and W′.

T-junctions

A T-junction, its equivalent circuit and circuit arrangement for its characterization [4] are shown in Figure 4.18. Only a symmetrical

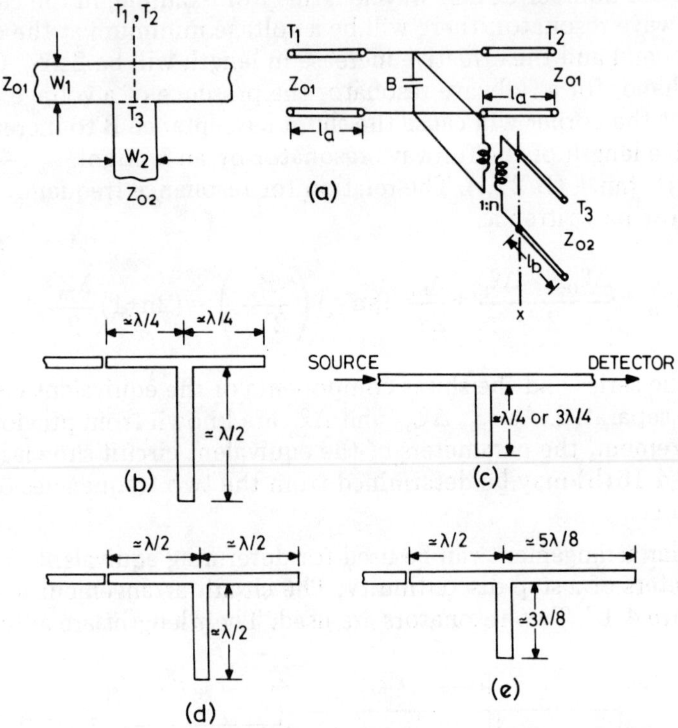

Figure 4.18 Circuit Arrangement Required for Characterization of a T-Junction (from [4])

T-junction, with its through arm having the same impedance on either side of the branch, is considered.

The circuit of Figure 4.18(b) enables an accurate determination of the line length ℓ_a by determining the resonance of the half wavelength along the through arm before and after removing the stub. It may be pointed out that the susceptance B is ineffective because of the presence of a voltage minimum at the location of B. The length ℓ_b may be obtained from the frequency of peak attenuation with the stub arm of Figure 4.18(c) an odd number of quarter wavelengths long. Due to the shunt resonance of the stub, peak attenuation is a strong function of stub length. The end effect of the open end of the stub is assumed to be known from previous measurements. The configuration of Figure 4.18(d) enables B to be determined. The impedance ratio n^2 is measured by using the configuration shown in Figure 4.18(e). Values of B and n^2 depend on previous measurements, but some cancellation in the uncertainty can be obtained if the stub in Figure 4.18(d) is etched off and measurements carried out to obtain ϵ_{re} from resonance of the "through arm." The accuracy of determination of n^2 has been estimated [4] as ± 2 percent. It may be noted that the transformation ratio n does not affect the resonance frequency for the configurations (b) to (d) because of the presence of an open or short circuit at plane XX (Figure 4.18(a)).

Measurements for a symmetrical cross junction may also be made by using circuits of Figures 4.18(b), (c), (d) and (e) and taking advantage of the symmetry of the junction. Similar measurement techniques may be designed for other discontinuity structures also.

The main advantage of the linear resonator method is that it involves shorter lengths which result in better accuracy. Since this method uses the open-ends of the resonator, it is necessary to characterize the open-ends accurately. This is one of the disadvantages associated with this method. The other disadvantage of this method is the need for fabricating a set of resonators for each frequency of interest. These problems are overcome in the ring resonator method which is discussed in next subsection.

4.2.2 Ring Resonator Method

Ring resonators have been described earlier (Section 1.4) while discussing the measurement of microstrip phase velocities. When a ring resonator is used in place of a linear resonator as discussed above, the open-end and gap reactances need not be calibrated and accounted for. This method is convenient particularly for symmetrical two-port discontinuities (with $S_{11} = S_{22}$).

A microstrip ring structure resonates if its electrical length is an integral multiple of the guide wavelength. When a discontinuity is introduced into the ring, each resonance degenerates into two distinct modes. This splitting is conveniently interpreted in terms of even and odd excitation of the discontinuity [12]. The even mode corresponds to the incidence of two waves of equal magnitude and phase upon the discontinuity, while in the odd mode, waves of equal magnitude but opposite phase are incident from two sides. Any one of these resonances can be excited by an appropriate choice of the point of excitation along the ring. In an experimental setup [12], this is achieved by shifting the position of the launcher along the ring as shown in Figure 4.19.

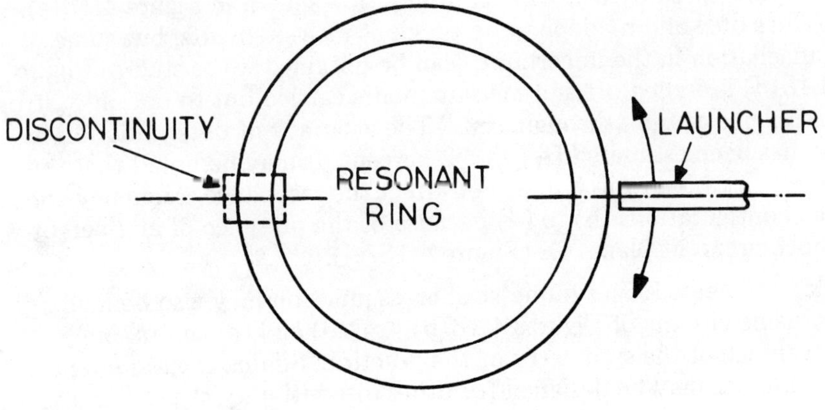

Figure 4.19 Ring Resonator Method for Measurement on a Two Port Symmetrical Discontinuity

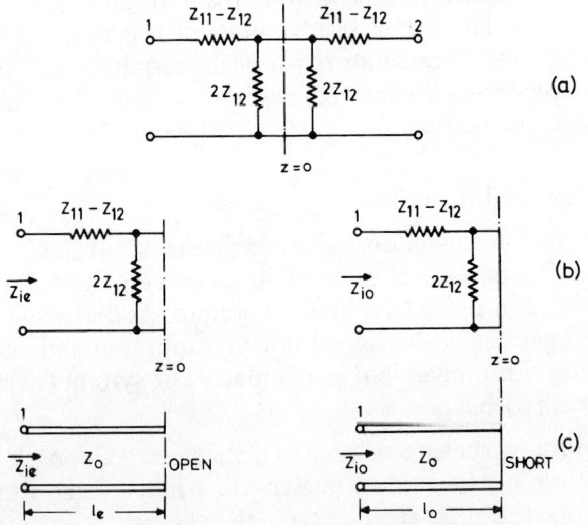

Figure 4.20(a) Representation of a Symmetrical Discontinuity by a T-Network

(b) Equivalent Circuits for Even and Odd Modes

(c) Equivalent Line Lengths for These Modes

A symmetrical discontinuity may be represented in terms of a T-network as shown in Figure 4.20(a). Parameters ofthe T-network can be evaluated from two impedances Z_{ie} and Z_{io} as shown in Figure 4.20(b) and obtained by introducing an open circuit and a short circuit, respectively, at the z = 0 plane. These impedances can be expressed in terms of two fictitious electrical lengths ℓ_e and ℓ_o (shown in Figure 4.20(c)) and given by

$$Z_{ie} = Z_{11} + Z_{12} = -j \cot k \ell_e \qquad \text{(even case)} \qquad (4.42)$$

$$Z_{io} = Z_{11} - Z_{12} = j \tan k \ell_o \qquad \text{(odd case)} \qquad (4.43)$$

where $k = 2\pi/\lambda_m$ is the propagation constant along the ring resonator and all the impedances have been normalized to the characteristic impedance of the microstrip ring. These equivalent lengths ℓ_e and ℓ_o add to the total length of the ring for even and odd excitation, respectively, as shown in Figures 4.21(a) and 4.21(b). Resonance conditions for the two cases may be written as

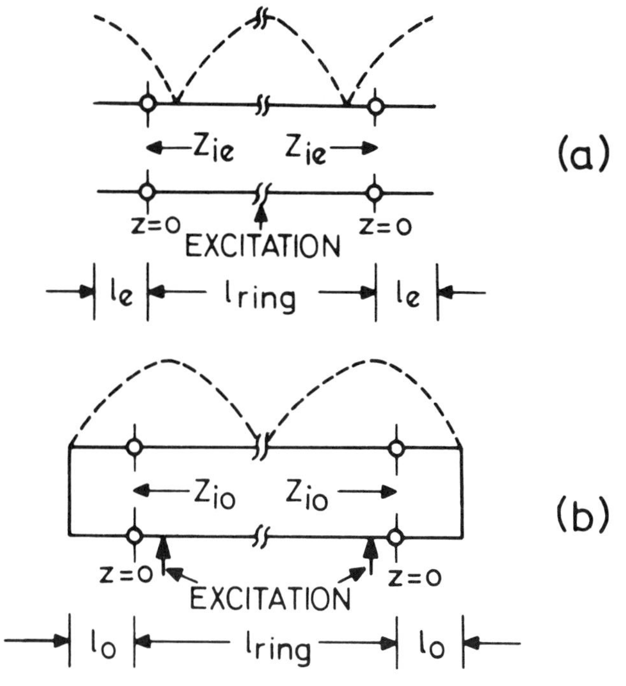

Figure 4.21 Standing Wave Patterns on the Ring for Even and Odd Modes of Excitation

$$\ell_{ring} + 2\ell_e = n\lambda_{me} \tag{4.44}$$

and

$$\ell_{ring} + 2\ell_o = n\lambda_{mo} \tag{4.45}$$

where λ_{me} and λ_{mo} are guide wavelengths corresponding to the even and odd mode resonance frequencies, respectively. ℓ_{ring} is the physical length of the ring resonator along the mean circumference. Equations (4.42 - 4.45) may be used for evaluating Z_{11} and Z_{12} and hence the equivalent circuit.

This method can also be extended for unsymmetrical discontinuities. An example of characterization of impedance steps in a ring resonator is given in reference [13]. The circuit arrangement used is shown in Figure 4.22. Two steps are located such that lengths ℓ_1 and ℓ_2 are electrically equal. Voltage maximum and minimum can be arranged to appear at the discontinuity locations successively by changing the point of excitation. Shunt and series parts of equivalent circuit are thus separated.

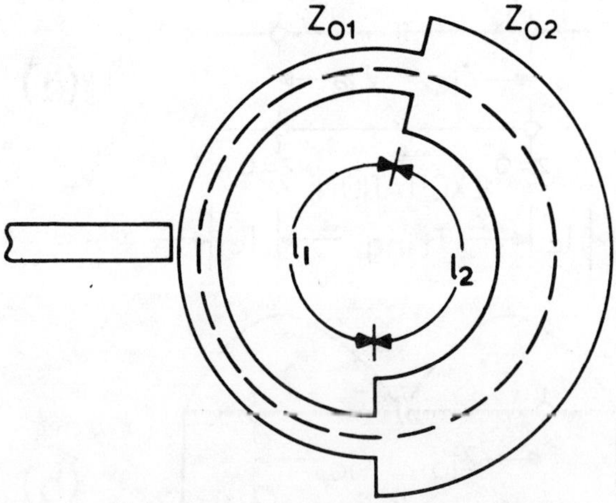

Figure 4.22 An Arrangement for Characterization of Step Discontinuity by Ring Resonator Method

REFERENCES

[1] Itoh, T., "Analysis of Microstrip Resonators," *IEEE Trans., Vol. MTT-22,* 1974, pp. 946-952.

[2] Wolff, I., G. Kompa, and R. Mehran, "Calculation Method for Microstrip Discontinuities and T-junctions," *Electron. Lett., Vol. 8,* 1972, pp. 177-179.

[3] Kompa, G., and R. Mehran, Planar waveguide model for calculating microstrip components, *Electron. Lett., Vol. 11,* 1975, pp. 459-460.

[4] Easter, B., "The Equivalent Circuits of some Microstrip Discontinuities," *IEEE Trans., MTT-23,* 1975, pp. 655-660.

[5] Kompa, G., "S-matrix Computation of Microstrip Discontinuities with a Planar Waveguide Model," *AEU, Vol. 30,* 1976, pp. 58-64.

[6] Mehran, R., "The Frequency-dependent Scattering Matrix of Microstrip Right-angle Bends, T-junctions and Crossings," *AEU, Vol. 29,* 1975, pp. 454-460.

[7] Mehran, R, "Frequency dependent Equivalent Circuits for Microstrip Right-angle Bends, T-junctions and Crossings," *AEU, Vol. 30,* 1976, pp. 80-82.

[8] Menzel, W. and I. Wolff, "A Method for Calculating the Frequency Dependent Properties of Microstrip Discontinuities," *IEEE Trans. Vol. MTT-25,* 1977, pp. 107-112.

[9] Altschuler, H.M. and A.A. Oliner, "Discontinuities in the Center Conductor of Strip Transmission Line," *IRE Trans. Vol. MTT-8,* 1960, pp. 328-338.

[10] Easter, B. *et al.*, "Resonant Techniques for the Accurate Measurement of Microstrip Properties and Equivalent Circuits," *Proc. 1973 European Microwave Conf.*, paper B 7.6.

[11] Stephenson, I.W. and B. Easter, "Resonant Techniques for Establishing the Equivalent Circuits of Small Discontinuities in Microstrip," *Electron. Lett., Vol. 7,* 1971, pp. 582-584.

[12] Hoefer, W.J.R. and A. Chattopadhyay, "Evaluation of the Equivalent Circuit Parameters of Microstrip Discontinuities through Perturbation of a Resonant Ring," *IEEE Trans. Vol. MTT-23,* 1975, pp. 1067-1071.

[13] Groll, H. and W. Weidmann, "Measurement of Equivalent Circuit Elements of Microstrip Discontinuities by a Resonant Method," *Nachrichtentech. Z., Vol. 28,* 1975, pp. 74-77.

Chapter 5
Slotlines I:
Analyses and Design Considerations

5.1 INTRODUCTION

Slotline is an alternative transmission structure proposed for use in MICs by Cohn in 1968. The basic slotline configuration is shown in Figure 5.1. It consists of a dielectric substrate with a narrow slot

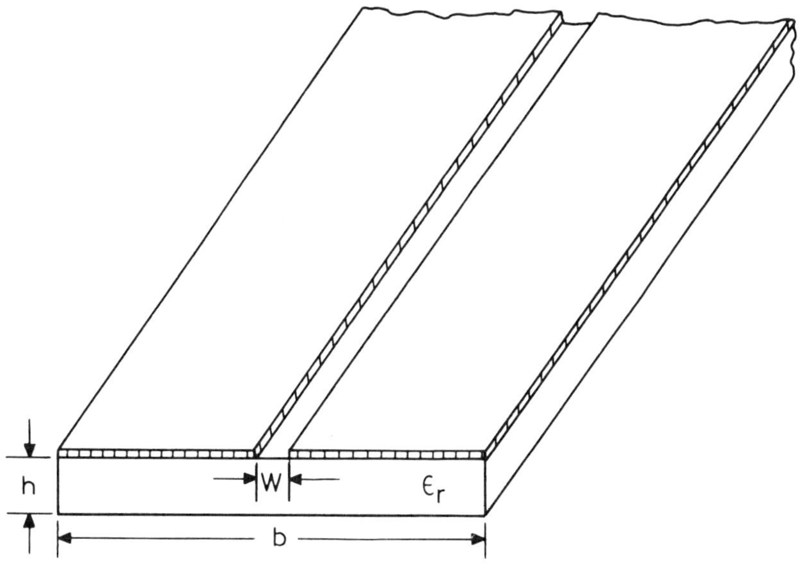

Figure 5.1 Slotline Configuration

etched in the metallization on one of the surfaces of the substrate. The other surface of the substrate is without any metallization. The geometry is planar and, as mentioned earlier in Chapter 1, is well suited for its usage in microwave integrated circuits.

Slotlines can be included in microstrip circuits by etching the slotline circuit in the ground plane of the substrate for microstrip circuits. This type of hybrid combination allows flexibility in the design of microwave circuits and has led to some new types of circuits such as hybrid branchline directional couplers which will be discussed later in Chapter 6. Also, some of the circuit elements, which cannot easily be achieved in microstrip configuration, can be incorporated in the slotline part of the circuit. These, for example, could be short circuits, high impedance lines or series stubs.

In a slotline, the wave propagates along the slot with the major electric field component oriented across the slot in the plane of metallization on the dielectric substrate. The mode of propagation is non-TEM and almost transverse electric in nature. However, unlike conventional waveguides, there is no low frequency cut-off because slotline is a two conductor structure. Approximate field distributions for slotline are shown in Figure 5.2.

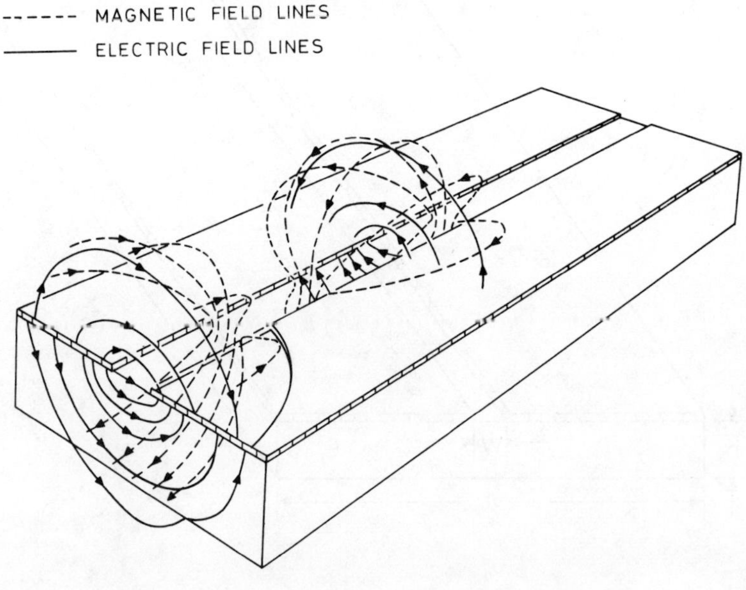

Figure 5.2 Field Distributions in a Slotline

The various methods used for the analysis of slotline are described in the following section. Design considerations are included in the last section of this chapter.

5.2 SLOTLINE ANALYSIS

The most widely used method of slotline analysis is the one given by Cohn [1] and employs a transverse resonance approach. There are other methods available, and various analytical techniques may be listed as:

i) approximate analysis [1],
ii) the transverse resonance method [1],
iii) Galerkin's method in FTD [2, 3], and
iv) analysis in elliptical coordinates [4].

These methods are discussed in the following sub-sections.

5.2.1 Approximate Analysis

Before attempting the rigorous analysis it is worthwhile to look at an approximate solution for slotline characteristics. It has the advantage of mathematical simplicity and provides a better qualitative picture of slotline characteristics. Approximate analysis for field distribution, polarization of magnetic field and expression for slot wavelength is presented below.

Field Distribution

For a waveguiding structure to be useful as a transmission line or a circuit element it is necessary to confine the fields near the structure. The analysis of the field distribution of the transmission line structure is helpful in determining the parameters necessary to prevent the spread of fields.

The slotline field contains six components; three electric field components and three magnetic field components. However, if the slot width W is much smaller than free space wavelength λ_o, the electric field across the slot may be represented by an equivalent line source of magnetic current and the far field contains only three components: H_x, H_r and E_ϕ. At a distance r ($\gg$ W) in the air region above the slot (Figure 5.3), these may be written as [1],

$$H_x = A\, H_o^{(1)}(k_c r) \tag{5.1}$$

$$H_r = -\frac{\gamma_x}{k_c^2}\frac{\partial H_x}{\partial r} = \frac{A}{\sqrt{1-(\lambda_s/\lambda_o)^2}}\, H_1^{(1)}(k_c r) \tag{5.2}$$

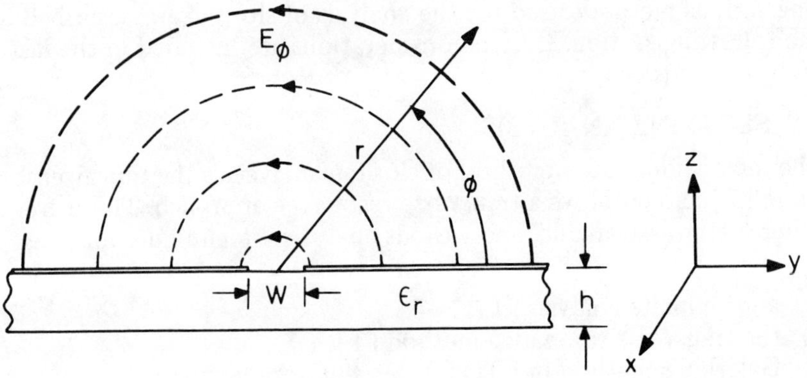

Figure 5.3 Cylindrical Coordinates Configuration for Approximate Analysis of Slotline

$$E_\phi = \frac{j\omega\mu}{k_c^2}\frac{\partial H_x}{\partial r} = -\eta\, H_r\, \lambda_s/\lambda_o \tag{5.3}$$

where γ_x is the propagation constant along the x-direction, and the direction of propagation and the coefficient k_c is related to the slot wavelength λ_s by the equation

$$k_c = j\frac{2\pi}{\lambda_o}\sqrt{\left(\frac{\lambda_o}{\lambda_s}\right)^2 - 1} \tag{5.4}$$

From the above expressions for the field components the following information may be obtained.

Rate of Decay of Field

For large $|p|$, $H_1^{(1)}(p)$ and $H_o^{(1)}(p)$ may be obtained from

$$H_n^{(1)}(j|p|) = \frac{2}{\sqrt{j\pi\,|p|}}\exp\left(-|p| - j\frac{n\pi}{2} - j\frac{\pi}{4}\right) \tag{5.5}$$

Therefore, if $k_c r$ is imaginary the field will decay with distance r. Equation (5.4) shows that $k_c r$ is imaginary for $\lambda_s/\lambda_o < 1$. Hence a relative wavelength ratio less than unity is a sufficient condition to ensure transverse decay of the field. To a zero order approximation, λ_s/λ_o is equal to $\sqrt{2/(\epsilon_r+1)}$. As λ_s/λ_o is decreased, i.e. ϵ_r increased, the rate of decay becomes faster and fields become more tightly bound to the slot. For example, the ratio of voltage V(r) at a distance r to the voltage V directly across the slot on a substrate with $\epsilon_r = 16$ is obtained (at 3 GHz) to be

$$V(r)/V = \frac{\pi}{2} \mid k_c r \, H_1^{(1)}(k_c r) \mid = 0.038 \text{ (r is one inch)} \tag{5.6}$$

Information regarding the rate of decay of fields is also helpful in determining the size of the enclosure for the slotline.

Polarization of the Magnetic Field

The polarization of the magnetic field in slotline can be obtained from the ratio $|H_x/H_r|$. Equations (5.1) and (5.2) give

$$\left|\frac{H_x}{H_r}\right| = \left|\frac{H_o^{(1)}(k_c r)}{H_1^{(1)}(k_c r)}\right| \sqrt{1-(\lambda_s/\lambda_o)^2} \tag{5.7}$$

From mathematical tables one knows that $H_1^{(1)}(j|p|)$ is always greater than $H_o^{(1)}(j|p|)$ and also $\lambda_s < \lambda_o$. Therefore $|H_x|$ is always less than $|H_r|$, and the magnetic field cannot have circular polarization. Nevertheless elliptical polarization exists for all values of r.

The field configuration in the slotline shown in Figure 5.2 indicates that the magnetic field has regions of elliptical polarization both in the air region above the slot and on the conducting surface constituting the slot. These regions of elliptical polarization can be utilized for the construction of non-reciprocal ferrite components. Robinson and Allen [5], have used slotline in the construction of ferrite devices.

The near field distribution of slotline has been described by Cohn [6].

Slot Wavelength

As shown in Figure 5.2 slotline field components are not confined to the substrate alone. They extend into the air regions above the slot and below the substrate also. Therefore, the energy is distributed between the substrate and the air regions. Consequently, the effective constant for slotline ϵ_{re} is less than substrate permittivity ϵ_r. Galejs [7] has shown that the zeroth order value of ϵ_{re} for a slot on an infinitely thick substrate is the average dielectric constant of the two media, i.e.,

$$\epsilon_{re} = \frac{\epsilon_r + 1}{2} \tag{5.8}$$

and therefore,

$$\frac{\lambda_s}{\lambda_o} = \sqrt{\frac{2}{\epsilon_r + 1}} \tag{5.9}$$

It has been observed by Garg and Gupta [8] that for slotline on a finite thickness substrate, the above value of λ_s/λ_o is approached for the cut-off thickness for the TE_{10} surface wave mode. The cut-off thickness $(h/\lambda_o)_c$ is given by

$$(h/\lambda_o)_c = 0.25/\sqrt{\epsilon_r - 1} \tag{5.10}$$

The approximate analysis discussed above gives a good physical picture of the field configuration of the slotline. But it does not lead to evaluation of the characteristic impedance of slotline. Moreover, the variation of slot wavelength λ_s with different geometrical parameters of slotline, i.e. h, W and b, is not provided by this analysis. To overcome these shortcomings, several rigorous analyses of slotline have been carried out [1-4]. These analyses take into account the effect of various parameters on slotline impedance Z_{os} and wavelength λ_s. One of these analyses, called the transverse resonance method, is described below.

5.2.2 Transverse Resonance Method [1]

In this method slotline is analysed as a rectangular waveguide problem. The key feature of this analysis is the introduction of boundary walls such that a rectangular waveguide configuration with a capacitance iris is obtained. It is then analysed in terms of waveguide modes propagating perpendicular to the slotline plane.

Development of Waveguide Model

A waveguide model for slotline is obtained by introducing (i) conducting planes normal to the slot and the substrate at x = 0 and x = a such that $a = \lambda_s/2$ as shown in Figure 5.4(a). Since the spacing between the two planes is $\lambda_s/2$, the introduction of these planes does not disturb the field variations. A standing wave field configuration with E_y and E_z equal to zero at x = 0 and x = a is obtained. (ii) Next, electric walls or magnetic walls are inserted in planes parallel to the slot and perpendicular to the substrate at $y = \pm b/2$ as shown in Figure 5.4(b) and Figure 5.4(c). Since fields are tightly bound to the slot, the walls at $y = \pm b/2$ will have a negligible effect when the distance b is sufficiently large. Introduction of electric walls creates the configuration of a capacitive iris in a rectangular waveguide as shown in Figure 5.4(d). The two cases of electric walls and magnetic walls are analyzed separately.

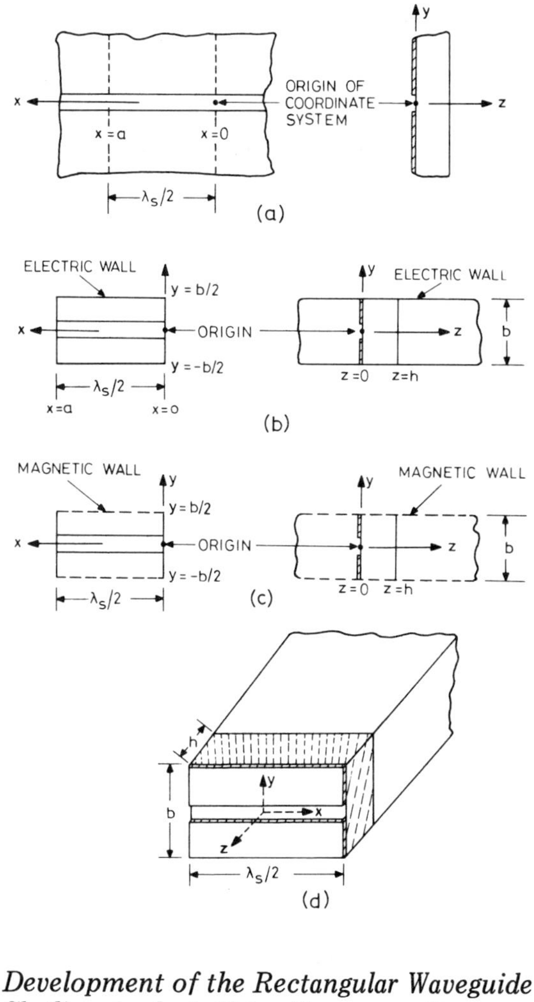

Figure 5.4 Development of the Rectangular Waveguide Model for Slotline Analysis Using Transverse Resonance Method

Slot Wavelength

Having developed the capacitive iris waveguide model the method of transverse resonance is applied to determine slot wavelength. In this method the sum of susceptances at the iris plane is equated to zero.

This sum includes the susceptances of the TE_{10} mode looking in the +z and -z directions and the capacitive iris susceptance due to higher order modes on both sides of the iris (the TE_{10} mode cannot exist for the magnetic wall case). The introduction of magnetic walls or electric walls at $y = \pm b/2$ gives rise to different sets of modes. These sets are $TE_{1,2n}$ and $TM_{1,2m}$ where n is an integer $\geqslant 0$ and $m \geqslant 1$ for electric walls, and n or m = 1/2, 3/2, 5/2 for magnetic walls.

Two separate expressions for the total susceptance ηB_t for the electric wall and magnetic wall cases are obtained. These are given in Appendix 5-A.

Evaluation of Slot Wavelength

Roots of the equation $\eta B_t = 0$, with ηB_t given by Equation (A-1) or Equation (A-2) for electric wall case or magnetic wall case, respectively, give the slot wavelength λ_s. It is a function of λ_o also, unlike in microstrips, because the mode of propagation in slotline is transverse electric.

Numerical computations by Cohn [1] show that, for large values of b, identical results are obtained for both electric wall and magnetic wall models. In the specific case when $\epsilon_r = 20$, h = 0.137 inch, W = 0.025 inch, $\lambda_o = 4.2$ inch and $\lambda_s = 1.360$ inch, the solutions for electric and magnetic walls approach each other for $b > 1.5$ inches, and are only slightly different for b = 1 inch.

Slotline Impedance

Because of the non-TEM nature of the mode in slotline, the characteristic impedance Z_{os} cannot be defined uniquely. The most useful definition is based on the power-voltage relationship and may be written as [1]

$$Z_{os} = V^2/2P \tag{5.11}$$

where V is the peak voltage across the slot. The average power P can be expressed in terms of energy storage W_t, which may be related to the rate of change of total susceptance B_t with frequency. For resonant cavities [9]

$$W_t = (V^2/4)(dB_t/d\omega) \tag{5.12}$$

and also since

$$W_t = \frac{2\pi P}{\omega} \frac{v}{v_g} \tag{5.13}$$

we can write

$$Z_{os} = (v/v_g)\ \pi/(\omega\partial B_t/\partial\omega)$$

It may also be written as

$$Z_{os} = \eta \frac{v}{v_g} \frac{\pi}{p} \frac{\Delta p}{-\Delta(\eta B_t)} \tag{5.14}$$

where $p = \lambda_o/\lambda_s$.

The ratio of phase velocity v to the group velocity v_g can be evaluated from the sensitivity of (λ_o/λ_s) with respect to frequency f. It is given as follows

$$\frac{v}{v_g} = 1 - \frac{f}{\lambda_s/\lambda_o} \frac{\Delta(\lambda_s/\lambda_o)}{\Delta f} \tag{5.15}$$

Evaluation of Slotline Impedance

For the given set of slotline parameters ϵ_r, W, h and b choose the frequency interval Δf centered around f, the frequency of operation. The value of $\Delta(\lambda_s/\lambda_o)$ is computed from two separate solutions of $\eta B_t = 0$ for the two values of h/λ_o corresponding to the ends of the frequency interval. Using the value of $\Delta(\lambda_s/\lambda_o)$ in Equation (5.15) gives the value of v/v_g. The change in susceptance $\Delta(\eta B_t)$ (needed for evaluating Z_{os}) is computed from Equation (A-1) or (A-2) with λ_s held constant (λ_s is obtained from the value of λ_s/λ_o at the frequency f) and p incremented slightly plus and minus from the value $p = \lambda_o/\lambda_s$ at $\eta B_t = 0$. (The two values of p are obtained from the two end values of λ_o for the frequency interval.)

Computations of slotline wavelength and impedance, based on the above method, have been carried out. They are shown in Figures 5.5 and 5.6 for two values of substrate dielectric constant. Mariani *et. al.* [10] have also reported slotline characteristics for $\epsilon_r = 9.6$, 11.0, 13.0, 16.0 and 20.0.

The method of transverse resonance is valid for the following set of parameters

$$W < 0.25\ \lambda_o/\sqrt{\epsilon_r} \tag{5.16a}$$

$$W/h \leqslant 1 \tag{5.16b}$$

and $$b \geqslant 7W \tag{5.16c}$$

Condition (5.16a) is necessary to avoid resonance across the slot.

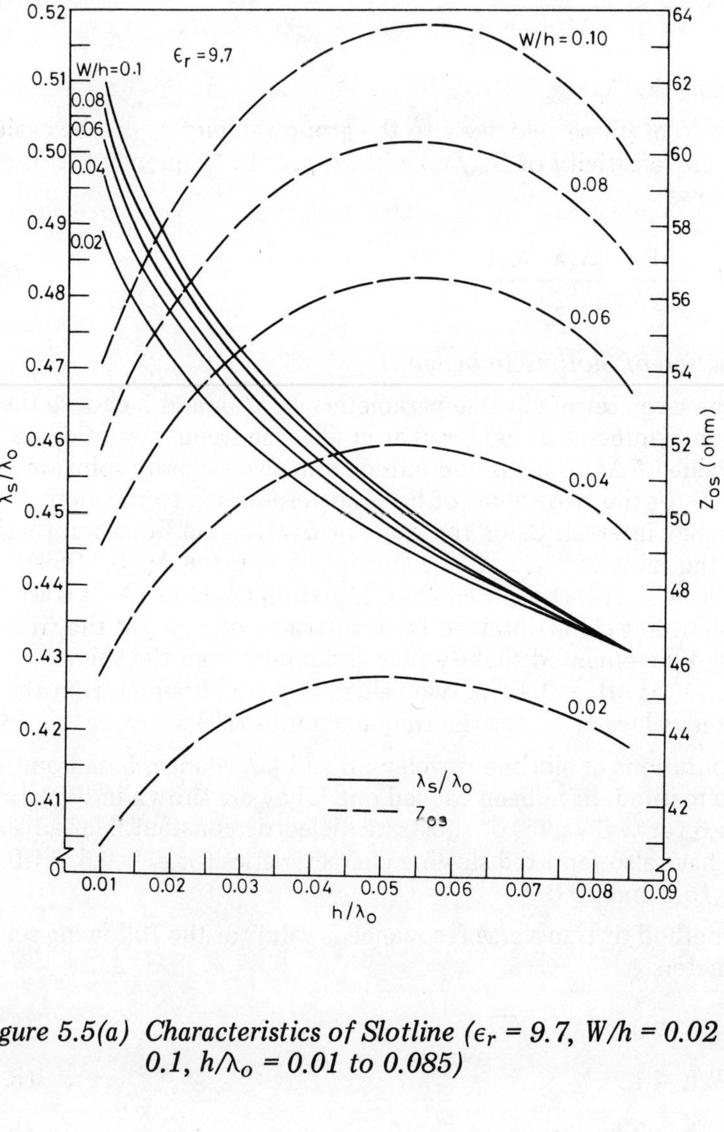

Figure 5.5(a) Characteristics of Slotline (ϵ_r = 9.7, W/h = 0.02 to 0.1, h/λ_o = 0.01 to 0.085)

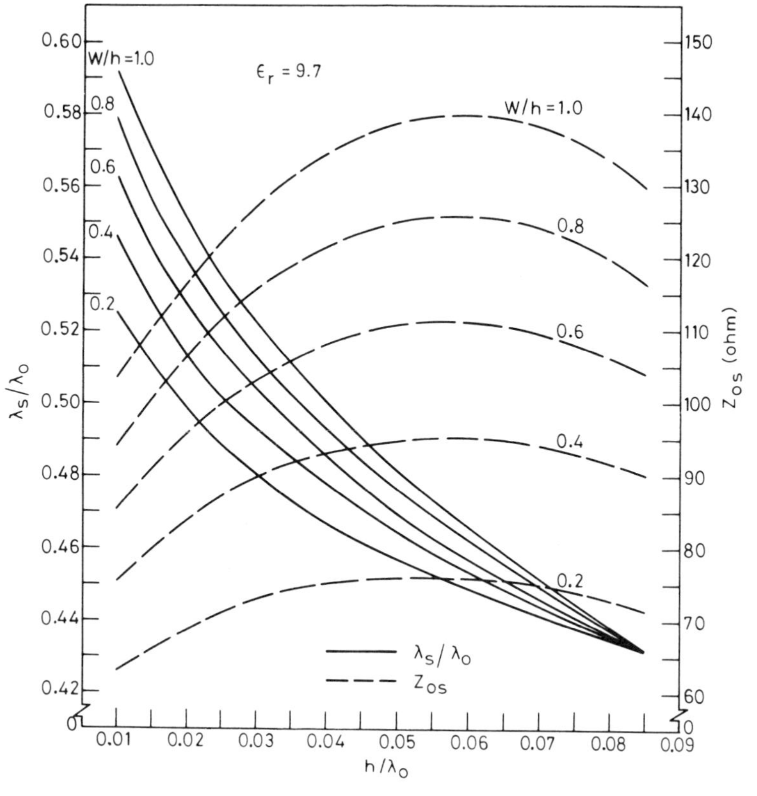

Figure 5.5(b) Characteristics of Slotline (ϵ_r = 9.7, W/h = 0.2 to 1.0, h/λ_o = 0.01 to 0.085)

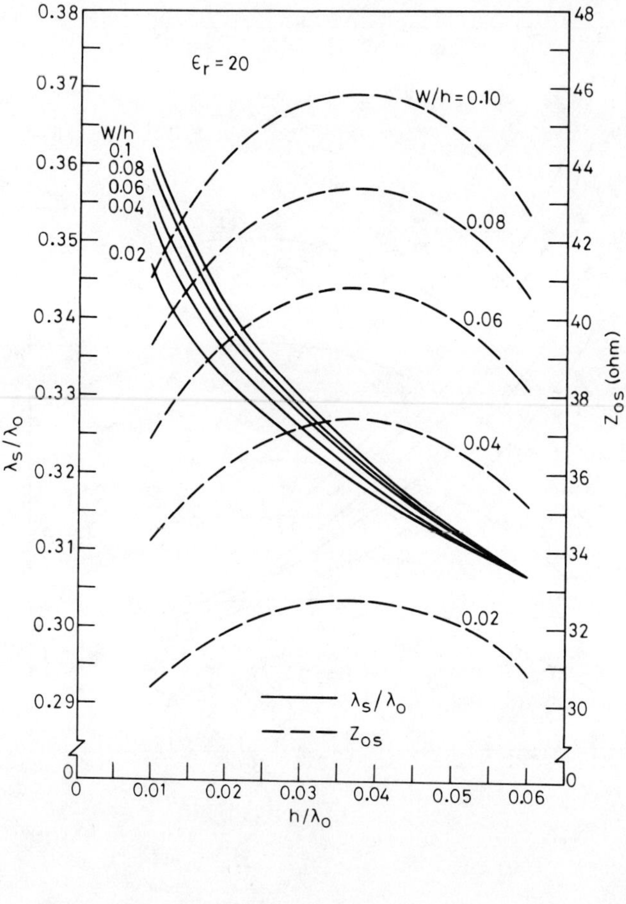

Figure 5.6(a) Characteristics of Slotline (ϵ_r = 20, W/h = 0.02 to 0.1, h/λ_o = 0.01 to 0.06)

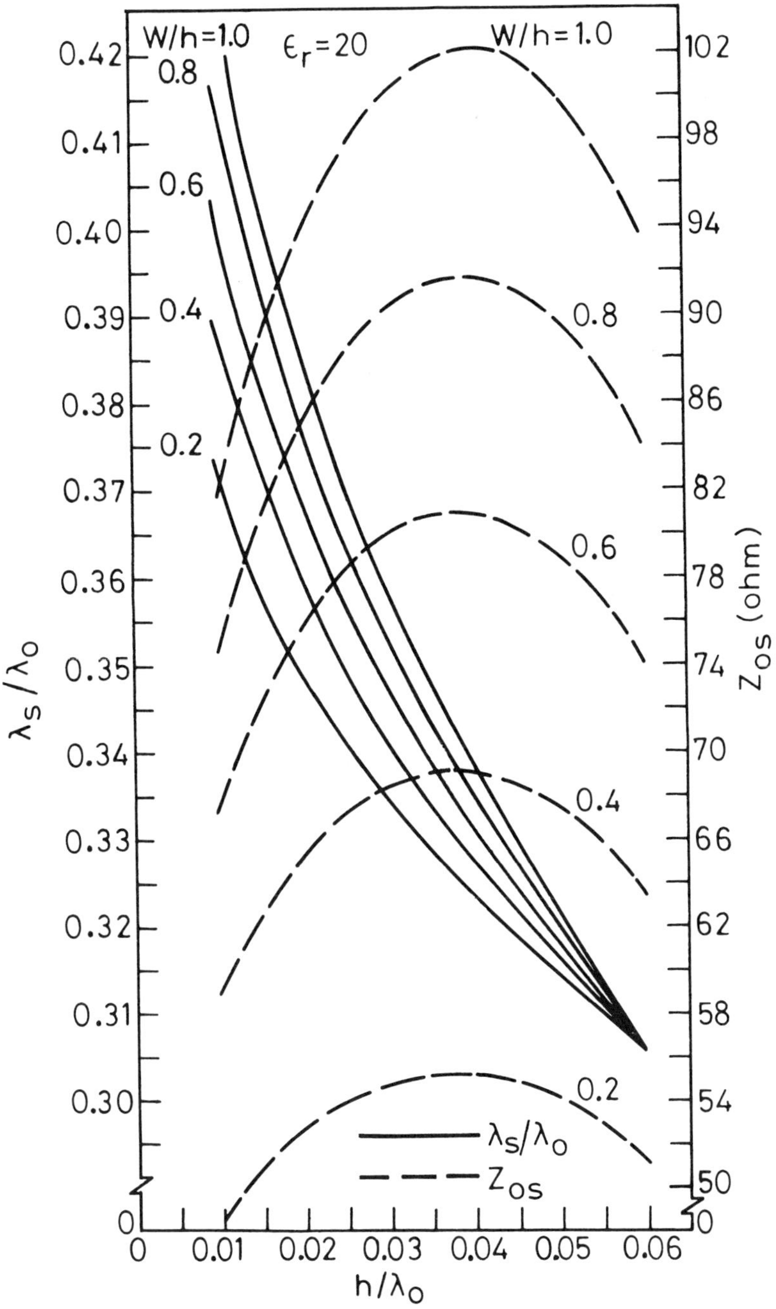

Figure 5.6(b) Characteristics of Slotline (ϵ_r = 20, W/h = 0.2 to 1.0, h/λ_o = 0.01 to 0.06)

Although this method can also be used to determine the effect of finite size of metal sheets enclosing the slot it cannot be employed for wide slots ($W/h > 1$). The method described next does not suffer from this limitation.

5.2.3 Galerkin's Method in FTD [2,3]

An alternative analysis of slotline is based on the use of Galerkin's method in the Fourier transform domain. This method is similar to those used for fullwave analysis of microstrip lines (in Section 2.3.2) and for analysis of microstrip discontinuities (in Section 3.2.3).

Field components in a slotline are expressed in terms of two scalar potentials $\psi^e(x,y)$ and $\psi^h(x,y)$. The longitudinal components are proportional to these potentials and are written as

$$E_z = k_c^2 \psi^e(x,y) \exp(\pm j\beta z) \tag{5.17}$$

$$H_z = k_c^2 \psi^h(x,y) \exp(\pm j\beta z) \tag{5.18}$$

where β is the propagation constant, and

$$k_c^2 = k_i^2 - \beta^2 \tag{5.19}$$

$$k_i = (\epsilon_i \mu_i)^{1/2}, \ i = 1, 2, 3$$

Values of i specify the three regions of slotline cross-section as shown in Figure 5.7. The next step is the Fourier transformation of the scalar wave equation along x. This transformation converts the second-order partial differential equation into an ordinary differential equation which can be solved easily. The solutions for transforms of scalar potentials in the three regions may be written as

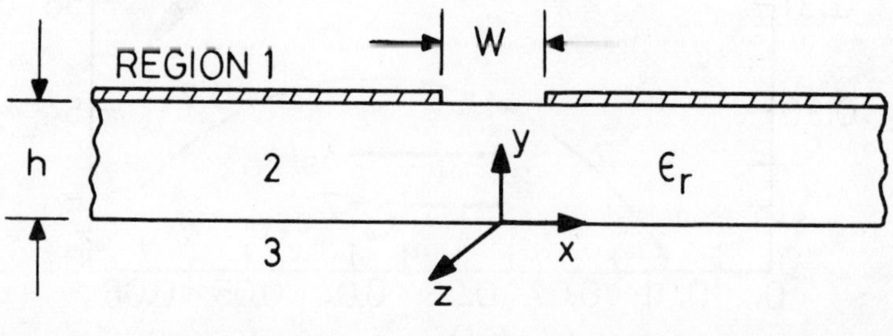

Figure 5.7 Configuration of Slotline for Analysis Using Galerkin's Method in FTD

$$\psi_1^e(\alpha, y) = A^e(\alpha) \exp[-\gamma_1 (y-h)]$$

$$\psi_2^e(\alpha, y) = B^e(\alpha) \sinh \gamma_2 y + C^e(\alpha) \cosh \gamma_2 y$$

$$\psi_3^e(\alpha, y) = D^e(\alpha) \exp(\gamma_1 y) \tag{5.20}$$

and

$$\psi_1^h(\alpha, y) = A^h(\alpha) \exp[-\gamma_1 (y-h)]$$

$$\psi_2^h(\alpha, y) = B^h(\alpha) \sinh \gamma_2 y + C^h(\alpha) \cosh \gamma_2 y$$

$$\psi_3^h(\alpha, y) = D^h(\alpha) \exp(\gamma_1 y) \tag{5.21}$$

where

$$\gamma_i^2 = \alpha^2 + \beta^2 - k_i^2$$

The eight unknown coefficients A^e through D^h are related to the tangential electric and magnetic field components at the interfaces $y = 0$ and $y = h$ by the continuity conditions, and can be related also to the surface current density on the metal and the electric field in the slot at $y = h$. If one denotes the Fourier transforms of the x- and z-directed current densities by $\tilde{J}_x(\alpha)$ and $\tilde{J}_z(\alpha)$, and electric field components by $\tilde{E}_x(\alpha)$ and $\tilde{E}_z(\alpha)$, one obtains a set of coupled equations of the form

$$\begin{bmatrix} M_1(\alpha,\beta), M_2(\alpha,\beta) \\ M_3(\alpha,\beta), M_4(\alpha,\beta) \end{bmatrix} \begin{bmatrix} \tilde{J}_x(\alpha) \\ \tilde{J}_z(\alpha) \end{bmatrix} = \begin{bmatrix} \tilde{E}_x(\alpha) \\ \tilde{E}_z(\alpha) \end{bmatrix} \tag{5.22}$$

The matrix M is now inverted to express transforms of current densities in terms of electric field transforms. If N-matrix is the inverse of M-matrix, Equation (5.22) gives

$$\begin{bmatrix} N_1(\alpha,\beta), N_2(\alpha,\beta) \\ N_3(\alpha,\beta), N_4(\alpha,\beta) \end{bmatrix} \begin{bmatrix} \tilde{E}_x(\alpha) \\ \tilde{E}_z(\alpha) \end{bmatrix} = \begin{bmatrix} \tilde{J}_x(\alpha) \\ \tilde{J}_z(\alpha) \end{bmatrix} \tag{5.23}$$

The matrix elements $N_1 \ldots N_4$ are known functions of α and β. Now $\tilde{E}_x(\alpha)$ and $\tilde{E}_z(\alpha)$ are expanded in terms of the Fourier transforms of basis functions, and Galerkin's method is applied to yield a homogeneous system of linear equations. The determinant of the coefficient matrix, corresponding to this set of linear equations, equated to zero gives the dispersion relation. An iteration scheme for β can be used to find a non-trivial solution of this dispersion relation.

The rate of convergence of this series representation depends upon the choice of basis functions. A successful choice [2,3] is given below

$$E_x = \begin{cases} [(W/2)^2 - x^2]^{-1/2} & |x| \leqslant W/2 \\ 0 & \text{elsewhere} \end{cases}$$

$$E_z = \begin{cases} x[(W/2)^2 - x^2]^{1/2} & |x| \leqslant W/2 \\ 0 & \text{elsewhere} \end{cases} \tag{5.24}$$

with the Fourier transforms given by

$$\widetilde{E}_x(\alpha) = \frac{\pi W}{4} J_o\left(\frac{W}{2}|\alpha|\right) \quad ; \quad \widetilde{E}_z(\alpha) = \frac{\pi W}{2\alpha} J_2\left(\frac{W}{2}|\alpha|\right)$$

The computation involved can be simplified by assuming $E_z = 0$. A comparison of the magnitudes of the x and z components of the electric field shows that E_z is about one-tenth of E_x and can therefore be neglected [3].

Results for slot wavelength, based on this method, are compared with previous analysis in Figure 5.8 (for $\epsilon_r = 20.0$, h = 3.48 mm and W = 0.625 mm). The difference is negligible for frequencies higher than 3 GHz.

This method can be extended to evaluate the characteristic impedance of slotlines. Power flow is calculated by integrating the Poynting vector over the cross-section. Parseval's theorem is used for performing the integral in the Fourier transform domain with respect to α and y. Again the computations involved can be simplified by neglecting E_z. Some results based on this method are compared with Cohn's results in Figure 5.9 (for $\epsilon_r = 11$, W/h = 0.1 and 2.0).

A comparison of Galerkin's method in FTD with Cohn's method indicates that the transverse resonance method used by Cohn [1] yields accurate results for slotline characteristics.

The transverse resonance method and Galerkin's method in FTD have been applied only to the fundamental mode in slotline. The elliptical waveguide model described next considers higher order modes also. It has been found that the modes in slotline are very much similar to the ridged guide modes in sandwich slotline [4].

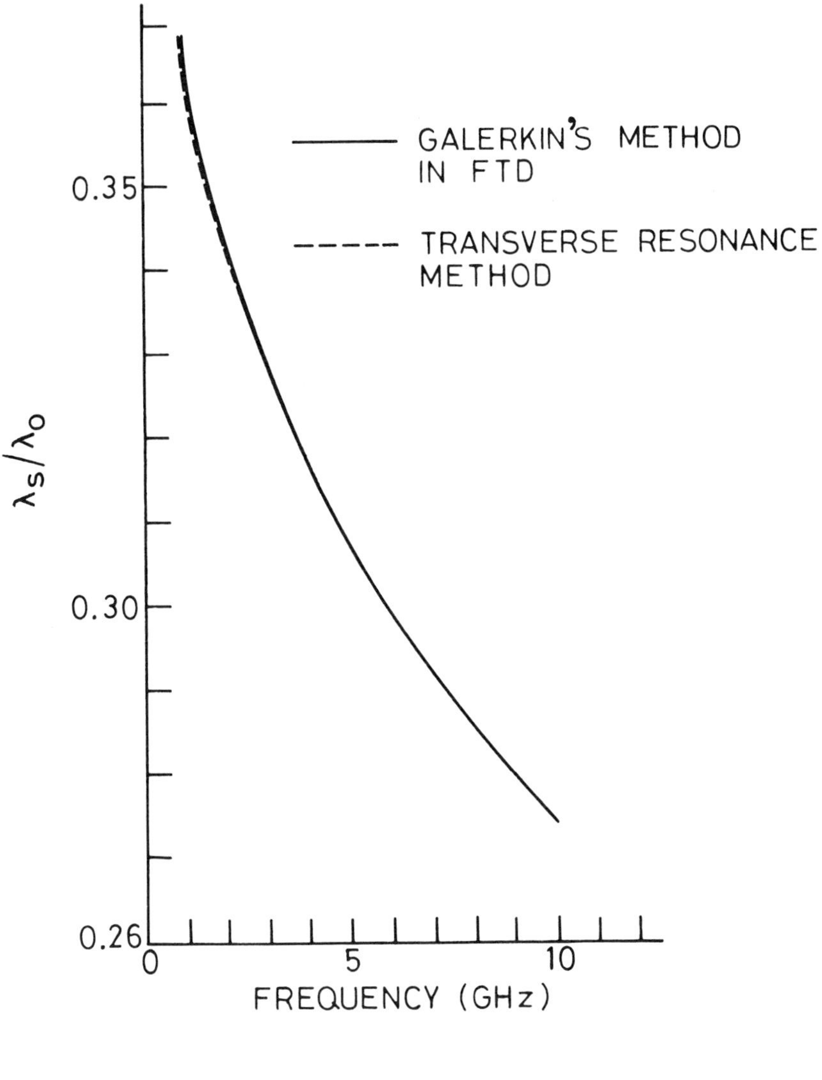

Figure 5.8 Comparison of Slot Wavelength Calculations Based on Galerkin's Method in FTD, and Transverse Resonance Method (from [3])

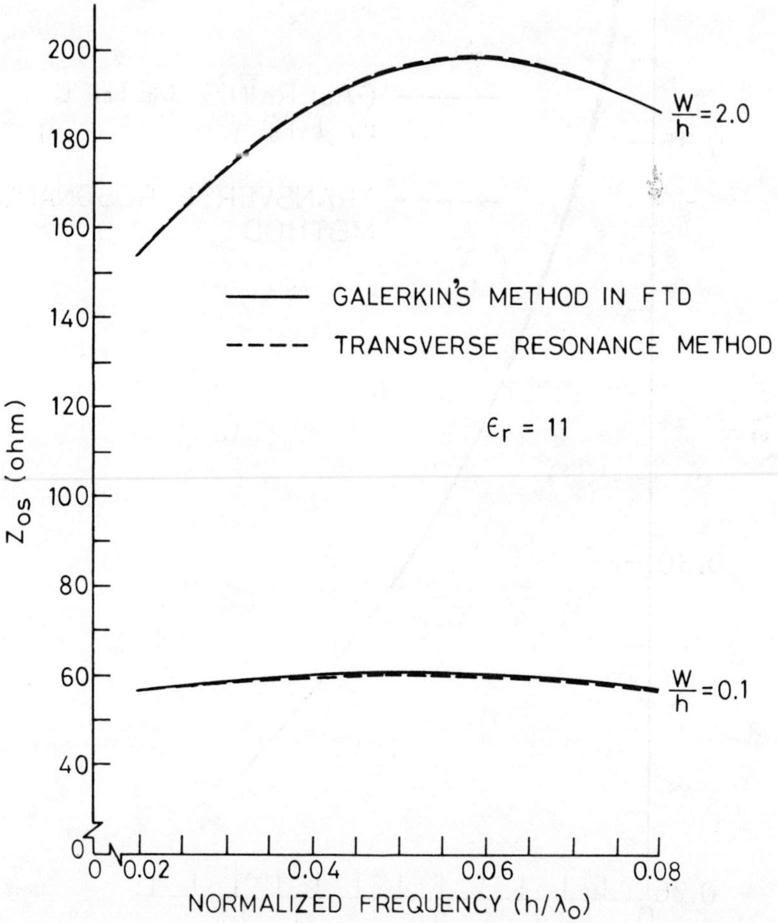

Figure 5.9 Comparison of Slotline Impedances Calculated Using Galerkin's Method in FTD, and Transverse Resonance Method (from [2])

5.2.4 Elliptical Waveguide Model of Slotline [4]

The slotline is modeled as a semi-elliptical dielectric ridged waveguide which is analyzed in elliptical cylindrical coordinate system. Figure 5.10 shows the model considered. The basic assumption in the

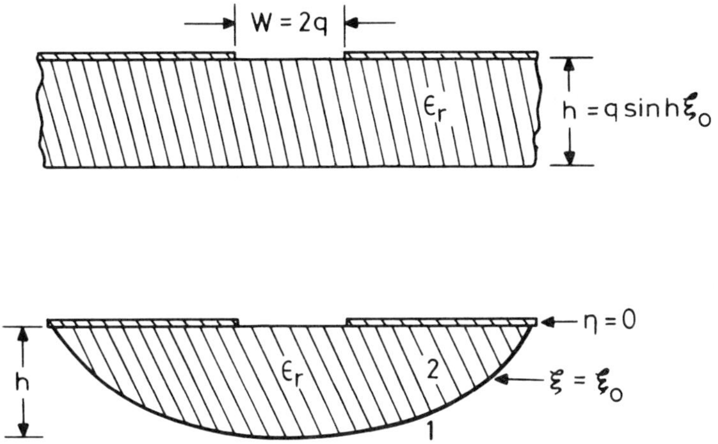

Figure 5.10 Elliptical Waveguide Model for Slotline

method is that the fringing field outside the substrate (on the side opposite to that containing the slot) is small, and therefore the modification of the dielectric boundary to an elliptical shape does not affect the propagation characteristics.

The transformation from the Cartesian coordinate system (x′, y′, z′) to the elliptical coordinate system (ξ, η, z) is specified by

$$\left.\begin{aligned} x' &= q \cosh\xi \cos\eta \\ y' &= q \sinh\xi \sin\eta \\ z' &= z \end{aligned}\right\} \quad (0 < \xi < \infty\, ; 0 \leqslant \eta \leqslant 2\pi) \tag{5.25}$$

where 2q is the separation between the two foci of the ellipse. The slot width W and substrate thickness h in the new coordinate system transform to W = 2q; h = q sinhξ_o. In the transformed coordinate system, the wave equation is written as

$$\left\{ \frac{\partial^2}{\partial \xi^2} + \frac{\partial^2}{\partial \eta^2} + q^2 \, (k^2 - \beta^2)\, (\cosh^2 \xi - \cos^2 \eta) \right\} \quad \Lambda(\eta, \xi) = 0 \tag{5.26}$$

where $k^2 = \omega^2 \mu_o \epsilon$ and $\Lambda(\eta, \xi)$ may be H_z or E_z for the mode considered. Equation (5.26) is separable in elliptical cylindrical coordinates and $\Lambda(\eta, \xi)$ may be written as the product of an azimuthal function $\theta(\eta)$ and a radial function $R(\xi)$. Differential equations determining $\theta(\eta)$ and $R(\xi)$ are the Mathieu equation and the modified Mathieu equation, respectively. Thus the field variations in η and ξ coordinates are given by Mathieu functions and modified Mathieu functions, respectively.

To solve the slotline problem, the field components in two regions (1 and 2) are expressed in terms of Mathieu functions, modified Mathieu functions and combinations thereof. Since the angular Mathieu functions are not only functions of η but also of the electrical properties of the medium in which they apply, the field components in both regions must be represented by infinite product terms of Mathieu and modified functions. The fields are matched at the interface of two regions, and application of the orthogonality relations of Mathieu functions leads to four sets of infinite homogeneous linear algebraic equations. The value of β is obtained by solving the truncated system of equations.

Some numerical results, based on this method, have been obtained for the dominant mode (HE_{01}) and two higher order (EH_{11} and HE_{02}) modes. These are shown in Figure 5.11.

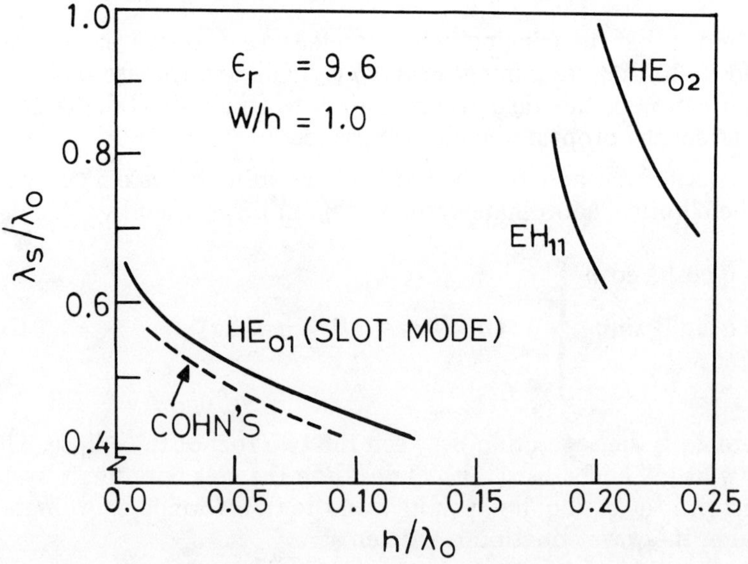

Figure 5.11 Slot Wavelength Results for the Dominant and the Next Two Higher Modes (Calculations Based on Elliptical Waveguide Model, from [4])

5.3 DESIGN CONSIDERATIONS

5.3.1 Closed Form Expressions

The various methods of analysis discussed above do not lead to any closed form expressions for slotline wavelength and impedance. This becomes a serious handicap for circuit analysis and design especially when computer-aided design techniques are used. Some attempts to overcome this difficulty have been reported [8]. Closed form expressions have been obtained by curve fitting the results based on Cohn's analysis. These expressions have an accuracy of about 2 percent for the following sets of parameters

$$9.7 \leqslant \epsilon_r \leqslant 20$$

$$0.02 \leqslant W/h \leqslant 1.0, \text{ and}$$

$$0.01 \leqslant h/\lambda_o \leqslant (h/\lambda_o)_c \tag{5.27}$$

where $(h/\lambda_o)_c$ is equal to the cut-off value for the TE_{10} surface-wave mode on the slotline, and is given by Equation (5.10).

The expressions obtained are

1) For $0.02 \leqslant W/h < 0.2$

$$\begin{aligned}\lambda_s/\lambda_o &= 0.923 - 0.448 \log \epsilon_r + 0.2\, W/h \\ &\quad - (0.29\, W/h + 0.047) \log (h/\lambda_o \times 10^2)\end{aligned} \tag{5.28}$$

$$\begin{aligned}Z_{os} &= 72.62 - 35.19 \log \epsilon_r + 50 \frac{(W/h - 0.02)(W/h - 0.1)}{W/h} \\ &\quad + \log (W/h \times 10^2)\,[44.28 - 19.58 \log \epsilon_r] \\ &\quad - [0.32 \log \epsilon_r - 0.11 + W/h\,(1.07 \log \epsilon_r + 1.44)] \\ &\quad \cdot (11.4 - 6.07 \log \epsilon_r - h/\lambda_o \times 10^2)^2\end{aligned} \tag{5.29}$$

2) For $0.2 \leqslant W/h \leqslant 1.0$

$$\begin{aligned}\lambda_s/\lambda_o &= 0.987 - 0.483 \log \epsilon_r + W/h\,(0.111 - 0.0022\, \epsilon_r) \\ &\quad - (0.121 + 0.094\, W/h - 0.0032\, \epsilon_r) \log (h/\lambda_o \times 10^2)\end{aligned} \tag{5.30}$$

$$\begin{aligned}Z_{os} &= 113.19 - 53.55 \log \epsilon_r + 1.25\, W/h\,(114.59 - 51.88 \log \epsilon_r) \\ &\quad + 20\,(W/h - 0.2)(1 - W/h) \\ &\quad - [0.15 + 0.23 \log \epsilon_r + W/h\,(-0.79 + 2.07 \log \epsilon_r)] \\ &\quad \cdot [10.25 - 5 \log \epsilon_r + W/h\,(2.1 - 1.42 \log \epsilon_r) \\ &\quad - h/\lambda_o \times 10^2]^2\end{aligned} \tag{5.31}$$

It is possible to derive more accurate expressions for slotline wavelength when the dielectric constant of the substrate is fixed. Expressions with 1 percent accuracy for dielectric constant values of 9.7 and 20.0 are given below [11],

(a) $\epsilon_r = 9.7 \qquad 0.01 \leqslant h/\lambda_o \leqslant (h/\lambda_o)_c$

(i) $0.02 \leqslant W/h \leqslant 0.1$

$$\lambda_s/\lambda_o = -(0.29\, W/h + 0.057) \log (h/\lambda_o \times 10^2) + 0.283\, W/h + 0.485 \tag{5.32}$$

(ii) $0.1 < W/h \leqslant 1.0$

$$\lambda_s/\lambda_o = -(0.11\, W/h + 0.077) \log (h/\lambda_o \times 10^2) + 0.104\, W/h + 0.507 \tag{5.33}$$

(b) $\epsilon_r = 20 \qquad 0.01 \leqslant h/\lambda_o \leqslant (h/\lambda_o)_c$

(i) $0.02 \leqslant W/h \leqslant 0.1$

$$\lambda_s/\lambda_o = -(0.269\, W/h + 0.047) \log (h/\lambda_o \times 10^2) + 0.2\, W/h + 0.345 \tag{5.34}$$

(ii) $0.1 < W/h \leqslant 1.0$

$$\lambda_s/\lambda_o = -(0.094\, W/h + 0.072) \log (h/\lambda_o \times 10^2) + 0.075\, W/h + 0.362 \tag{5.35}$$

The logarithms are to the base 10 in expressions (5.28) through (5.35) above.

5.3.2 Slotline Discontinuities

As in the case of microstrip circuits, the characterization of slotline discontinuities is needed for the design of slotline circuits. However, there are no analytical results available for various slotline discontinuities. Only very limited experimental results are available.

Experimental characteristics of a slotline short-end have been reported by Knorr and Saenz [12]. A short-end (shown in Figure 5.12) is created by merely ending the slot or equivalently filling the slot with a conducting surface lying in the plane of the slot. In such a case, current flows around the end of the slot and there is appreciable energy storage beyond the termination. This situation is illustrated in Figure 5.12. The net result is a predominance of stored magnetic energy giving rise to an inductive reactance as seen at a reference plane normal to the slot axis and coincident with the end of the slot.

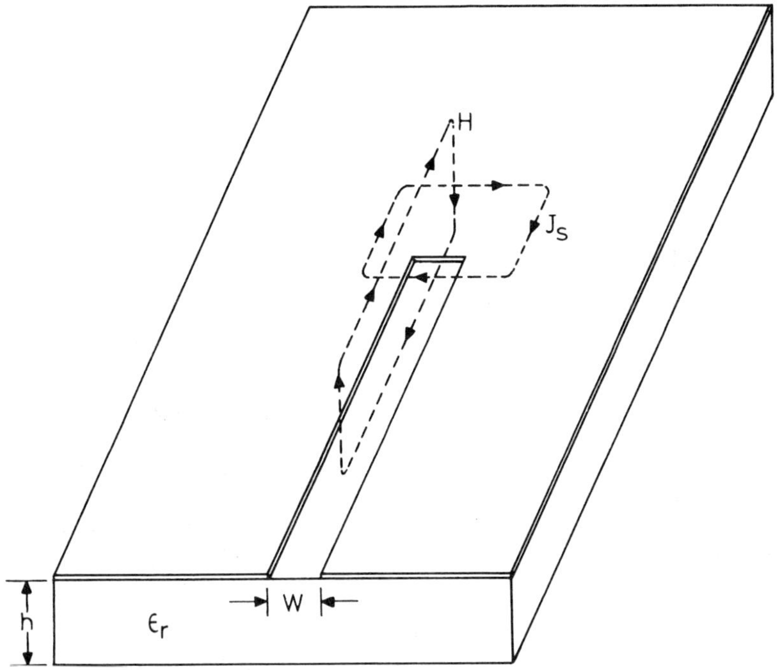

Figure 5.12 Field and Current Distributions in the Vicinity of a Slotline Short-End

In [12], the normalized inductive reactance of the shorted slots were determined from VSWR measurements. Two sets of reactance curves based on these measurements are shown in Figures 5.13 and 5.14. The end effect is seen to be significant. The equivalent electrical length of the short-ends is up to 0.1 λ_s. It may be mentioned that the slotline short-end is frequently used in slotline circuits and has the same significance as an open-end in microstrip circuits.

5.3.3 Effect of Metal Thickness

It has been assumed in the analysis presented in Section 5.2 that the metal conductors constituting the slot have zero thickness. In practice it is not possible. Kitazawa *et. al.* [13] have evaluated the effect of finite metal thickness on the phase constant. It is observed that the phase constant decreases (i.e. λ_s/λ_o increases) with the increase in metal thickness t. For ϵ_r = 20, the decrease in the phase constant is about 1 percent for a t/W ratio of 0.02.

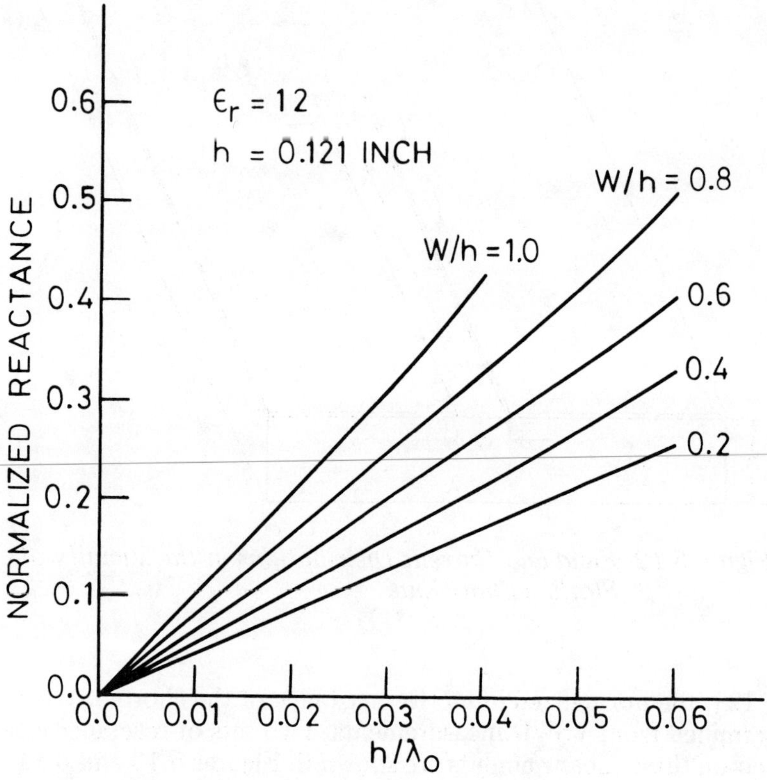

Figure 5.13 Short-End Reactance Data for Slotline, ϵ_r = 12 (from [12])

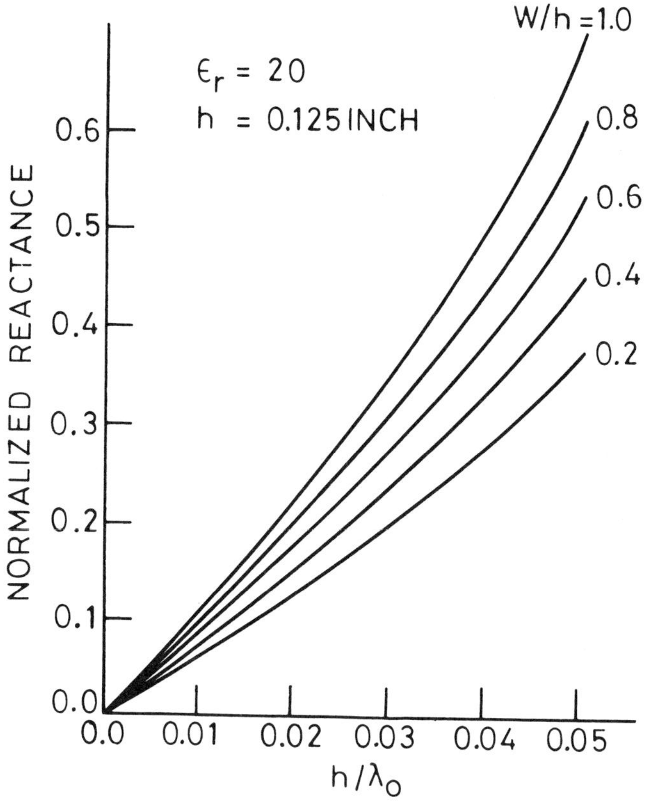

Figure 5.14 Short-End Reactance Data for Slotline, $\epsilon_r = 20$ (from [12])

5.3.4 Effect of Tolerances

The effect of tolerances in various parameters on the performance of slotline can be carried out using sensitivity analysis, as has been done for microstrip in Section 2.4.3. The worst case behavior for a given set of tolerances is represented by the maximum change in characteristic impedance and slot wavelength. Expressions for these quantities are given below (for a fixed λ_o)

$$\frac{|\Delta Z_{os}|_{max}}{Z_{os}} = \left|\frac{\Delta W}{W} S_W^{Z_{os}}\right| + \left|\frac{\Delta h}{h} S_h^{Z_{os}}\right| + \left|\frac{\Delta \epsilon_r}{\epsilon_r} S_{\epsilon_r}^{Z_{os}}\right| \tag{5.36}$$

$$\frac{|\Delta \epsilon_{re}|_{max}}{\epsilon_{re}} = \left|\frac{\Delta W}{W} S_W^{\epsilon_{re}}\right| + \left|\frac{\Delta h}{h} S_h^{\epsilon_{re}}\right| + \left|\frac{\Delta \epsilon_r}{\epsilon_r} S_{\epsilon_r}^{\epsilon_{re}}\right| \tag{5.37}$$

where $\epsilon_{re} = (\lambda_o/\lambda_s)^2$ (5.38)

The sensitivity expressions can be obtained by using closed form equations for Z_{os} and λ_s/λ_o, Equations (5.28-5.31). These expressions are given in Appendix 5-B and plotted as sensitivity curves in Figures 5.15 and 5.16 [14].

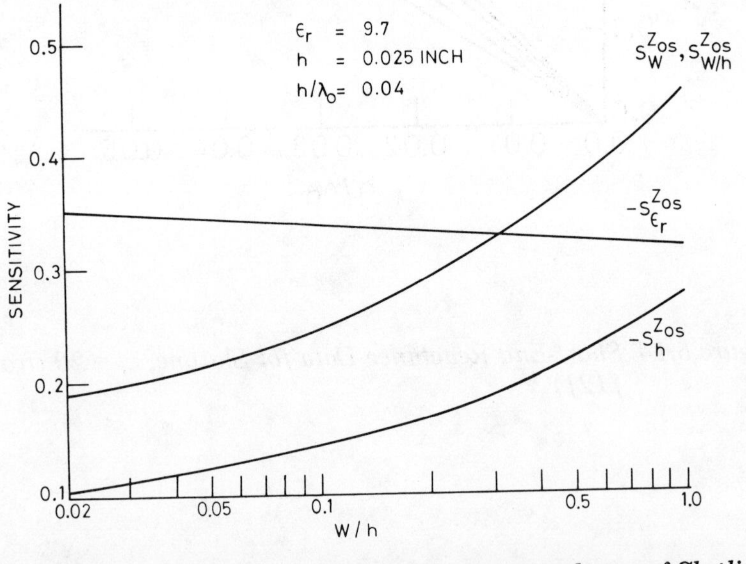

Figure 5.15 Sensitivities of Characteristic Impedance of Slotline With Respect to its Parameters (from [14])

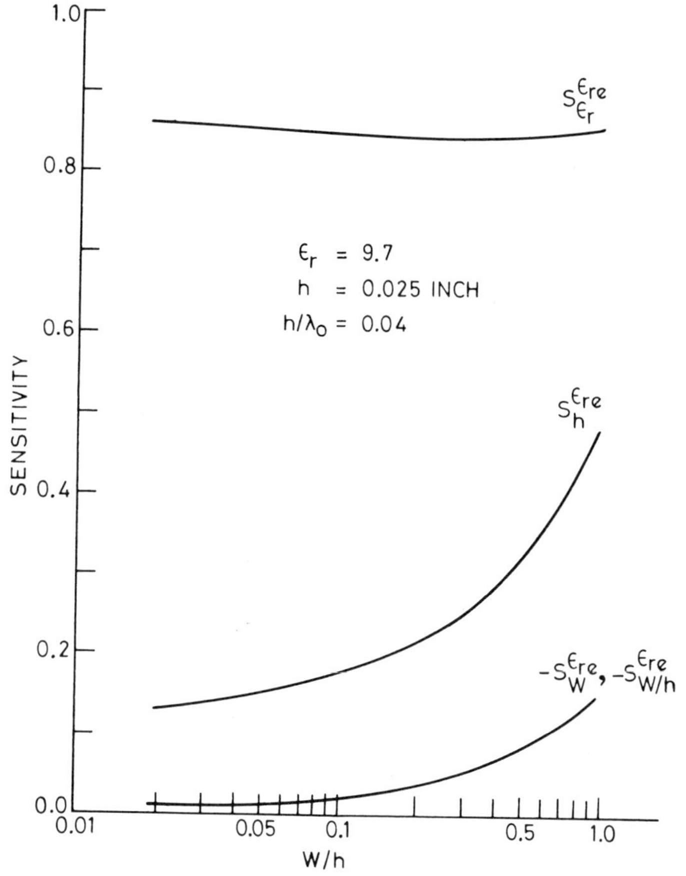

Figure 5.16 Sensitivities of Effective Dielectric Constant of Slotline With Respect to its Parameters (from [14])

For a given set of slotline parameters the sensitivity values are calculated and substituted in Equation (5.36) to determine $(\Delta Z_{os})_{max}$. This value of $(\Delta Z_{os})_{max}$ is used to calculate slotline VSWR. It is shown in Figure 5.17 for $\epsilon_r = 9.7$. The inverse problem of determining the fabrication tolerance for a given set of other tolerances can be solved in the same manner as has been done for microstrip in Section 2.4.3. The required fabrication accuracy in slot width for a VSWR of 1.05 and a given set of other tolerances is shown in Figure 5.18 [14].

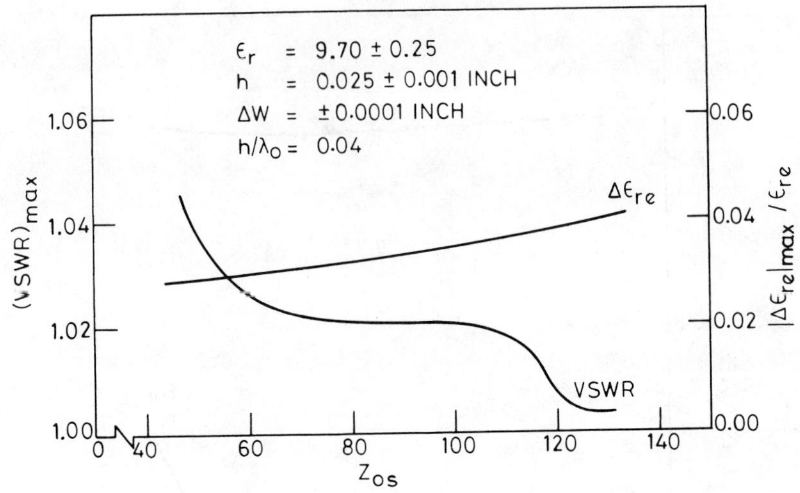

Figure 5.17 Effect of Tolerances on the Characteristics of Slotline (from [14])

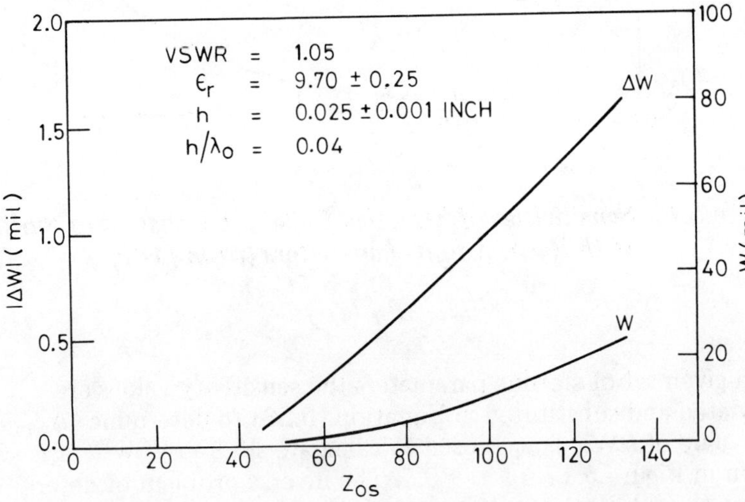

Figure 5.18 Fabrication Accuracy Requirement for Slot Width W for the Given Substrate Tolerances in ϵ_r and h, and the Required VSWR Performance (from [14])

5.3.5 Losses in Slotline

There is no comprehensive treatment available concerning losses in slotline. Robinson and Allen [5] have compared losses in slotline and microstrip for the same substrate thickness with $\epsilon_r = 16$. Their observations indicate that losses in slotline are about the same as for microstrip. Losses in slotline increase linearly from 0.15 dB/in at 4 GHz to about 0.3 dB/in at 8 GHz. Also, it increases with decrease in slot width. Experimental results given in [15] show that the relative value for unloaded Q factors of microstrip and slotline resonators are 280 and 120, respectively.

It may be pointed out that Wheeler's incremental inductance rule involves calculation of inductance and is difficult to apply to non-TEM lines.

APPENDIX 5-A: SUSCEPTANCE CALCULATION FOR THE TRANSVERSE RESONANCE METHOD

The formula for susceptance B_t for the case of electric walls at $y = \pm b/2$ is given below

$$\eta B_t = \frac{a}{2b}\left[-v + u \tan\left(\frac{\pi h u}{ap} - \tan^{-1}\frac{v}{u}\right)\right] + \frac{1}{p}\left\{\left(\frac{\epsilon_r + 1}{2} - p^2\right) \ln\frac{2}{\pi\delta} + \tfrac{1}{2} \sum_{n=1,2,3\ldots} \left[v^2\left(1 - \frac{1}{F_n}\right) + M_n\right] \frac{\sin^2(\pi n\delta)}{n(\pi n\delta)^2}\right\}. \tag{A-1}$$

For magnetic walls at $y = \pm b/2$ the expression for B_t is

$$\eta B_t = \frac{1}{p}\left\{\left(\frac{\epsilon_r + 1}{2} - p^2\right) \ln\frac{8}{\pi\delta} + \tfrac{1}{2} \sum_{n=1/2,\,3/2,\,5/2\ldots} \left[v^2\left(1 - \frac{1}{F_n}\right) + M_n\right] \frac{\sin^2(\pi n\delta)}{n(\pi n\delta)^2}\right\} \tag{A-2}$$

where $\eta = \sqrt{\mu_o/\epsilon_o} = 376.7$ ohm, $\delta = W/b$, $p = \lambda_o/\lambda_s$, and

$$u = \sqrt{\epsilon_r - p^2}, \quad v = \sqrt{p^2 - 1} \tag{A-3}$$

$$F_n = \sqrt{1 + \left(\frac{b}{2an}\,\frac{v}{p}\right)^2}\,, \tag{A-4}$$

$$F_{n1} = \sqrt{1 - \left(\frac{b}{2an}\,\frac{u}{p}\right)^2} \tag{A-5}$$

For F_{n1} real, M_n is

$$M_n = \frac{\epsilon_r \tanh r_n - p^2 F_{n1}^{\,2} \coth q_n}{\left[1 + \left(\frac{b}{2an}\right)^2\right] F_{n1}} - u^2 \tag{A-6}$$

where

$$r_n = \frac{2\pi n h F_{nl}}{b} + \tanh^{-1}\left(\frac{F_{n1}}{\epsilon_r F_n}\right) \tag{A-7}$$

$$q_n = \frac{2\pi n h F_{n1}}{b} + \coth^{-1}\left(\frac{F_n}{F_{n1}}\right) \tag{A-8}$$

For F_{n1} imaginary, M_n is

$$M_n = \frac{\epsilon_r \tan r_n' - p^2 \, |F_{n1}|^2 \cot q_n'}{[1 + \left(\frac{b}{2an}\right)^2] \, |F_{n1}|} - u^2 \tag{A-9}$$

where

$$r_n' = \frac{2\pi n h \, |F_{n1}|}{b} + \tan^{-1}\left(\frac{|F_{n1}|}{\epsilon_r F_n}\right) \tag{A-10}$$

$$q_n' = \frac{2\pi n h \, |F_{n1}|}{b} + \cot^{-1}\left(\frac{F_n}{|F_{n1}|}\right) \tag{A-11}$$

APPENDIX 5-B: SENSITIVITY EXPRESSIONS FOR SLOTLINE IMPEDANCE AND WAVELENGTH

The following expressions can be obtained by using the definition of sensitivity, Equation (2.104) and the expressions for slotline impedance and wavelength, Equations (5.28 - 5.31),

(i) For $0.02 \leqslant W/h < 0.2$

$$S_W^{Z_{os}} = \frac{50}{Z_{os}} \left\{ 2\frac{W}{h} - 0.12 - \frac{(W/h-0.02)(W/h-0.1)}{W/h} + \frac{0.4343}{50} \cdot (44.28 - 19.58 \log \epsilon_r) \right\} - \frac{W/h}{Z_{os}} (1.07 \log \epsilon_r + 1.44) \cdot (11.4 - 6.072 \log \epsilon_r - h/\lambda_o \times 10^2)^2 \tag{B-1}$$

$$S_h^{Z_{os}} = - S_W^{Z_{os}} + \frac{h}{Z_{os}} \frac{1}{\lambda_o} \frac{\partial Z_{os}}{\partial (h/\lambda_o)} \tag{B-2}$$

where

$$\frac{\partial Z_{os}}{\partial (h/\lambda_o)} = -200\,(11.4 - 6.07 \log \epsilon_r - h/\lambda_o \times 10^2) . [0.32 \log \epsilon_r - 0.11 + \frac{W}{h} (1.07 \log \epsilon_r + 1.44)]$$

$$S_{\epsilon_r}^{Z_{os}} = - \frac{0.4343\, \epsilon_r}{Z_{os}} [35.19 + 19.58 \log (W/h \times 10^2) + (0.32 + 1.07\, W/h)(11.4 - 6.07 \log \epsilon_r - h/\lambda_o \times 10^2)^2 - 12.14\,(11.4 - 6.07 \log \epsilon_r - h/\lambda_o \times 10^2) \cdot [0.32 \log \epsilon_r - 0.11 + W/h\,(1.07 \log \epsilon_r + 1.44)]] \tag{B-3}$$

$$S_W^{\epsilon_{re}} = -2S_W^{\lambda_s/\lambda_o} = - \frac{2W/h}{\epsilon_{re}} [0.2 - 0.29 \log (h/\lambda_o \times 10^2)] \tag{B-4}$$

$$S_h^{\epsilon_{re}} = -S_W^{\epsilon_{re}} + \frac{0.8686}{\epsilon_{re}} (0.29\, W/h + 0.047) \tag{B-5}$$

$$S_{\epsilon_r}^{\epsilon_{re}} = 0.389/\epsilon_{re} \tag{B-6}$$

(ii) For $0.2 \leqslant W/h \leqslant 1.0$

$$S_W^{Z_{os}} = \frac{W/h}{Z_{os}} \Big[1.25\,(114.59 - 51.88 \log \epsilon_r) + 24 - 40\,W/h - \left\{ 10.25 - 5 \log \epsilon_r + W/h\,(2.1 - 1.42 \log \epsilon_r) - h/\lambda_o \times 10^2 \right\} \cdot \left\{ (2.07 \log \epsilon_r - 0.79)\,[10.25 - 5 \log \epsilon_r + W/h\,(2.1 - 1.42 \log \epsilon_r) - h/\lambda_o \times 10^2] + 2(2.1 - 1.42 \log \epsilon_r)\,[0.15 + 0.23 \log \epsilon_r + W/h\,(2.07 \log \epsilon_r - 0.79)] \right\} \Big] \tag{B-7}$$

$$S_h^{Z_{os}} = -S_W^{Z_{os}} + \frac{h}{Z_{os}}\,\frac{1}{\lambda_o}\,\frac{\partial Z_{os}}{\partial (h/\lambda_o)} \tag{B-8}$$

where

$$\frac{\partial Z_{os}}{\partial (h/\lambda_o)} = 200\,[10.25 - 5 \log \epsilon_r + W/h\,(2.1 - 1.42 \log \epsilon_r) - h/\lambda_o \times 10^2]\,[0.15 + 0.23 \log \epsilon_r + W/h \cdot (2.07 \log \epsilon_r - 0.79)]$$

$$S_{\epsilon_r}^{Z_{os}} = \frac{0.4343\,\epsilon_r}{Z_{os}} \Big\{ 53.55 + 64.85\,W/h + (0.23 + 2.07\,W/h) \cdot [10.25 - 5 \log \epsilon_r + W/h\,(2.1 - 1.42 \log \epsilon_r) - h/\lambda_o \times 10^2]^2 - 2(5 + 1.42\,W/h)\,[0.15 + 0.23 \log \epsilon_r + W/h\,(2.07 \log \epsilon_r - 0.79)] \cdot [10.25 - 5 \log \epsilon_r + W/h\,(2.1 - 1.42 \log \epsilon_r) - h/\lambda_o \times 10^2] \Big\} \tag{B-9}$$

$$S_W^{\epsilon_{re}} = -\frac{2W/h}{\epsilon_{re}}\,[0.111 - 0.0022\,\epsilon_r - 0.094 \log (h/\lambda_o \times 10^2)] \tag{B-10}$$

$$S_h^{\epsilon_{re}} = -S_W^{\epsilon_{re}} + \frac{0.8686}{\epsilon_{re}} (0.121 + 0.094\ W/h - 0.0032\ \epsilon_r) \qquad \text{(B-11)}$$

$$S_{\epsilon_r}^{\epsilon_{re}} = \frac{2}{\epsilon_{re}} [0.21 + 0.0022\ \epsilon_r\ W/h - 0.0032\ \epsilon_r \log (h/\lambda_o \times 10^2)] \qquad \text{(B-12)}$$

The logarithms are to the base 10 in the above expressions.

REFERENCES

[1] Cohn, S.B., "Slotline on a Dielectric Substrate," *IEEE Trans., Vol. MTT-17*, 1969, pp. 768-778.

[2] Knorr, J.B. and K.D. Kuchler, "Analysis of Coupled Slots and Coplanar Strips on Dielectric Substrates," *IEEE Trans., Vol. MTT-23*, 1975, pp. 541-548.

[3] Itoh, T. and R. Mittra, "Dispersion Characteristics of Slotlines," *Electron. Lett., Vol. 7*, 1971, pp. 364-365.

[4] Citerne, J. *et. al.*, "Fundamental and Higher Order Modes in Microslot Lines," *Proc. 5th European Microwave Conf.*, Hamburg, 1975, pp. 273-277.

[5] Robinson, G.H. and J.L. Allen, "Slotline Application to Miniature Ferrite Devices," *IEEE Trans., Vol. MTT-17*, 1969, pp. 1097-1101.

[6] Cohn, S.B., "Slotline Field Components," *IEEE Trans., Vol. MTT-20*, 1972, pp. 172-174.

[7] Galejs, J., "Excitation of Slots in a Conducting Screen Above a Lossy Dielectric Half Space," *IRE Trans., Vol. AP-10*, 1962, pp. 436-443.

[8] Garg, R. and K.C. Gupta, "Expressions for Wavelength and Impedance of Slotline," *IEEE Trans., Vol. MTT-24*, 1976, p. 532.

[9] Montgomery, C.G., *et. al.*, *Principles of Microwave Circuits*, 1948, McGraw-Hill Book Company, New York, p. 230.

[10] Mariani, E.A., *et. al.*, "Slotline Characteristics," *IEEE Trans., Vol. MTT-17*, 1969, pp. 1091-1096.

[11] Garg, R., and K.C. Gupta, "Slot Line and its Applications in MICs," *ACES Tech. Rept. TR-34-75*, 1975, I.I.T. Kanpur (India).

[12] Knorr, J.B. and J. Saenz, "End Effect in a Shorted Slot," *IEEE Trans., Vol. MTT-21*, 1973, pp. 579-580.

[13] Kitazawa, T., *et. al.*, "Slotline with Thick Metal Coating," *IEEE Trans., Vol. MTT-21*, 1973, pp. 580-582.

[14] Garg, R., "Effect of Tolerances on Microstripline and Slotline Performances," *IEEE Trans., Vol. MTT-26*, 1978, pp. 16-19.

[15] Kurpis, G.P., "Coplanar and Slotlines — Are They Here to Stay?," *Proc. Int. Microelectric Symp.*, Washington, 1972, pp. 3B.6.1 - 3B.6.5.

Chapter 6
Slotlines II:
Transitions and Applications

6.1 SLOTLINE TRANSITIONS

In order to test and design slotline circuits it is necessary to have a transition between a slotline and the measuring equipment. A coaxial to slotline transition is commonly used for this purpose. Transitions between slotline and other transmission lines are also useful and increase the applications of slotlines. One such transition is slotline to microstrip. These two types of transitions are discussed in this section.

It is also possible to design a transition from a rectangular waveguide to a slotline. A double ridged waveguide structure oriented such that its E-field direction matches with the E-field of slotline appears to be suitable for this purpose.

6.1.1 Coaxial to Slotline Transitions

A commonly used coaxial line to slotline transition is shown in Figure 6.1(a). It consists of a miniature coaxial line placed perpendicular to and at the end of an open circuited slotline. The outer conductor of the cable is electrically connected (with solder or epoxy) to the metallization in the left half of the slot plane. The inner conductor is extended over the slot and connected to the metallization on the opposite side of the slot. This transition has been analysed in reference [1] by assuming that the inner conductor of the coaxial line has a semicircular shape over the slot as shown in Figure 6.1(b).

An equivalent circuit suggested [1] for the coax-slot transition of Figure 6.1 is shown in Figure 6.2. The impedances Z_{os} and $Z_{c\ell}$ are characteristic impedances of the slotline and the coaxial line, respectively. The fringe capacitance at the open end of the slot is represented by the lumped capacitor C. The inductance L represents

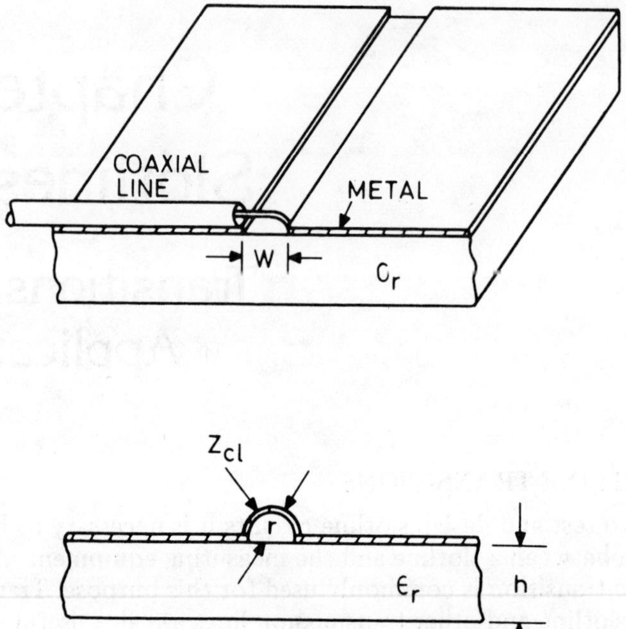

Figure 6.1 A Coaxial-to-Slotline Transition and its Model for Analysis

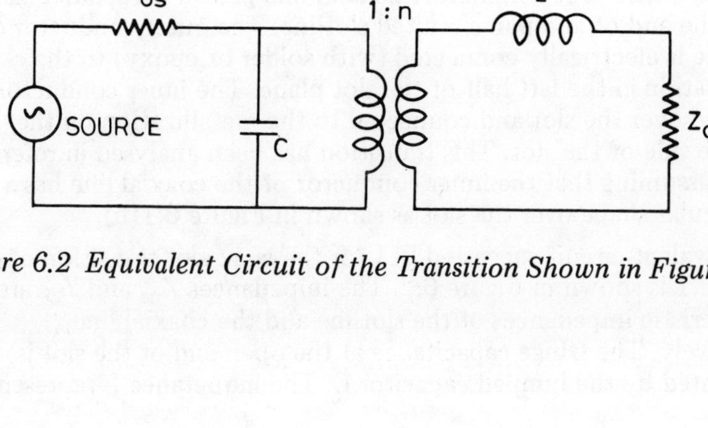

Figure 6.2 Equivalent Circuit of the Transition Shown in Figure 6.1

self-inductance of the semicircular loop. The transformation ratio n can be evaluated approximately by using Equation (5.6) which gives the ratio of the voltage at a distance r to the voltage across the slot. We have

$$n = \frac{\pi}{2} \left| k_c r H_1^{(1)} (k_c r) \right| \tag{6.1}$$

where

$$k_c = j \frac{2\pi}{\lambda_s} \left\{ 1 - (\lambda_s/\lambda_o)^2 \right\}^{1/2} \tag{6.2}$$

From Equation (6.1), it may be noted that the value of the transformer ratio n decreases with increase in frequency. Thus we can expect the performance of the transition to worsen at higher frequencies.

A comparison between experimental VSWR for a coaxial-slotline transition and the values based on the above model is shown in Figure 6.3. This transition has been constructed with a 50-ohm 0.141 inch

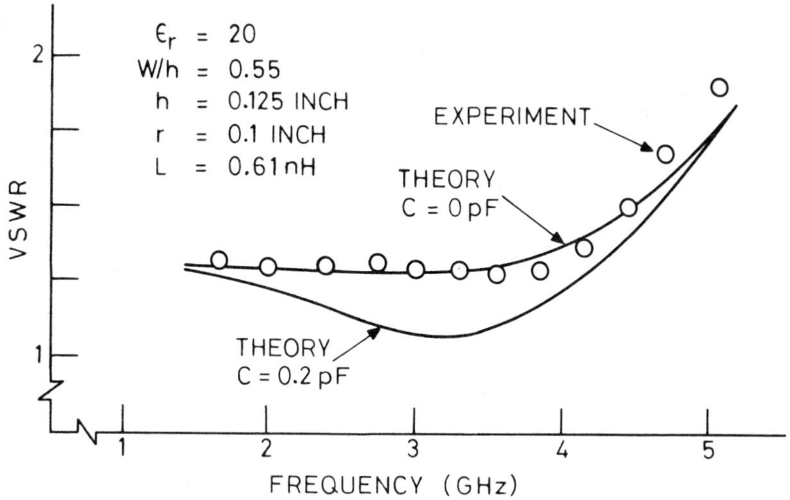

Figure 6.3 Comparison of Theoretical and Experimental VSWR for Coaxial to Slotline Transition (from [1])

semirigid coaxial cable which is coupled to a slotline etched from a 0.125-inch thick substrate with $\epsilon_r = 20.0$. Slot impedance is about 75 ohm (W/h = 0.55). The measured value of L is found to be 0.61 nH and the capacitance C has a typical value of 0.2 pF. It is seen that the experimental curve is in reasonable agreement with the theoretical curve for C = 0 pF. Also, for achieving this agreement, the value of r used is 0.1 inch which is about 50 percent greater than the actual height of the inner conductor of coaxial line above the slot. There are two possible reasons for the lack of any better agreement between the model and the actual performance. Firstly, the inner conductor of the coaxial line does not form a loop of an exactly semicircular shape. Secondly, the Hankel function approximation does not describe accurately the variations of electric field near the slot [2].

The transition described above has been successfully used in S-band as it presents a good VSWR (less than 1.15) in the frequency range 1.65 to 4.0 GHz. Lower VSWR value over a narrow frequency range can be obtained by using an additional movable short as shown in Figure 6.4.

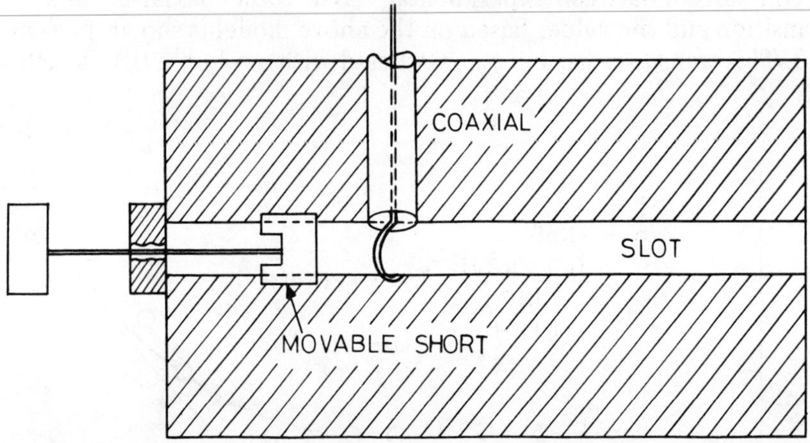

Figure 6.4 Coaxial to Slotline Transition with a Movable Short

This transition is very useful for feeding and testing slotline circuits.

6.1.2 Microstrip to Slotline Transition

Most of the circuits, wherein a slotline is used, also incorporate microstrip lines. Thus a microstrip to slotline transition is desired. Also the fabrication of the microstrip-slot transition can be easily included in the MIC fabrication routine when an arrangement is made for etching the substrate on both the sides.

Microstrip to Slotline Transition Using a Cross-Junction

A microstrip-slot transition is shown in Figure 6.5(a). The slotline,

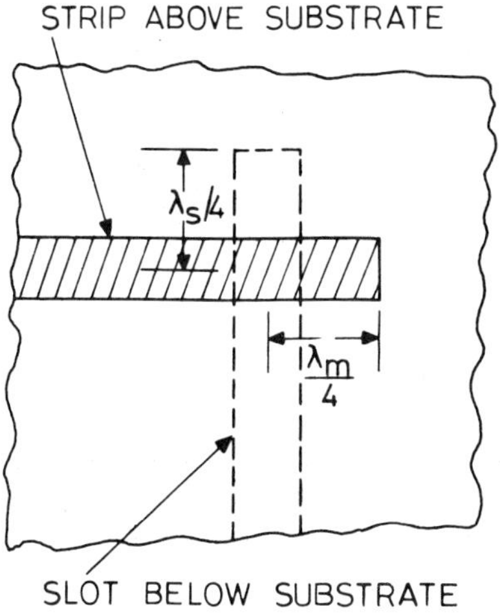

Figure 6.5(a) Microstrip-Slotline Transition

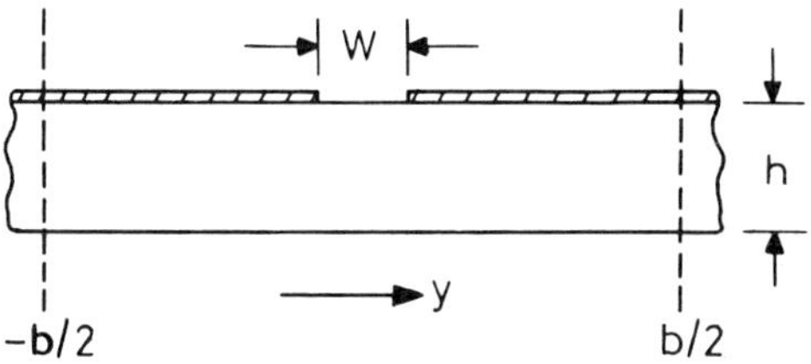

Figure 6.5(b) Slotline Cross-Section

which is etched on one side of the substrate, is crossed at a right angle by a microstrip conductor on the opposite side. The microstrip extends about one quarter of a wavelength beyond the slot and similarly, the slot extends about one-quarter of a wavelength beyond the microstrip. The transition can be fabricated using the usual photo-etching process and is thus easily reproducible. Also, as the microstrip part of the circuit can be placed on one side of the substrate and the slotline part on the other side, this transition makes two-level circuit design possible.

An equivalent circuit of the microstrip transition is shown in Figure 6.5(c). The reactance X_{os} represents the inductance of a shorted

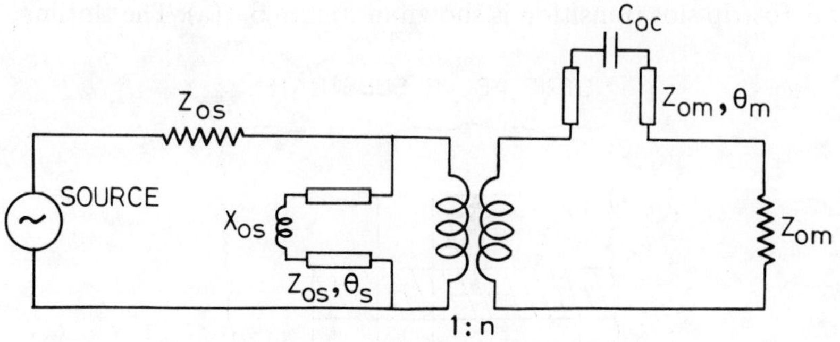

Figure 6.5(c) Equivalent Circuit of (a)

slotline (see Section 5.3.2), and C_{oc} is the capacitance of an open microstrip (see Section 3.4.1). Z_{os} and Z_{om} are slotline and microstrip impedances respectively. θ_s and θ_m represent the electrical lengths (quarter wave at center frequency) of the extended portions of the slotline and the microstrip. The value of the transformer ratio, n, is determined from the knowledge of slotline field components [2]. In the approximate analysis reported by Knorr [1], n is defined as

$$n = V(h)/V_o \tag{6.3}$$

where

$$V(h) = -\int_{-b/2}^{b/2} E_y(h)\, dy \tag{6.4}$$

V_o is the voltage across the slot and $E_y(h)$ is the electric field of the slotline on the other surface of the dielectric substrate. Limits of integration in Equation (6.4) correspond to the locations of electric (or magnetic) walls in Cohn's analysis discussed in Section 5.2.2 (see Figure 5.4). From Cohn's analysis $E_y(h)$ may be written as

$$E_y(h) = -\frac{V_o}{b}\left\{\cos\frac{2\pi u}{\lambda_o}h - \cot q_o \sin\frac{2\pi u}{\lambda_o}h\right\} \tag{6.5}$$

where

$$q_o = \frac{2\pi u}{\lambda_o} h + \tan^{-1}(u/v) \quad (6.6)$$

$$u = \left\{ \epsilon_r - (\lambda_o/\lambda_s)^2 \right\}^{1/2}, v = \left\{ (\lambda_o/\lambda_s)^2 - 1 \right\}^{1/2} \quad (6.7)$$

A comparison between the experimental results and the theoretical values of VSWR is shown in Figure 6.6. For theoretical values, lengths

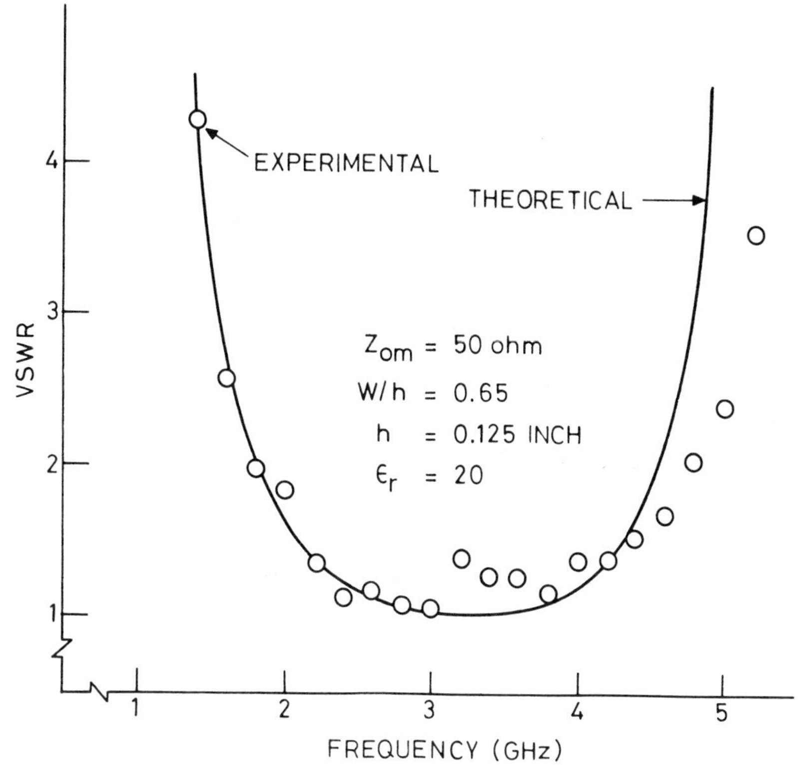

Figure 6.6 Experimental and Theoretical VSWR for Microstrip Slotline Transition (from [1])

of the extended lines were measured from the edge of the opposite line in each case. It has been reported [1] that the agreement is not good when the lengths are measured from the line center to the stub end.

An X-band version of this transition has been tested by Robinson and Allen [3]. The geometry of the transition is slightly different. The microstrip is terminated in an open-circuit quarter wave radial stub as shown in Figure 6.7. Microstrip impedance is 50 ohm and slotline

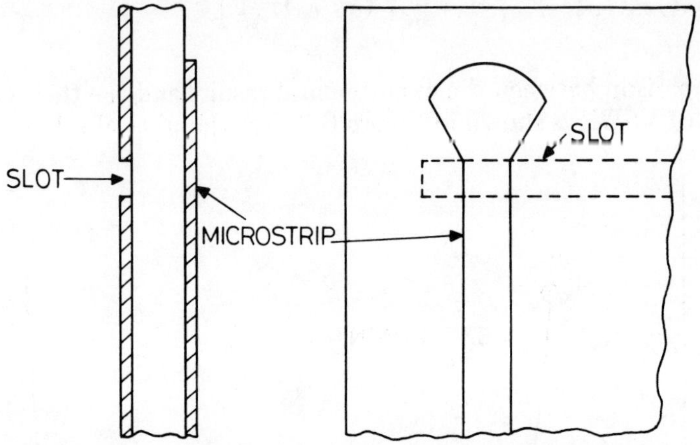

Figure 6.7 A Different Type of Microstrip-Slotline Transition

impedance is 72 ohm. For this transition, a VSWR value less than 1.10 is obtained from 8.0 to 10.0 GHz (20 percent bandwidth).

Different variations of this transition have been reported [4] for wide band applications. These are shown in Figure 6.8(a), (b) and (c). The

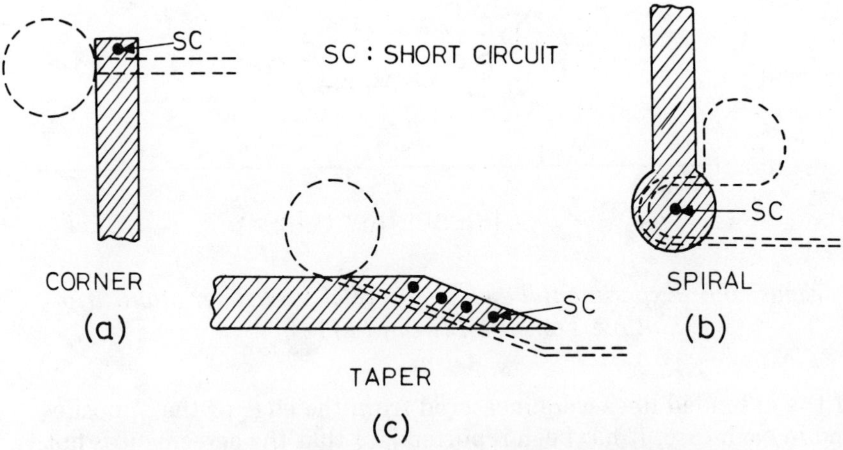

Figure 6.8 Wide Band Microstrip-Slotline Transitions

metal contact between the strip and the ground plane is indicated by "SC". No detailed results or analysis is available for these transitions, but the spiral configuration shown in Figure 6.8(b) is reported [4] to have a VSWR less than 1.1 in 1.0 GHz to 10 GHz frequency range.

Microstrip-Slot Transition Using a Six-Port Junction [5]

An improved microstrip-slotline transition, based on a different principle, has been proposed [5]. This is a broadband transition with an insertion loss less than 0.2 dB and is not critical in its dimensions.

A detailed analysis of this new transition is not available but a qualitative explanation may be given based on the characteristics of 6-port junction shown in Figure 6.9(a). This circuit is matched at port 1 and

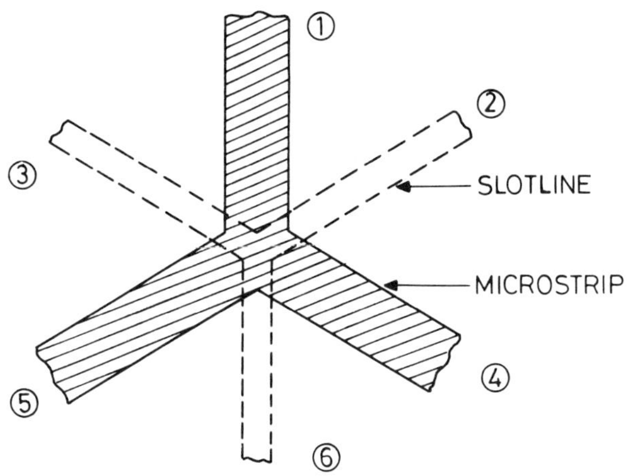

Figure 6.9(a) 6-Port Junction Used in an Improved Microstrip Slotline Transition

port 6 when

- the ports 2 through 5 are terminated by matched loads
- the characteristic impedances of all the microstrips and slotlines are equal (e.g. 50 ohm), and
- the junction effects can be ignored.

First of all, we note that there is no direct coupling between ports 1 and 6. This could be explained qualitatively on the basis of field configurations for the microstrip (at port 1) and the slotline (at port 6) shown in Figures 6.9(b) and 6.9(c). The two lines are collinear. We note that the E-field of microstrip has even symmetry while that of

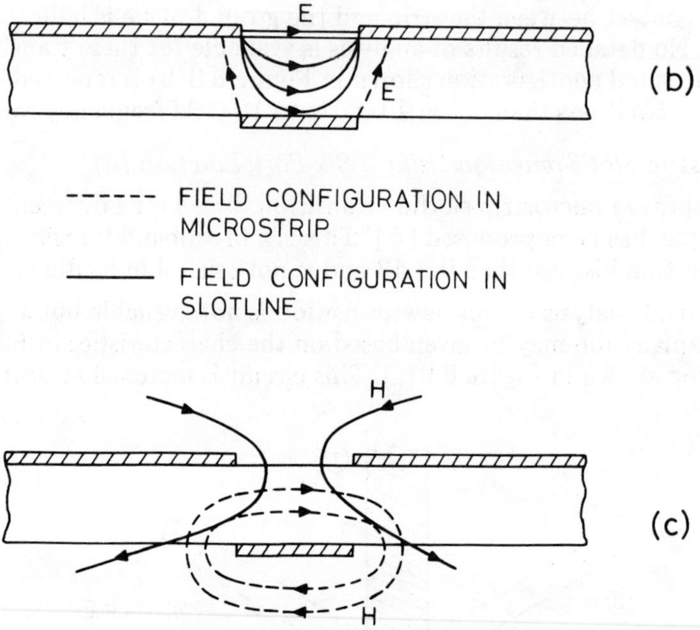

Figure 6.9(b) and (c) Coupling of Electromagnetic Waves From Microstrip to Slotline

slotline has odd-symmetry as shown in Figure 6.9(b). Thus there is no net coupling. A similar argument holds for magnetic field distribution as shown in Figure 6.9(c).

Now let us examine the equivalent circuits as seen from ports 1 and 6. Looking from port 1, the slotlines leading to ports 2 and 3 are parallel to each other and in series to the two parallel microstrip lines that lead to ports 4 and 5. This situation is shown in Figure 6.10(a). Two-wire symbolic representation is used for both microstrip and slotline but they are distinguished by letters m and s. As a result of this, the input impedance looking from port 1 is 50 ohms. Similarly, looking from port 6, the slotlines leading to ports 2 and 3 are in series to each other and parallel to the series connected microstrips leading to ports 4 and 5. This arrangement is shown in Figure 6.10(b). Thus, also looking from port 6, the input impedance of the junction is 50 ohms. In a similar manner it can be proved that the input impedance of the junction is 50 ohms when looked at from any port.

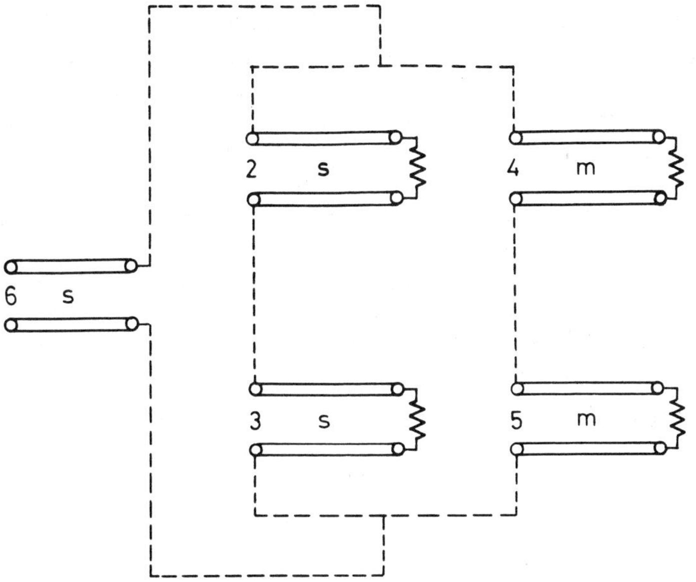

Figure 6.10(a) Transmission Line Equivalent Circuit for Figure 6.9(a) When Viewed From Port 1

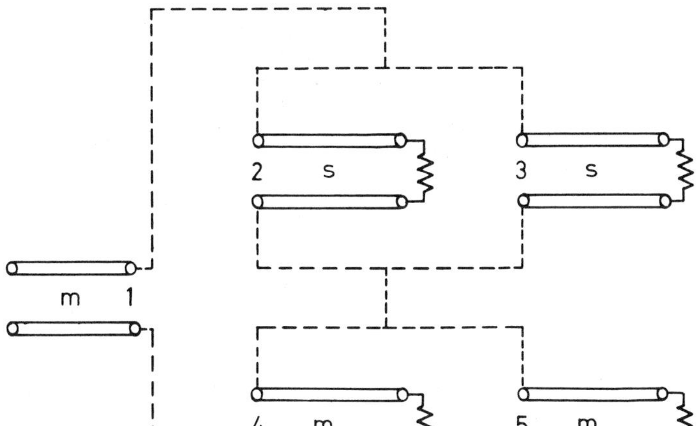

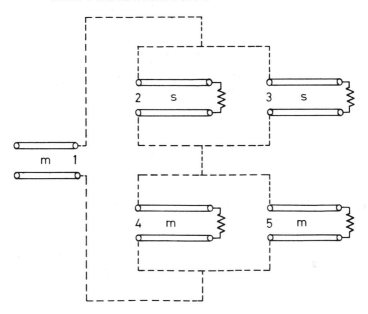

Figure 6.10(b) Transmission Line Equivalent Circuit for Figure 6.9(a) When Viewed From Port 6

Also under these conditions ports 1 and 6 are decoupled. Let us consider a signal incident at port 1. This input signal will be equally distributed into ports 2 through 5 (port 6 is decoupled). If these components are totally reflected from identical reactive terminals connected to ports 2 to 5, they will constitute the signal reflected back into port 1. Similarly, an input signal at port 6 will also be equally transmitted into ports 2-5, but in phase opposition to ports 2 and 5 with respect to ports 3 and 4. Again, equal reflection coefficients at ports 2-5 will reflect the signals back into port 6. However, reflection coefficients of $\exp(j\phi)$ at ports 2 and 5 and of $\exp j(\phi + 180^\circ)$ at ports 3 and 4 cause a perfect transmission of input signal (port 1) into the output port 6.

Figure 6.11 shows realization of this transition with short and open

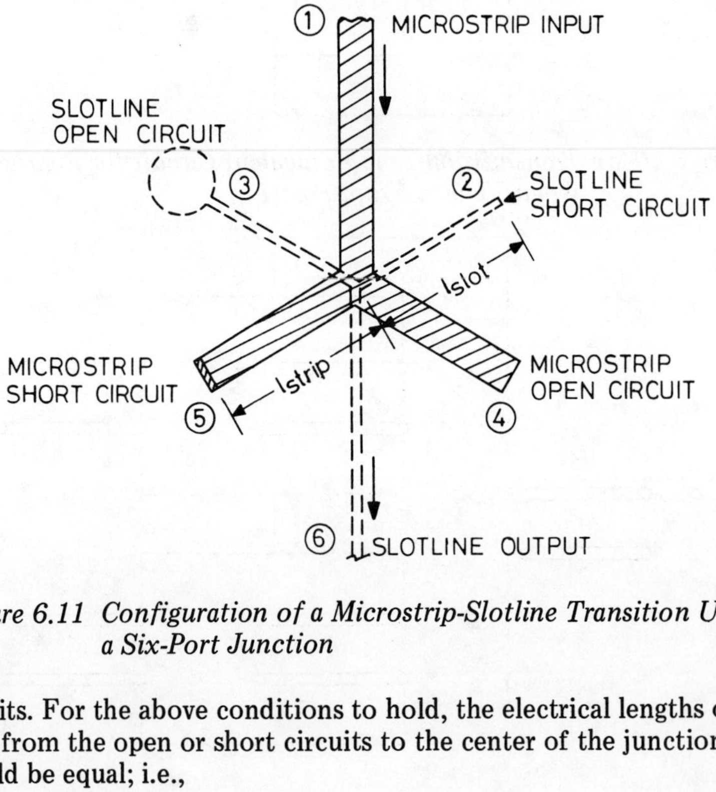

Figure 6.11 Configuration of a Microstrip-Slotline Transition Using a Six-Port Junction

circuits. For the above conditions to hold, the electrical lengths of the lines from the open or short circuits to the center of the junction should be equal; i.e.,

$$\beta_m \ell_m = \beta_s \ell_s = \theta \tag{6.8}$$

where β_m and β_s are the phase constants and ℓ_m and ℓ_s are the line lengths for microstrips and slotlines, respectively.

In experimental realization ℓ's are made conveniently small. Note that 2ℓ should be made smaller than a quarter wavelength to avoid radiation effects.

Experimental results for this transition are shown in Figure 6.12.

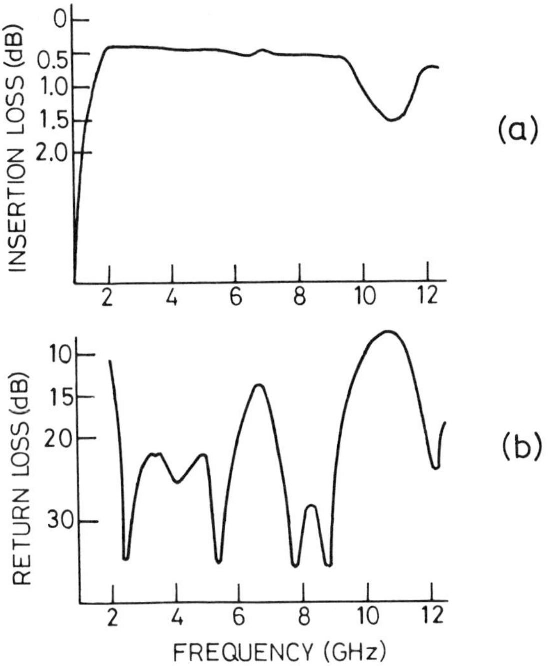

Figure 6.12 Experimental Performance of Microstrip-Slotline Transition Using a Six-Port Junction (from [5])

Measurements were conducted on two transitions in cascade fabricated on 1 x 1 inch alumina substrate of thickness 0.51 mm. The losses, which also include the connector losses ($\simeq$ 0.2 dB), are rather low, going below 0.5 dB. This means that loss for one transition should be below 0.15 dB in the frequency range 2-6 GHz and below 0.2 dB in the range 6-9 GHz. The return loss, which includes the interference of four discontinuities, i.e. two connectors and two transitions, is mostly better than 20 dB.

It may be mentioned that this improved transition and also the wide band transitions shown in Figure 6.8 require a hole through the ceramic substrate to realize microstrip short circuits. This complicates the fabrication procedure for circuits using such transitions.

6.2 SLOTLINE APPLICATIONS

It was mentioned in Chapter 5 that slotlines can be incorporated in microstrip circuits by etching the slotline circuit in the ground plane of the microstrip circuit. This type of hybrid combination allows some flexibility in the design, saves substrate area, and has led to some novel circuits with improved performance such as hybrid branchline directional couplers. Also, some of the circuit elements, which are not easily accessible in microstrip configuration, can be incorporated in the slotline part of the circuit. These could be, for example, short circuits, high impedance lines, series stubs, etc.

Some of the circuit applications of slotline are discussed in this section. The discussion is limited only to those slotline circuits which either have some advantages over corresponding microstrip configurations or which are possible only with slotlines. Circuits using slotlines with coplanar waveguides are discussed in Chapter 7.

6.2.1 Circuits Using Series T-junction

Perhaps the most important class of slotline circuits is the one using slotline-microstrip-junction as a circuit element. This junction can be used as a series T circuit element in microstrip circuits.

Although a T-junction was suggested some time back [4], there is no analysis or detailed characterization available for this component. Measurements on the series impedance presented by a slotline to the microstrip (see Figure 6.13(a)) have been carried out by Schiek [6].

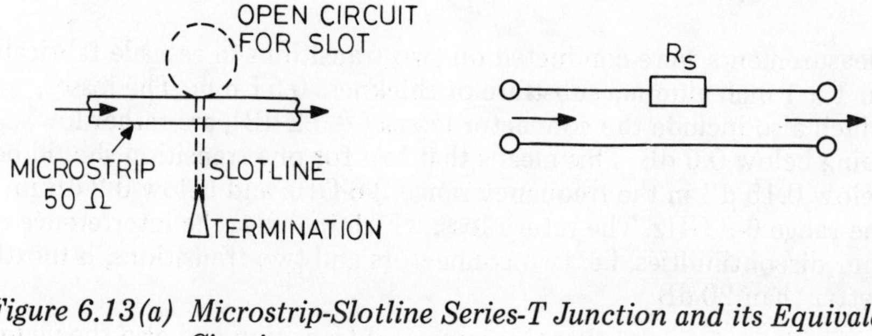

Figure 6.13(a) Microstrip-Slotline Series-T Junction and its Equivalent Circuit

These results are shown in Figure 6.13(b). The slot impedance can be

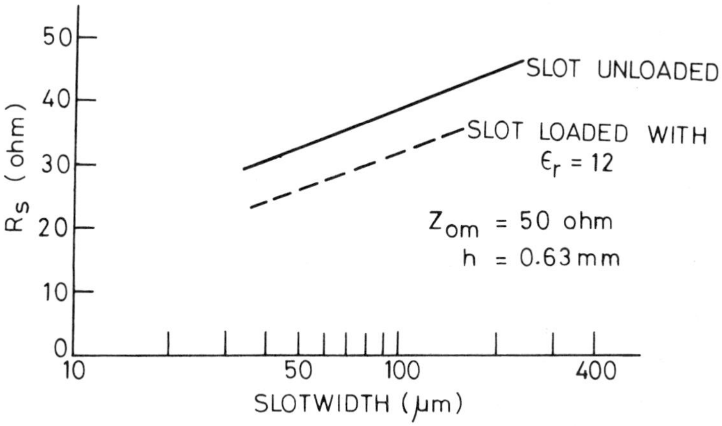

Figure 6.13(b) Measured Values of Series Impedance R_s for a Series-T Junction (from [6])

reduced by loading it with a dielectric, the results of which are also shown in this figure. The substrate has a dielectric constant of 12 and a thickness of 0.63 mm. This type of series-T junction has been combined with a microstrip shunt-T to yield a hybrid magic-T junction [4]. The configuration of the magic-T is shown in Figure 6.13(c). In

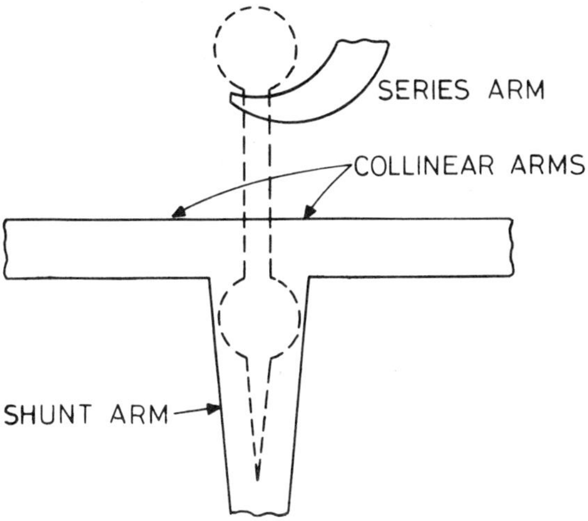

Figure 6.13(c) A Magic Tee Using Microstrip-Slotline Series-T Junction

the microstrip-T part of this circuit, a linear taper acts as an impedance transformer, while the reflections at the 90° corners are compensated by a series inductance in the ground plane as shown in the figure. Also the slotline should be open circuited at the junction of the series-T. This is obtained by having a $\lambda_s/4$ long slot in the ground plane below the shunt microstrip arm. This $\lambda_s/4$ length is the factor limiting the bandwidth of the magic-T. In an experimental model tested at 2-4 GHz (on 1 x 1 inch alumina substrate) the following performance has been obtained [4]:

Isolation between shunt and series arm	$\geqslant$ 40 dB
Isolation between collinear arms	$\geqslant$ 20 dB
Unbalance between opposite arms	$\leqslant$ 0.3 dB
Insertion loss between any two ports	$\simeq$ 3.2 dB

As the series-T junction has not been analyzed so far, theoretical limitations on the performance of this type of circuit are not known.

The use of a series T-junction as described above has led to a new class of branchline couplers [6] called hybrid branchline couplers. Let us consider the branchline coupler configurations shown in Figure 6.14. A conventional microstrip branchline coupler is shown in Figure 6.14(a) along with its transmission line equivalent circuit

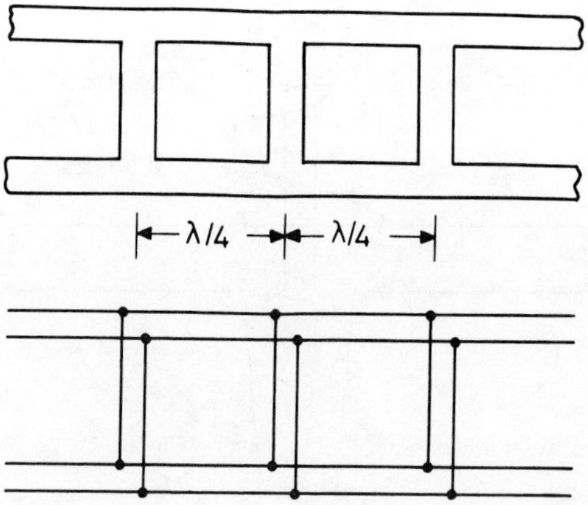

Figure 6.14(a) Branchline Coupler Configurations Using Microstrip Lines, and Two-Wire Lines

(neglecting junction effects). All the branchlines in this circuit are connected in shunt. Series connections of the branchline are not possible by the use of microstrips. However, use of slotlines also allows the designer the flexibility of incorporating series connected branches if desired. As shown in Figure 6.14(b), a shunt connected

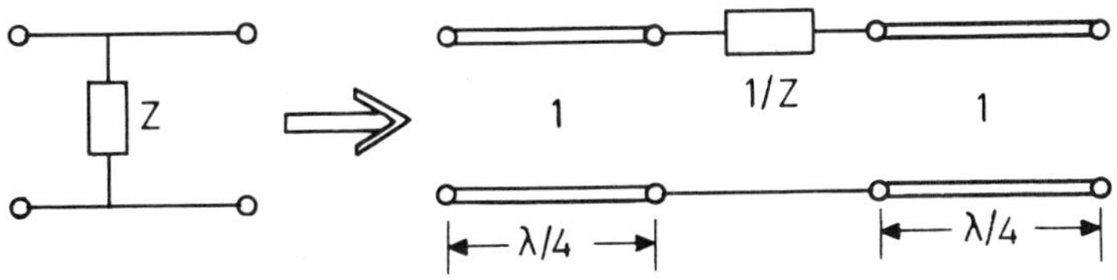

Figure 6.14(b) Equivalence Between a Shunt and a Series Connected Branch

element can be transformed into an equivalent series connected element provided two additional quarter wave sections are included on each side of the series connected element. If the middle branch of the 3-branch coupler, shown in Figure 6.14 (a), is replaced by a series connected branch in this manner, we obtain the configuration shown in Figure 6.14(c). In this arrangement, there are two half-wave

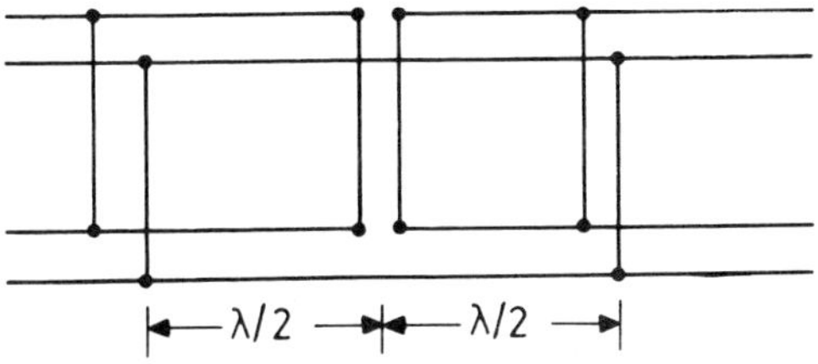

Figure 6.14(c) Modified Coupler With a Series Branch

sections between the shunt and series connected branches. These half-wave sections can be eliminated altogether and the three branches put together at one place as shown in Figure 6.14(d). This coupler has been analyzed, like any other branchline coupler, using the method of even- and odd-mode excitations.

The modified branchline coupler has two advantages over the conventional microstrip branchline coupler: smaller size and wider bandwidth. Both of these advantages result from the elimination of the two quarter-wave lengths shown in Figure 6.14(a).

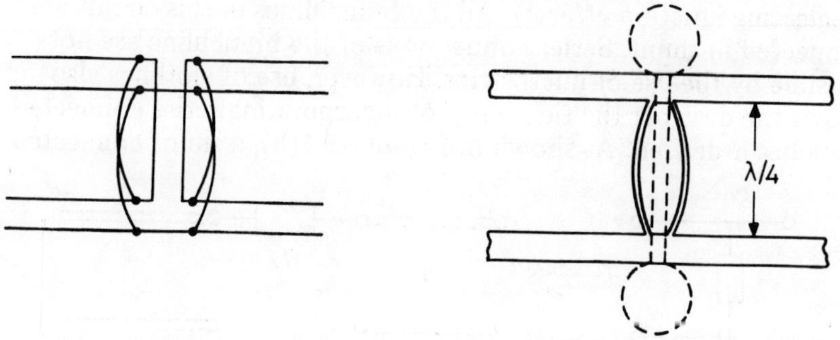

Figure 6.14(d) Hybrid Branchline Coupler

The final version of the hybrid branchline coupler, shown in Figure 6.14(d), is very similar to the coupler configuration shown in Figure

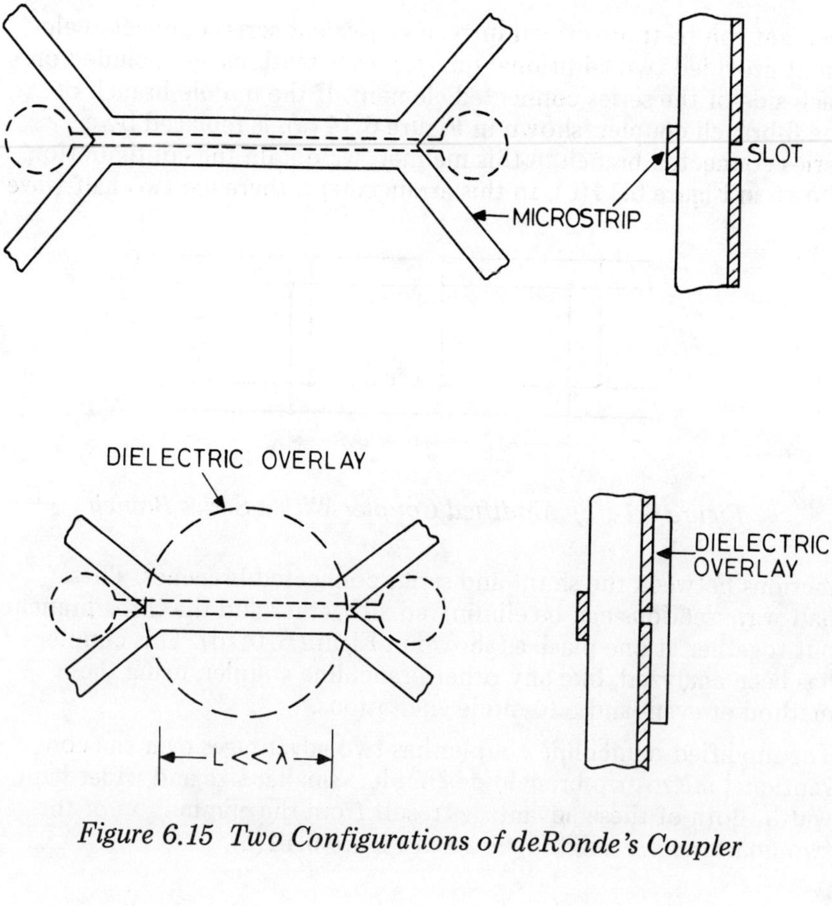

Figure 6.15 Two Configurations of deRonde's Coupler

6.15 which was suggested earlier empirically by de Ronde [4] and is known after his name. One can consider de Ronde's coupler to be derived from the configuration of Figure 6.14(d) in the following manner. Two shunt connected branches are combined together and realized by the microstrip on the top surface of the dielectric substrate. The series connected branch is obtained by the slotline in the ground plane. The performance of de Ronde's coupler has been measured [6] and the results are shown here in Figure 6.16. The

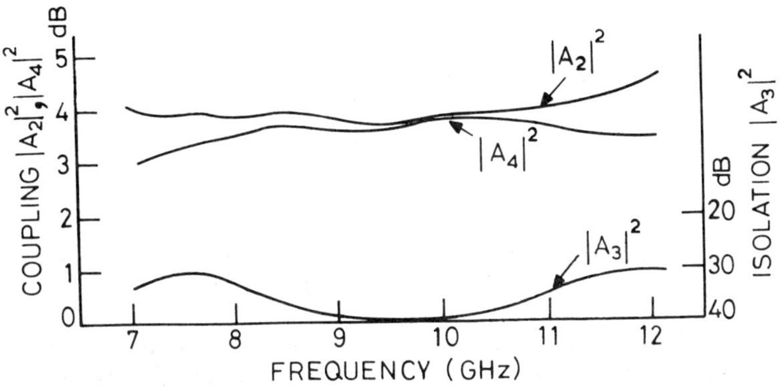

Figure 6.16 Measured Performance of deRonde's Coupler (from [6])

circuit details are as follows:

Substrate thickness	0.38 mm
Slot width	50 μm
ϵ_r	12
Substrate size	2 x 2 cm
Microstrip impedance	60.4 ohm
Slotline impedance	50 ohm
Frequency range	X-band

It may be noted that de Ronde's coupler differs from the hybrid branchline coupler discussed above in some respects. The microstrip and the slotline in de Ronde's configuration are in close proximity and are continuously coupled all along the length of the branchline. In the branchline coupler, the coupling exists only at the junctions. Also, in the modified version of the branchline coupler (Figure 6.14(d)) two shunt branches are separated from each other by the series branch and, therefore, cannot be combined in parallel to yield de Ronde's configuration. A complete analysis of de Ronde's coupler is not available.

6.2.2 Circuits Using Wide Band 180° Phase Shift

When two microstrip to slotline transitions are connected back-to-back as shown in Figure 6.17(a), an additional 180 degree phase

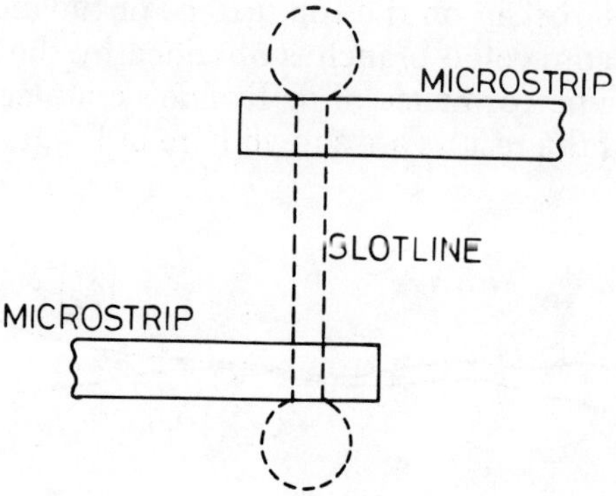

Figure 6.17(a) Two Microstrip-Slotline Transitions Connected Back-to-Back for 180° Phase Change

shift is introduced in the signal path. This can be explained qualitatively by considering the E-field distribution associated with the microstrip-slotline transition. Referring to Figure 6.17(b), we note

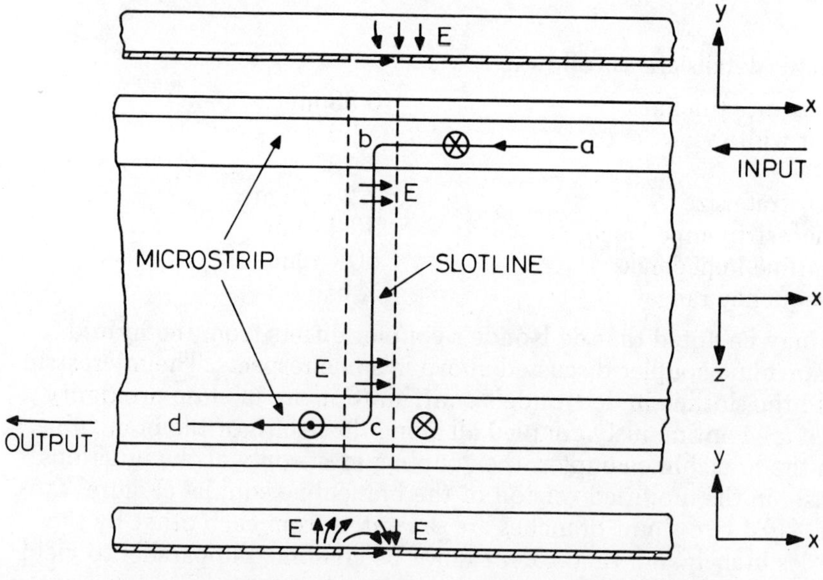

Figure 6.17(b) Mechanism for 180° Phase Change

that the E-field in the input microstrip line (near the transition) is in the -y direction. This produces a slotline wave with the E-field in the x direction. At the second transition an x-directed component of E will cause the E-field in the output microstrip to lie in the y-direction. Thus, in addition to the phase change introduced by the line length, the E-field direction changes from -y to y which amounts to an equivalent 180° phase change. This phase change is independent of frequency (at least in a first order analysis) and can thus be used in wide band circuits. Its application in a rat-race circuit is discussed below.

The usual microstrip rat-race circuit shown in Figure 6.18(a) consists of a $3\lambda/2$ microstrip ring with the four ports located radially as

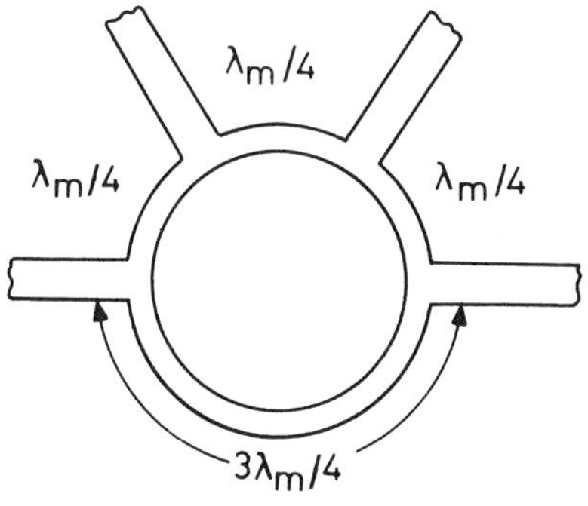

Figure 6.18(a) A Rat-Race Hybrid Using Microstrip Lines Only

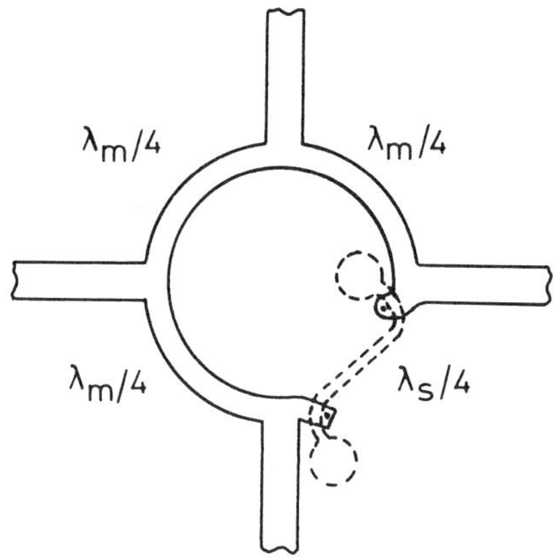

Figure 6.18(b) Rat-Race Hybrid Using Slotline in (a)

shown. The three adjacent sections are each $\lambda/4$ long while the fourth section is $3\lambda/4$. Typically this circuit will have a bandwidth of 20 percent. A modified version of this circuit [7] involves replacement of the $3\lambda/4$ microstrip section with a $\lambda/4$ slotline etched on the other side of the substrate as shown in Figure 6.18(b). The remaining 180° electrical length of the microstrip section is compensated by the two microstrip-slotline junctions required for introducing a slotline in the circuit. Since this phase change is frequency independent, the resulting rat-race circuit has a wider bandwidth. Experimental measurements [7] presented in Figure 6.18(c) show that a bandwidth of two octaves can be realized.

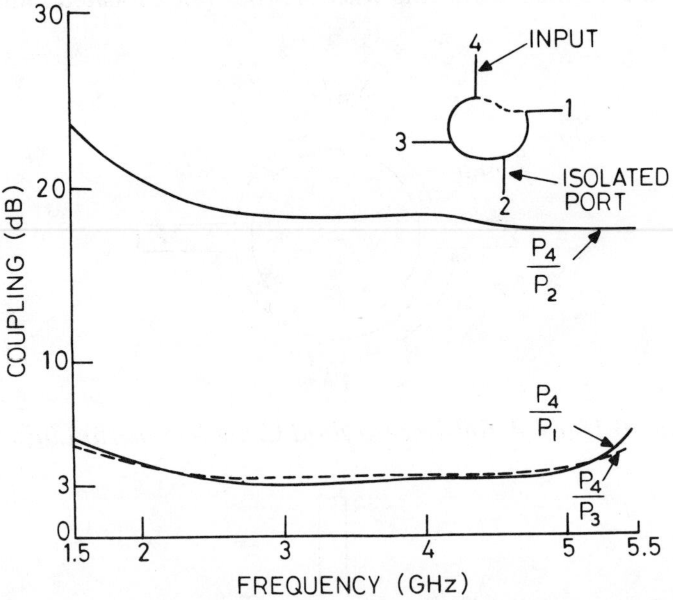

Figure 6.18(c) Performance of Rat-Race Hybrid Shown in (b) (from [7])

In the above example, the use of slotline provides a method of obtaining a broad-band 180° phase change. This technique can be used successfully in other circuits where a broad-band 180° phase shift may be needed. A broad-band pulse inverter has also been designed on this principle [8]. The input pulse is fed to one of the microstrip lines (see Figure 6.19(a)) and the inverted pulse output appears at the other microstrip. This pulse inverter was designed using a 25 mil

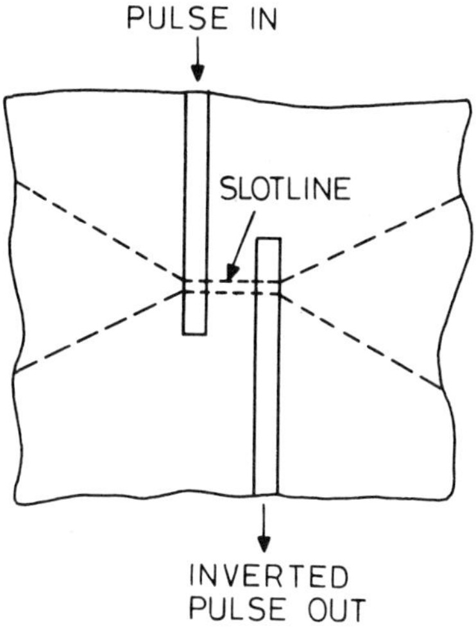

Figure 6.19(a) Configuration of a Microstrip-Slotline Pulse Inverter

alumina substrate. The oscilloscope traces of the input and the output pulse trains at 250 MHz are shown in Figure 6.19(b). As seen in

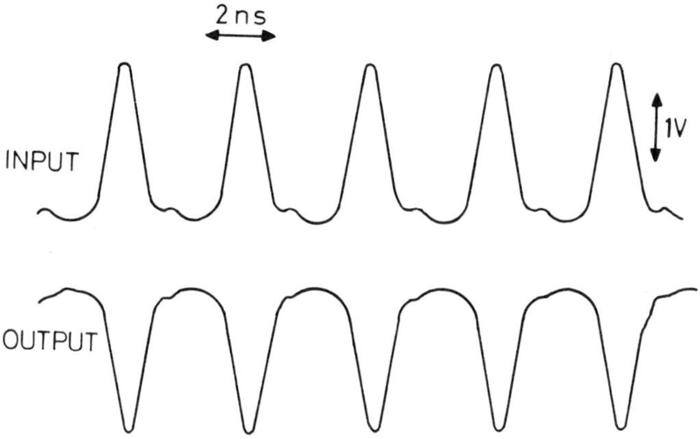

Figure 6.19(b) Oscilloscope Trace of the Performance of a Microstrip-Slotline Pulse Inverter (from [8])

this figure, the output pulses are almost identical to the input pulses except for the change in polarity. The bandwidth measurement of the pulse inverter indicates that the circuit works up to 1 GHz.

6.2.3 Other Types of Slotline Circuits

The circuits mentioned in this section are based on the properties of slotlines only. They do not have the hybrid composition as described in earlier circuits using slotlines. These circuits can be classified into two categories: circuits using slotline resonators (filters, etc.) and ferrite devices using slotline.

Circuits Using Slotline Resonators

Slotline resonators have been used for the design of filters, both band-pass and band-rejection types [9]. The design procedure for slotline filters is the same as that for any other transmission line; i.e., it is based on the coupling coefficient between either two end-coupled or two parallel-coupled sections of transmission line. The necessary theory for the determination of the coupling coefficient for parallel coupled slotlines will be given in Section 8.6.1. However, for end-coupled slotlines only some empirical design information is available. The experimental results [9] indicate that the performance of slotline filters is not superior to those using other transmission lines.

Ferrite Devices Using Slotline

When the slotline was introduced as an alternative transmission structure for MICs, it was expected that the slotline would be more suitable than the microstrip line for non-reciprocal ferrite devices. This expectation was based on the existence of an elliptically polarized magnetic field distribution in the slot as discussed in Section 5.2.1. However, the experimental and analytical studies reported so far on differential phase shifters [3], circulators and isolators [10-12], have not pointed out any significant advantage of ferrite devices using slotline.

REFERENCES

[1] Knorr, J.B., "Slotline Transitions," *IEEE Trans., Vol. MTT-22,* 1974, pp. 548-554.

[2] Cohn, S.B., "Slotline Field Components," *IEEE Trans., Vol. MTT-20,* 1972, pp. 172-174.

[3] Robinson, G.H., and J.L. Allen, "Slotline Application to Miniature Ferrite Devices," *IEEE Trans., Vol. MTT-17,* 1969, pp. 1097-1101.

[4] de Ronde, F.C., "A New Class of Microstrip Directional Couplers," *Digest of Tech. Papers, G-MTT Symp. 1970,* pp. 184-189.

[5] Schiek, B., and J. Kohler, "An Improved Microstrip-to-Microslot Transition," *IEEE Trans., Vol. MTT-24,* 1976, pp. 231-233.

[6] Schiek, B., "Hybrid Branchline Couplers — A Useful New Class of Directional Couplers," *IEEE Trans., Vol. MTT-22,* 1974, pp. 864-869.

[7] Chua, L.W., "New Broadband Matched Hybrids for Microwave Integrated Circuits," *Proc. European Microwave Conf. (Stockholm), 1971,* pp. C4/5:1 - C4/5:4.

[8] C. Hede, "High Speed Logic, Part 3," *Tech. Report IR 127,* Electromagnetics Institute, Technical University of Denmark (1977).

[9] Mariani, E.A. and J.P. Agrios, "Slotline Filters and Couplers," *IEEE Trans., Vol. MTT-18,* 1970, pp. 1089-1095.

[10] Ogasawara, N. and M. Kaji, "Coplanar-Guide and Slot-Guide Junction Circulators," *Electron. Lett., Vol. 7,* 1971, pp. 220-221.

[11] De Vecchis, M., *et. al.,* "A New Slotline Broadband Isolator," *Proc. European Microwave Conf. (Brussels), 1973,* Paper B.9.6.

[12] Courtois, L. and M. De Vecchis, "A New Class of Non-Reciprocal Components Using Slotline," *IEEE Trans., Vol. MTT-23,* 1975, pp. 511-516.

Chapter 7
Coplanar Lines:
Coplanar Waveguide and Coplanar Strips

7.1 INTRODUCTION

The term "coplanar lines" is used for those transmission lines for which all the conductors are in the same plane; namely, on the top surface of the dielectric substrate. These transmission lines include slotline, coplanar waveguide (CPW) and coplanar strips (CPS). Slotline has been discussed in Chapters 5 and 6. Coplanar waveguide and coplanar strips are discussed in this chapter. A distinct advantage of these two lines lies in the fact that mounting of lumped (active or passive) components in shunt or series configuration is much easier. Drilling of holes or slots through the substrate is not needed.

Coplanar waveguide was proposed by Wen [1] in 1969. As shown in Figure 7.1(a), it consists of a center strip with two ground planes located parallel to and in the plane of the strip (i.e. on the same surface of the dielectric slab). The electric and magnetic field configurations for quasi-static approximation are shown in Figure 7.1(b). At higher frequencies the mode of propagation in CPW becomes non-TEM because a longitudinal component of the magnetic field exists. In such a case CPW has an elliptically polarized magnetic field in the slots at the air-dielectric interface and becomes suitable for non-reciprocal ferrite devices.

A configuration of coplanar strips which is complementary to CPW is shown in Figure 7.2(a). It consists of two strips (generally of equal widths) running parallel on the same surface of the dielectric slab. The electric and magnetic field configurations are shown in Figure 7.2(b). At lower regions of microwave frequencies, CPS is also useful for carrying signals for high-speed computer circuits.

Methods of analysis for CPW and CPS are discussed in the following sections. Design considerations for these lines are given. Circuits using CPW are included in Section 7.4.

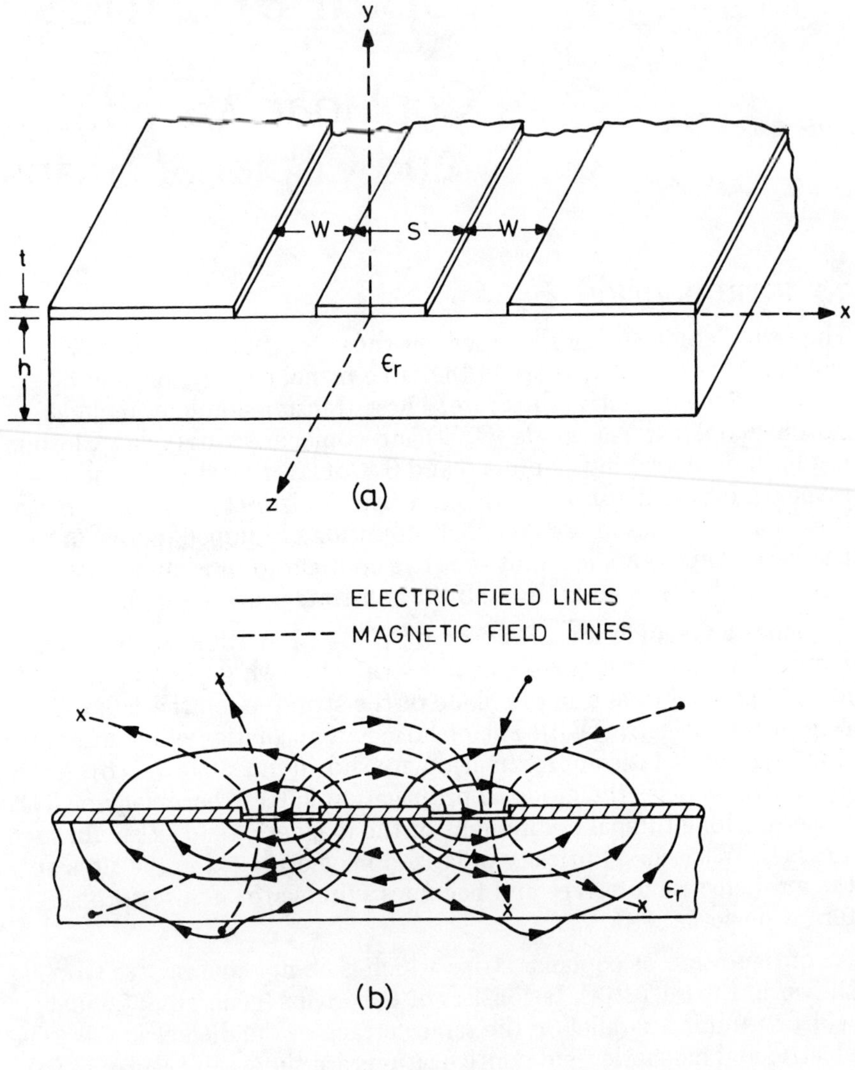

Figure 7.1(a) Coplanar Waveguide (CPW) Geometry (b) Electric and Magnetic Field Distributions in CPW

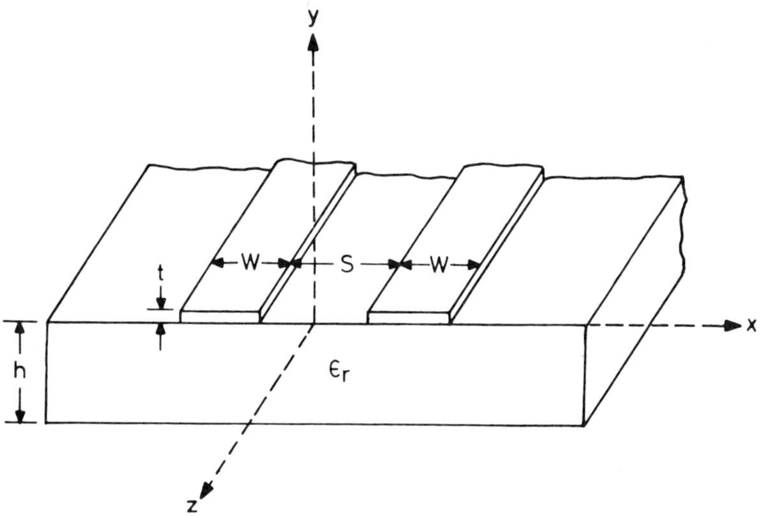

(a)

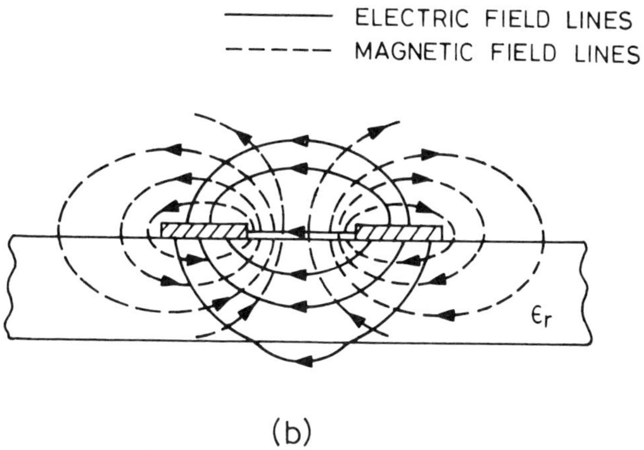

(b)

Figure 7.2(a) Coplanar Strips (CPS) Geometry (b) Electric and Magnetic Field Distributions in CPS

7.2 ANALYSES

Coplanar lines have been studied using quasi-static approximation as well as fullwave analysis. Wen [1] has carried out a quasi-static analysis of these transmission lines using conformal mapping and with the assumption that the dielectric substrate is thick enough to be considered infinite. For commonly used thicknesses this assumption is valid for large values of the dielectric constant. A modification of the method studied by Wen is given by Davis *et al.* [2] and takes the finite thickness of the dielectric substrate into consideration. The effect of enclosure on the characteristics of CPW has been determined using the finite difference method [3]. A fullwave analysis of coplanar lines which provides information regarding frequency-dependence of phase velocity and characteristic impedance has been carried out by using Galerkin's method in the spectral domain [4, 5], by the variational method [6] and also by nonuniform discretization of integral equations [7].

7.2.1 Quasi-static Analysis

Conformal Mapping Method

A quasi-static analysis for CPW can be carried out by using conformal transformation for the case when the dielectric substrate thickness is sufficiently large and can be considered infinite in the analytical model. The strip and the ground plane metallization thickness is considered negligible. The conformal transformation which maps the dielectric half plane z_1 (Figure 7.3(a)) of CPW into an interior of a rectangle in

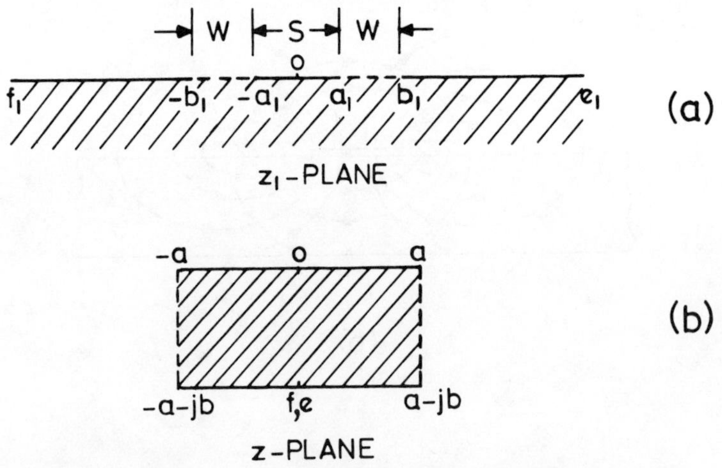

Figure 7.3 Conformal Transformation Planes for CPW and CPS Analysis

the z-plane (Figure 7.3(b)), with conductor surface on the top and the bottom and air-dielectric interfaces on the sides, is given by

$$\frac{dz}{dz_1} = \frac{A}{(z_1^2 - a_1^2)^{1/2} (z_1^2 - b_1^2)^{1/2}} \tag{7.1}$$

where A is a constant. The ratio a/b of the rectangle in the z-plane may be evaluated by carrying out the integration

$$a + jb = \int_0^{b_1} \frac{A\, dz_1}{(z_1^2 - a_1^2)^{1/2} (z_1^2 - b_1^2)^{1/2}} \tag{7.2}$$

and is given by

$$a/b = K(k)/K'(k) \tag{7.3}$$

where K(k) is the complete elliptic integral of the first kind and

$$k = a_1/b_1 = \frac{S}{S+2W}$$

$$K'(k) = K(k')$$

$$k' = (1 - k^2)^{1/2}$$

The capacitance per unit length of the line contributed by the dielectric half space may be written as

$$C = \epsilon_o\, \epsilon_r\, 2a/b \tag{7.4a}$$

The total line capacitance including the empty space half-plane may be written as

$$C = (\epsilon_r + 1)\, \epsilon_o\, 2a/b \tag{7.4b}$$

Using the quasi-static approximation one can write the phase velocity and characteristic impedance as

$$v_{cp} = \left(\frac{2}{\epsilon_r + 1}\right)^{1/2} c \tag{7.5}$$

and

$$Z_{ocp} = \frac{1}{C\, v_{cp}} = \frac{30\pi}{\sqrt{\frac{\epsilon_r + 1}{2}}} \frac{K'(k)}{K(k)} \text{ (ohm)} \tag{7.6}$$

where c is the velocity of electromagnetic waves in free space. Values of characteristic impedance Z_{ocp} computed from Equation (7.6) are shown in Figure 7.4. Measured values of Z_{ocp} for $\epsilon_r = 9.6$, 16 and 130

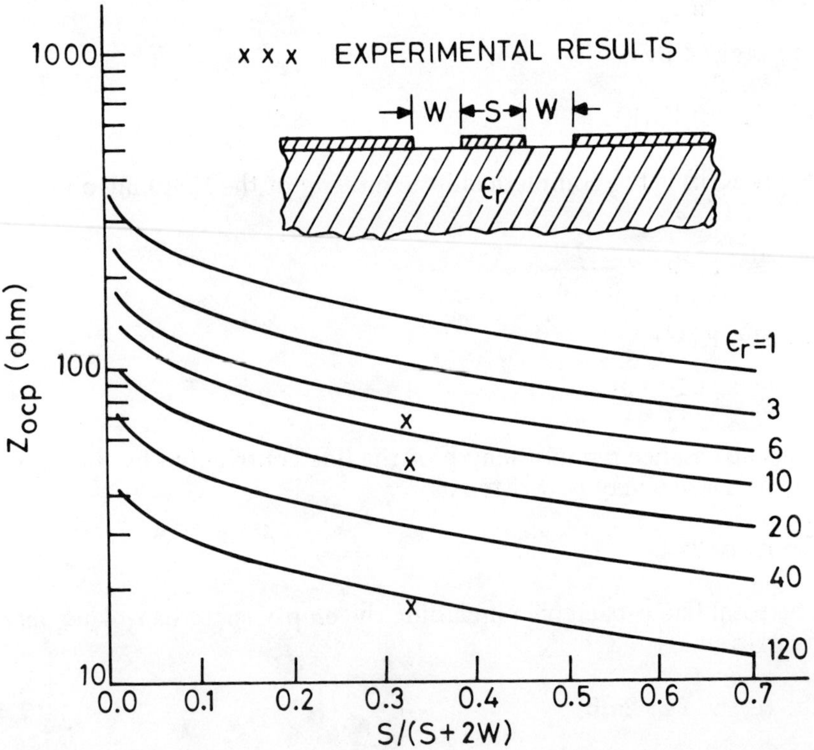

Figure 7.4 Characteristic Impedance of Coplanar Waveguides (from [1])

are also shown in this figure. Wen [1] points out that Z_{ocp} increases by less than 10 percent, for large values of ϵ_r, when the thickness of the substrate is reduced from infinite to W, the width of the slots (that is, when $W/h \rightarrow 1$).

A quantitative estimate of the modification caused by finite thickness of the substrate is given by Davis *et. al.* [2]. Conformal transformation is used again but the lower boundary of the dielectric substrate is also mapped. This appears approximately as an ellipse as shown in Figure 7.5. Mapping of the points away from the x_1-axis in the z_1-plane

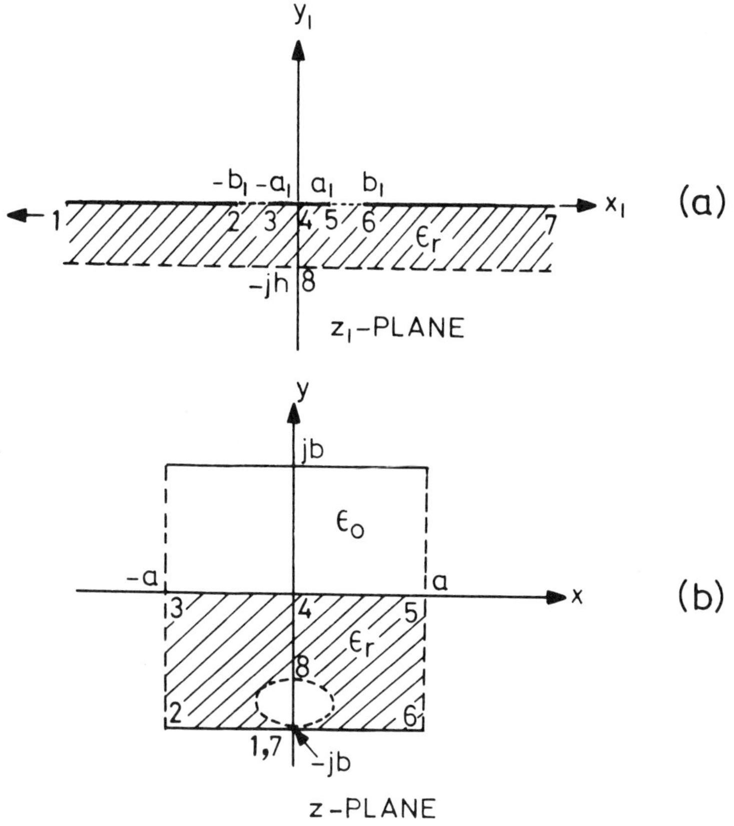

Figure 7.5 Conformal Transformation for CPW With Finite Substrate Thickness (from [2])

(Figure 7.5) leads to incomplete elliptic integrals. The equivalent dielectric constant is calculated numerically by modeling the configuration with the elliptical 'void' in form of a distributed shunt-series capacitance as in the case of microstrip analysis. Effect of finite substrate thickness on the effective dielectric constant for $\epsilon_r = 10$ and 120 is shown in Figures 7.6(a) and (b) respectively. These figures show

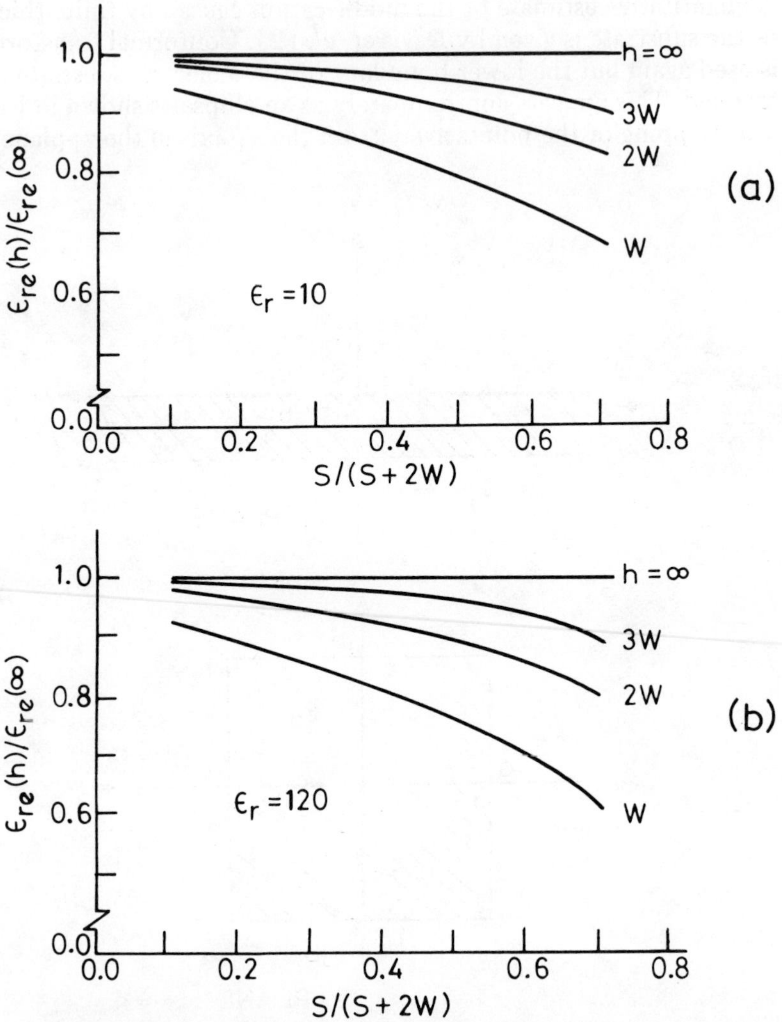

Figure 7.6 Effective Dielectric Constant of CPW for Finite Substrate Thickness (from [2])

that the Wen's analysis holds only for small aspect ratios and for substrate thicknesses greater than twice the slot width. Table 7.1 compares CPW characteristics for various substrate thicknesses (for $\epsilon_r = 10$ and $S/(S+2W) = 0.5$). Factor η represents percentage of energy in the substrate. For $\epsilon_r = 10$ the quasi-static approximation predicts that 91 percent of the energy will be contained in the dielectric.

Table 7.1
Comparison of CPW Characteristics
for Various Thicknesses
(ϵ_r = 10, S/(S+2W) = 0.5)

Parameter	Substrate thickness		
	Infinite	3W	W
V_{cp}	0.43	0.44	0.48
Z_{ocp}	51.4	52.4	57.7
η*	91	89.0	79.0

(*percentage of energy in the dielectric)

Since coplanar strips and coplanar waveguide configurations are complementary to each other, conducting and air-dielectric walls in Figure 7.3(b) get interchanged for CPS analysis. Thus, the capacitance per unit length of the line may be written as

$$C = (\epsilon_r+1)\, \epsilon_o \, \frac{b}{2a} \tag{7.8}$$

and the characteristic impedance becomes

$$Z_{ocs} = \frac{120\pi}{\sqrt{\dfrac{\epsilon_r+1}{2}}} \, \frac{K(k)}{K'(k)} \text{ (ohm)} \tag{7.9}$$

Values of characteristic impedance computed from Equation (7.9) are shown in Figure 7.7.

Finite Difference Method

The characteristics of CPW enclosed in a box, as shown in Figure 7.8, are evaluated by employing the finite difference method. This method has been discussed in Chapter 1.

Calculated results [3] for the characteristic impedance Z_{ocp} and phase velocity ratio v_{cp}/c as functions of $S'/(0.5S+W)$ are shown in Figure 7.9. Here S' is the width of the ground plane, and 2L and H are the width and height of the enclosure, respectively. For these calculations

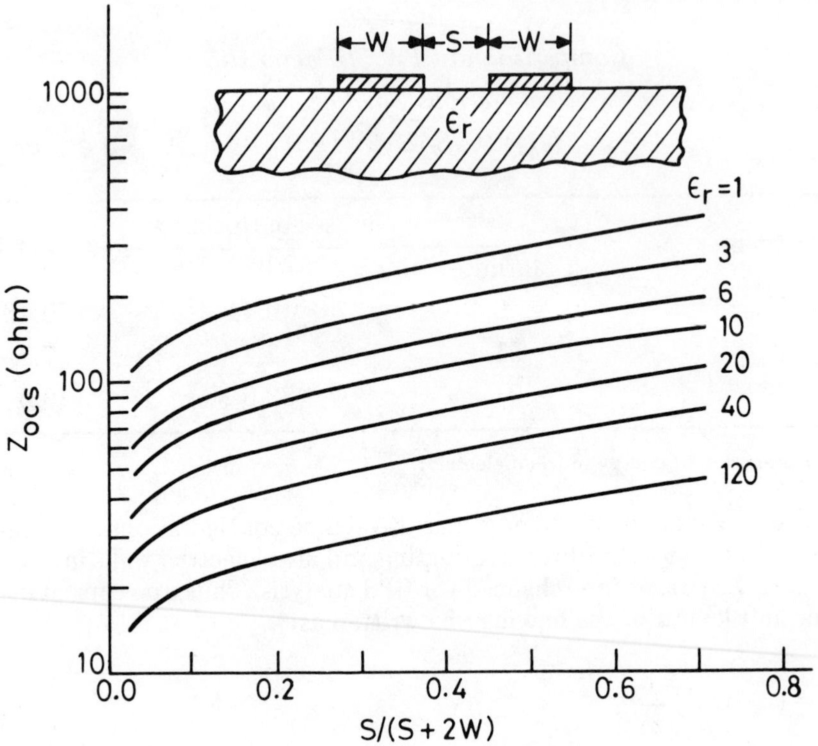

Figure 7.7 Characteristic Impedance of Coplanar Strips (from [1])

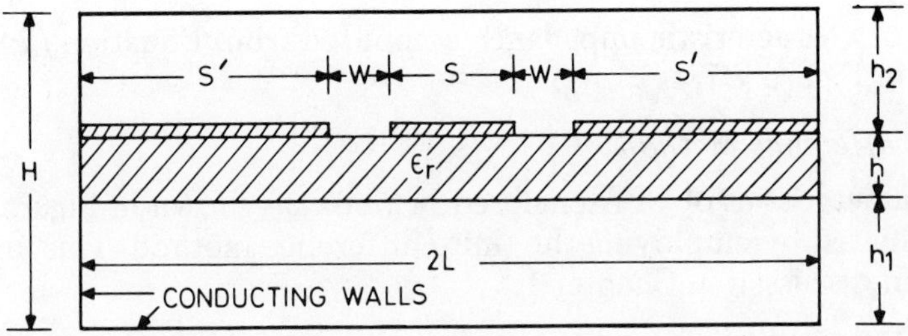

Figure 7.8 Coplanar Waveguide Enclosed in a Box

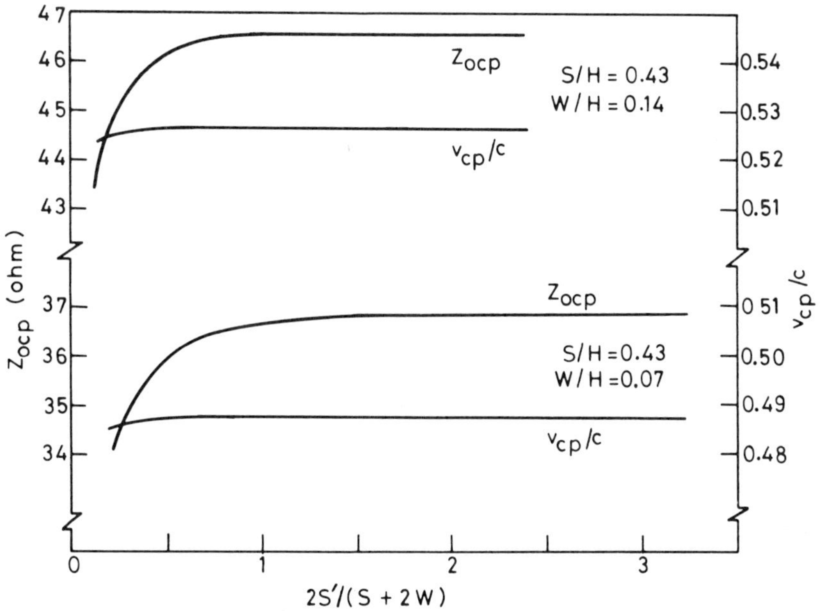

Figure 7.9 Effect of Enclosure on CPW Characteristics (from [3])

H = 4.3 mm, h = 0.61 mm and ϵ_r = 9.4. It may be observed that for wider slot width (W/H = 0.14), Z_{ocp} approaches a constant value asymptotically when the ratio S′/(0.5S+W) is larger than 1.0; for narrower slot width (W/H = 0.07), Z_{ocp} becomes constant when S′/(0.5S+W) is larger than 2.0. The phase velocity ratio v_{cp}/c becomes constant when this ratio is larger than 0.5.

Coplanar strips can also be analyzed by using the finite difference method.

7.2.2 Fullwave Analysis

A rigorous fullwave analysis of CPW has been carried out [4,5] by using Galerkin's method in the spectral domain. The analysis of CPW is identical to the analysis for the odd-mode of coupled slotlines to be discussed later in Chapter 8. It differs from fullwave analysis of a single slotline (Section 5.2) only in respect to the basis functions which now correspond to the physical configuration (Figure 7.1(a)) and field distributions of CPW. The basis functions for electric fields in the present case are written as

$$E_x(x) = \begin{cases} \left[1 - \left(\frac{x-x_o}{W/2}\right)^2\right]^{-1/2} & S/2 \leqslant x \leqslant 0.5S + W \\ -\left[1 - \left(\frac{x+x_o}{W/2}\right)^2\right]^{-1/2} & -(0.5S+W) \leqslant x \leqslant -S/2 \\ 0 & \text{elsewhere} \end{cases} \tag{7.10}$$

$$E_z(x) = \begin{cases} j\frac{x-x_o}{W/2}\left[1 - \left(\frac{x-x_o}{W/2}\right)^2\right]^{1/2} & S/2 \leqslant x \leqslant 0.5S+W \\ -j\frac{x+x_o}{W/2}\left[1 - \left(\frac{x+x_o}{W/2}\right)^2\right]^{1/2} & -(0.5S+W) \leqslant x \leqslant -S/2 \\ 0 & \text{elsewhere} \end{cases} \tag{7.11}$$

where $x_o = (S+W)/2$. The characteristic impedance is calculated using

$$Z_{ocp} = \frac{V_o^2}{2P_{avg}} \tag{7.12}$$

As in case of slotline, P_{avg} is calculated in the spectral domain by the following equation

$$P_{avg} = \frac{1}{4\pi} \text{Re} \int_{-\infty}^{\infty}\int_{-\infty}^{\infty} [\tilde{E}_x(\alpha,y)\tilde{H}_y^*(\alpha,y) - \tilde{E}_y(\alpha,y)\tilde{H}_x^*(\alpha,y)]\,d\alpha\,dy \tag{7.13}$$

where α is the variable in the Fourier transform domain and the superscript ~ denotes the transform of the field.

The details of the method are similar to those used for analyzing microstrip lines (Section 2.2.2) and slotlines (Section 5.2) and will not be discussed here. Results for λ_{cp}/λ_o and Z_{ocp} are shown in Figure 7.10(a) for W/h = 0.25 and ϵ_r = 11.0, and in Figure 7.10(b) for W/h = 0.4 and ϵ_r = 16. A comparison of fullwave results with the quasi-static results [2] is shown in Figure 7.11 for W/h = 1 and ϵ_r = 10 at frequencies of 1, 3 and 5 GHz.

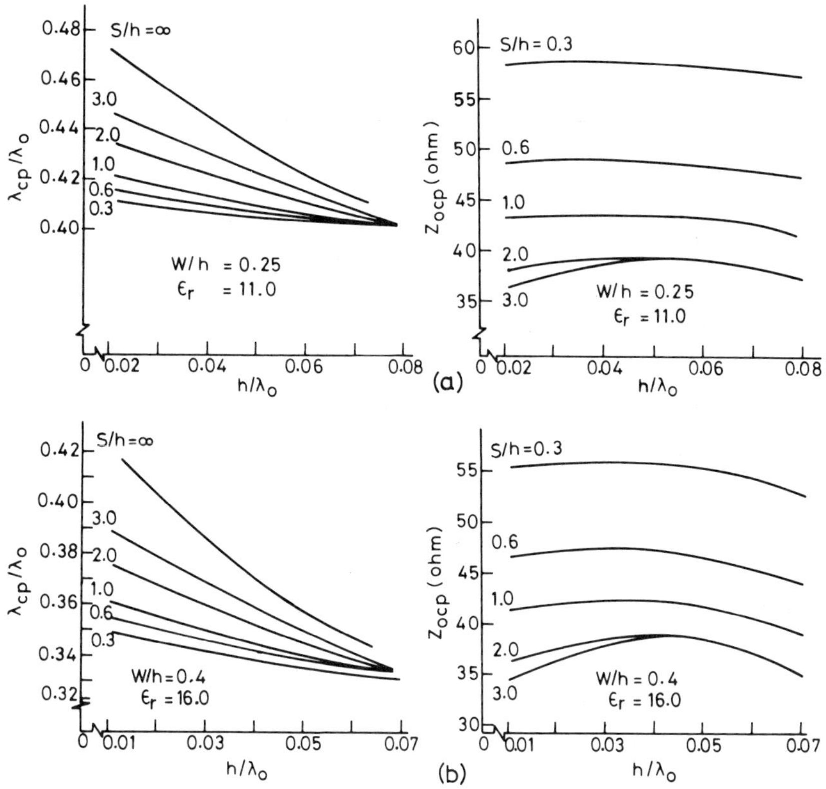

Figure 7.10 Guide Wavelength and Characteristic Impedance of CPW (Based on Fullwave Analysis, from [4])

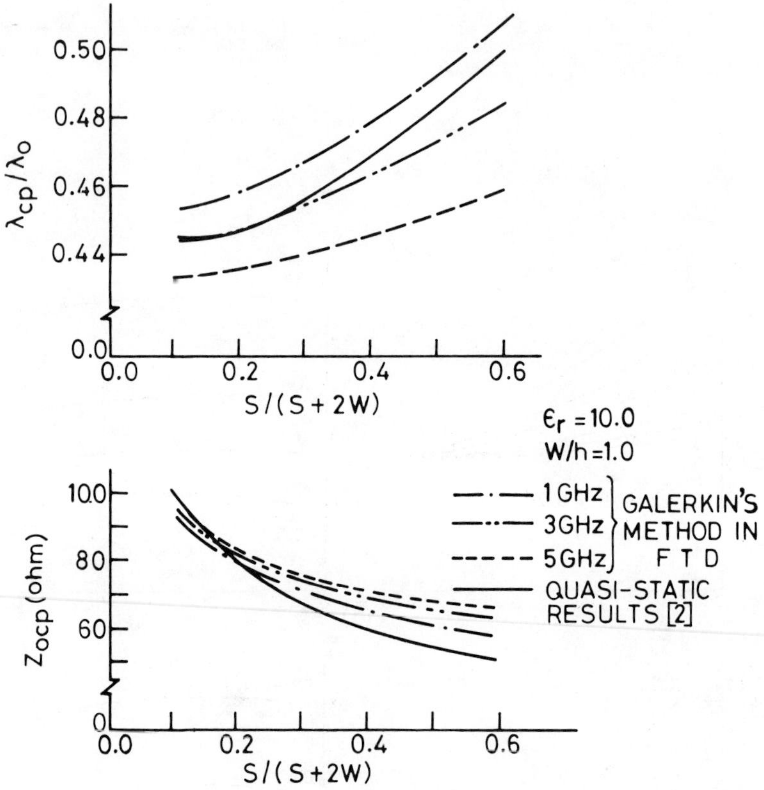

Figure 7.11 Comparison of Fullwave and Quasi-Static Results for CPW (from [4])

Higher order modes on CPW have also been investigated [5] by using the above method of analysis. In the configuration used in this study (Figure 7.8 with top and ground conducting walls removed) the ground planes are finite in the transverse direction and are bounded by perpendicular conducting side walls. The results are presented in Figure 7.12 for $\epsilon_r = 9.6$, S = 0.4 mm, W = 1.3 mm and S′ = 6.0 mm, where S′ is the width of the ground plane. The height of the substrate is 1.0 mm for Figure 7.12(a) and 2.0 mm for Figure 7.12(b). Two higher order waveguide modes are shown in each case. These results show that higher order modes are not present for $h/\lambda_o < 0.05$ and the dispersion is also small for $h/\lambda_o < 0.05$. When h < 1.0 mm the dispersion is very small up to 10 GHz.

The effect of top and bottom conducting walls (Figure 7.8) on the

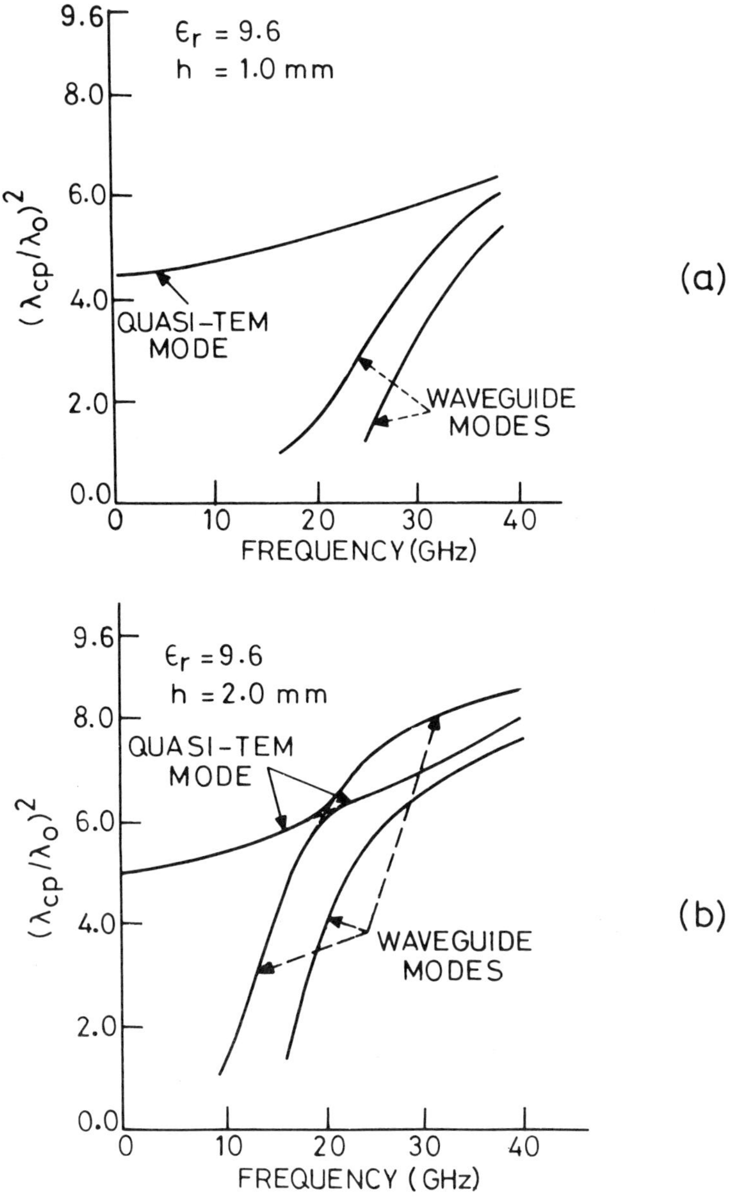

Figure 7.12 Dispersion Curves for Quasi-TEM and Higher Order Modes in CPW (S = 0.4 mm, W = 1.3 mm and S′ = 6.0 mm), (a) h = 1 mm and (b) h = 2 mm (from [5])

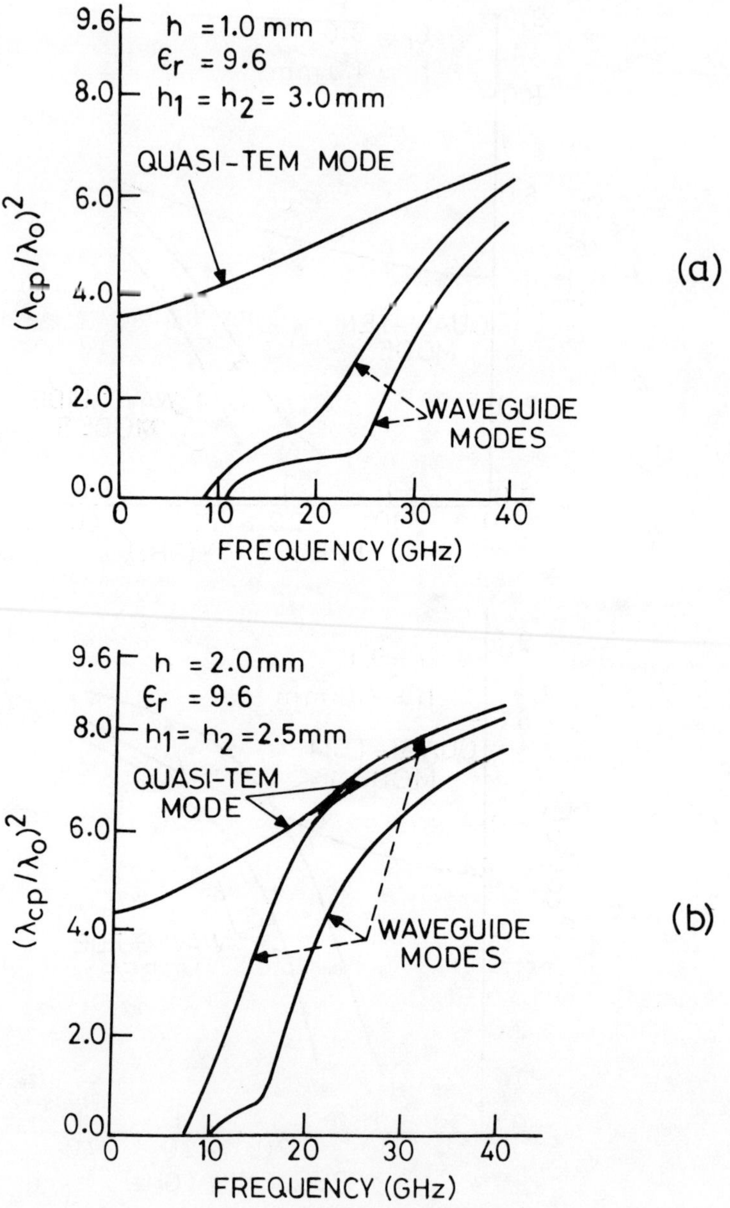

Figure 7.13 Dispersion Curves for Quasi-TEM and Higher Order Modes in Enclosed CPW ($S = 2.0$ mm, $W = 1.0$ mm, $S' = 5.5$ mm), (a) $h = 1$ mm and (b) $h = 2$ mm (from [5])

dispersion characteristics has also been studied. The results are shown in Figure 7.13 for ϵ_r=9.6, S=2.0 mm, W=1.0 mm, S′=5.5 mm and $h_1 = h_2$. For h = 2.0 mm (Figure 7.13(b)), one can observe that mutual interaction occurs between the waveguide and quasi-TEM modes [5].

Fullwave analysis using Galerkin's method in the spectral domain has also been carried out for coplanar strips. In this case, the problem is formulated in terms of surface currents on the strip, and these currents are expressed in terms of basis functions. A first order solution is obtained assuming that the surface current in the x-direction is negligible and the surface current $J_z(x)$ in the z-direction is of the same form [4] as $E_x(x)$ for CPW, that is

$$J_z(x) = \begin{cases} \left[1 - \left(\frac{x-x_o}{W/2}\right)^2\right]^{-1/2} & S/2 \leqslant x \leqslant 0.5S+W \\ -\left[1 - \left(\frac{x+x_o}{W/2}\right)^2\right]^{-1/2} & -(0.5S+W) \leqslant x \leqslant -S/2 \\ 0 & \text{elsewhere} \end{cases} \tag{7.14}$$

In the case of CPS, the characteristic impedance is calculated by evaluating the average power flow in the Fourier transform domain and using the power-current relationship given below:

$$Z_{ocs} = 2\, P_{avg}/I_o^2 \tag{7.15}$$

where I_o is the total current on one strip.

The variations of the guide wavelength ratio λ_{cs}/λ_o and the characteristic impedance Z_{ocs}, with normalized frequency, are shown in Figures 7.14(a) and (b) for ϵ_r = 2.5 and 9.0, respectively. The ratio W/h in these figures is 1.5. Reasonable agreement for the impedances is found by comparing these results for $h/\lambda_o \simeq 0.01$ with the quasi-static results shown in Figure 7.7. However, as one might expect, the present method yields somewhat larger values for the impedance due to the finite thickness of the dielectric substrate.

7.3 DESIGN CONSIDERATIONS

The numerical methods for the characterization of coplanar lines discussed above involve extensive computations. For easy design of coplanar line circuits, closed form design equations are needed.

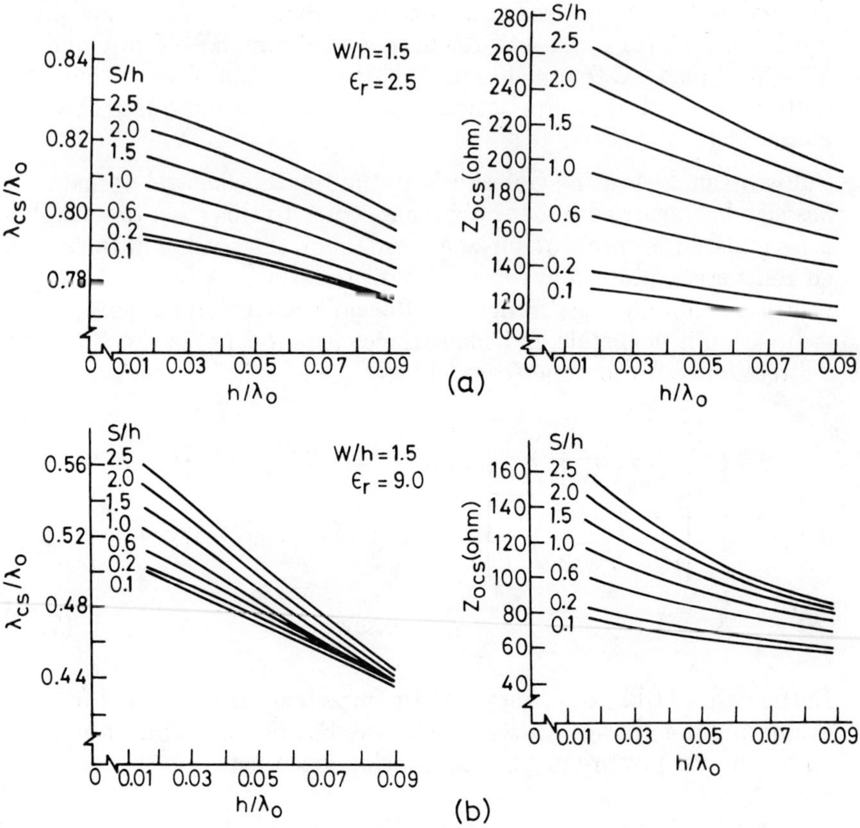

Figure 7.14 Dispersion Characteristics of Coplanar Strips (from [4])

These design equations for CPW and CPS are presented in this section. They include closed form expressions for the characteristic impedance and effective dielectric constant, and their variations with metal strip thickness. Effect of tolerances and expressions for losses are also described.

All the design equations and data presented in this section are based on the quasi-static analysis. Dispersion effects in coplanar lines have been studied in reference [7] and found to be of the same order as for microstrip. Also, the dispersion for low dielectric constant substrates is almost negligible [7]. The results indicate that the quasi-TEM analysis may be used below X-band frequencies.

7.3.1 Design Equations

Closed form expressions for the characteristic impedance and effective dielectric constant for coplanar lines are described below.

Characteristic Impedance and Effective Dielectric Constant

The quasi-static results for CPW due to Wen [1] may be modified as

$$Z_{ocp} = \frac{30\pi}{\sqrt{\epsilon_{re}}} \frac{K'(k)}{K(k)} \tag{7.16}$$

where $k = \dfrac{S}{S+2W}$.

Accurate and simple expressions for the ratio K/K' are available in the literature [8]. These are reproduced below:

$$\frac{K(k)}{K'(k)} = \frac{1}{\pi} \ln \left[2 \frac{1+\sqrt{k}}{1-\sqrt{k}} \right] \text{ for } 0.707 \leqslant k \leqslant 1 \tag{7.17a}$$

$$\frac{K(k)}{K'(k)} = \frac{\pi}{\ln \left[2 \dfrac{1+\sqrt{k'}}{1-\sqrt{k'}} \right]} \text{ for } 0 \leqslant k \leqslant 0.707 \tag{7.17b}$$

Equations (7.17) and therefore Equation (7.16) are accurate to within 3 parts per million.

The numerical results of Davis *et. al.* [2] have been curve fitted to obtain the following closed form expression for ϵ_{re} [9]

$$\epsilon_{re} = \frac{\epsilon_r + 1}{2} \left[\tanh \left\{ 1.785 \log (h/W) + 1.75 \right\} + \frac{kW}{h} \left\{ 0.04 - 0.7\, k + 0.01 (1 - 0.1\, \epsilon_r)(0.25 + k) \right\} \right] \tag{7.18}$$

Accuracy of this expression is better than 1.5 percent for $h/W \geqslant 1$, $\epsilon_r \gtrsim 9$, and $o \leq k \leq 0.7$, when compared with the results of Davis *et al.* [2].

Experimental results of Dupuis and Campbell [10] for Z_{ocp} are compared with the theoretical values, calculated from Equations (7.16) and (7.18), in Figure 7.15. The agreement between the two results is good.

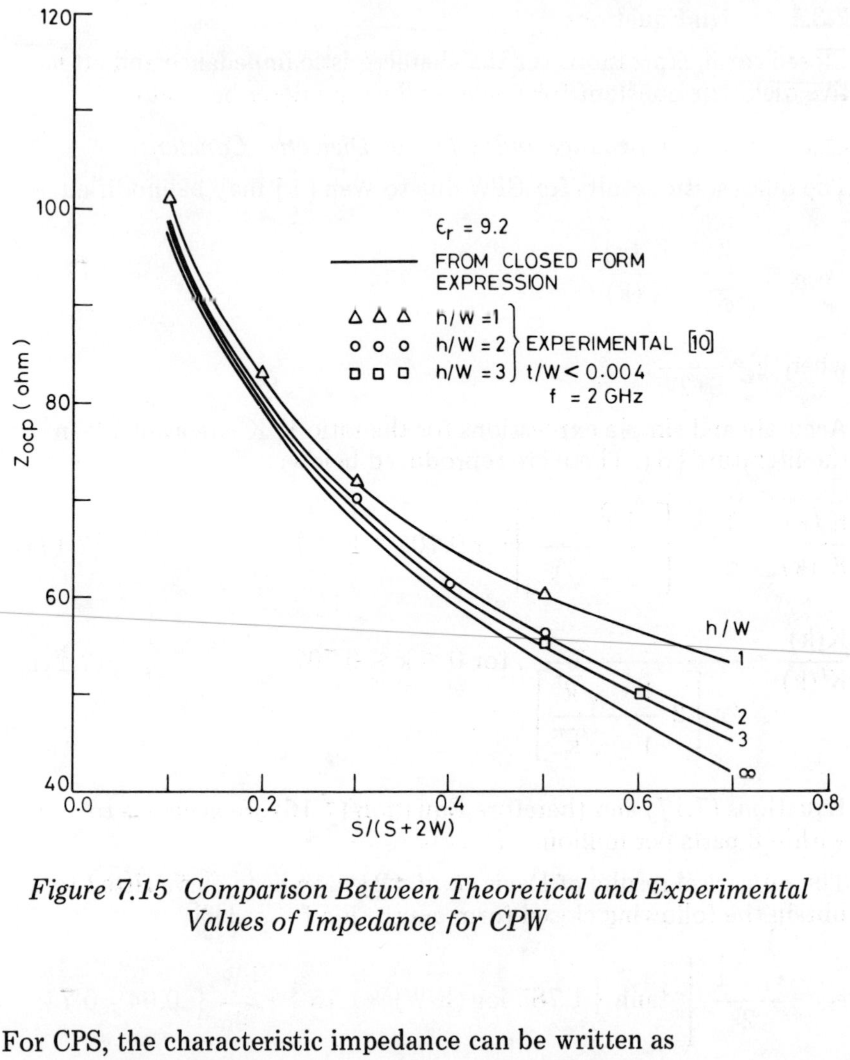

Figure 7.15 Comparison Between Theoretical and Experimental Values of Impedance for CPW

For CPS, the characteristic impedance can be written as

$$Z_{ocs} = \frac{120\pi}{\sqrt{\epsilon_{re}}} \quad \frac{K(k)}{K'(k)} \tag{7.19}$$

where ϵ_{re} is again given by Equation (7.18) in which W is now the strip width and S is the spacing between the strips for CPS. A good agreement is found between the values calculated using the above relation and available results [4]. The variation of Z_{ocs} with aspect ratio for various values of ϵ_r and h/W is shown in Figure 7.16.

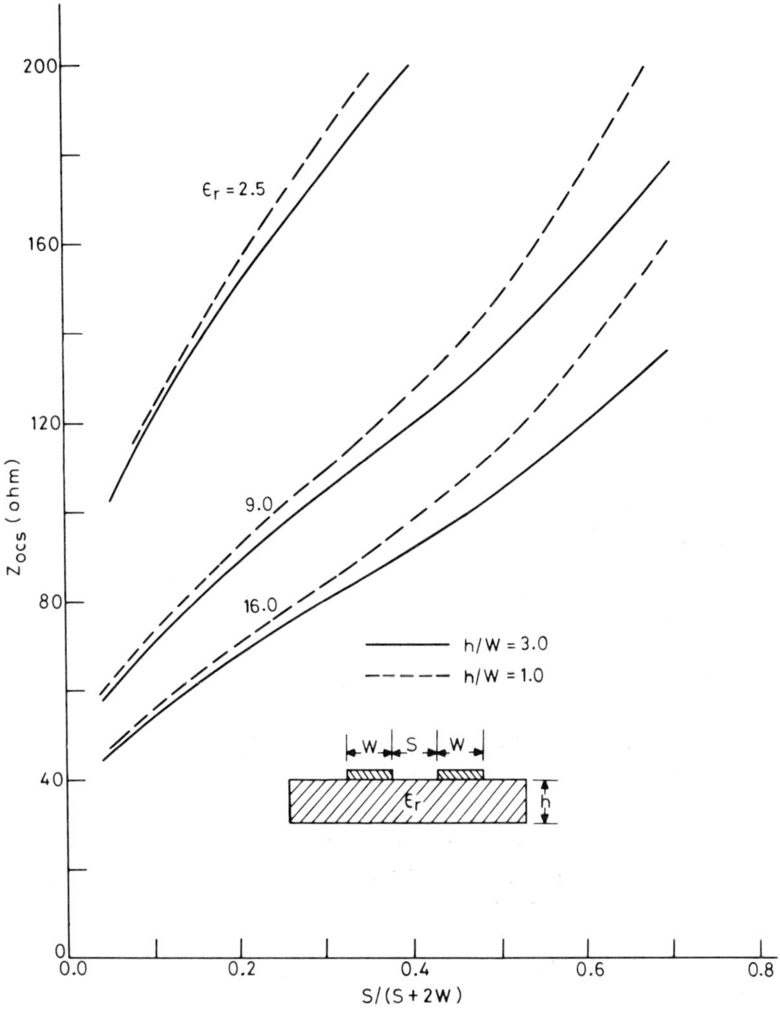

Figure 7.16 Characteristic Impedance of CPS

Effect of Strip Thickness

The results discussed above assume infinitesimally thin metallic strip conductor and ground planes. But in practice, metallization has a finite thickness "t" which affects the characteristics. The effect of strip thickness on impedance of coplanar lines can be taken into account by defining effective values of strip width and spacing. This is similar to the concept of increase in microstrip width W due to thickness t, discussed in Section 2.4.5. For CPW, we can write

$$S_e = S + \Delta$$

and therefore

$$W_e = W - \Delta$$

where

$$\Delta = (1.25t/\pi)\,[1 + \ln(4\pi S/t)]$$

The characteristic impedance is found as

$$Z_{ocp} = \frac{30\pi}{\sqrt{\epsilon_{re}^{t}}}\,\frac{K'(k_e)}{K(k_e)} \tag{7.20}$$

where k_e is the effective aspect ratio given by

$$k_e = S_e/(S_e + 2W_e) \simeq k + (1 - k^2)\,\Delta/2W$$

and ϵ_{re}^{t} is the effective dielectric constant for thick CPW. An expression for ϵ_{re}^{t} is derived by adding a term due to metal thickness to the expression for capacitance of CPW and modifying the subsequent result empirically such that the results agree with numerically evaluated values given in [11] (for $\epsilon_r = 20$ and $t/W \leq 0.1$). The final expression for ϵ_{re}^{t} may be written as

$$\epsilon_{re}^{t} = \epsilon_{re} - \frac{0.7(\epsilon_{re} - 1)\,t/W}{[K(k)/K'(k)] + 0.7t/W} \tag{7.21}$$

Variations of Z_{ocp} and the effective dielectric constant for CPW with aspect ratio for various values of t/W are shown in Figure 7.17. As expected Z_{ocp} and ϵ_{re}^{t} decrease with increasing t/W. The effect of t/W on these characteristics is higher for smaller values of the aspect ratio. These results are in good agreement with those reported by Kitazawa [11].

For coplanar strips, the effect of strip thickness on Z_{ocs} and ϵ_{re} is similar to that in CPW, and the closed form expressions are obtained as

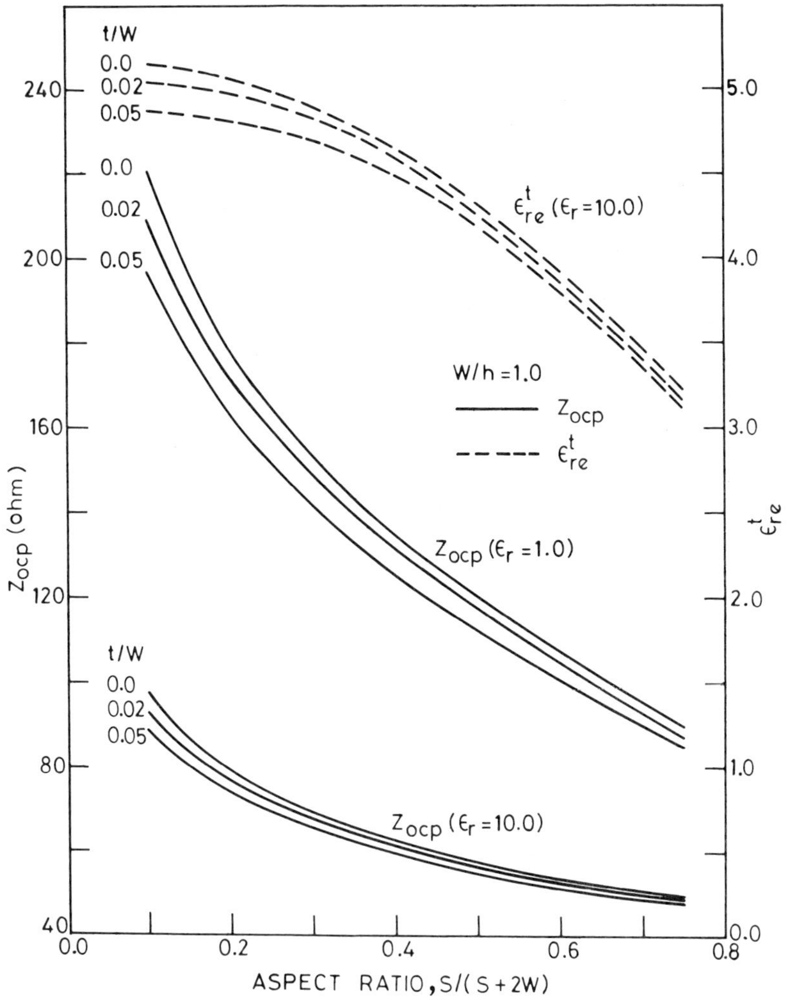

Figure 7.17 Effect of Strip Thickness on CPW Characteristics

$$Z_{ocs} = \frac{120\pi}{\sqrt{\epsilon_{re}^t}} \frac{K(k_e)}{K'(k_e)} \tag{7.22}$$

where $k_e = S_e/(S_e + 2W_e) \simeq k - (1-k^2)\Delta/2W$

and $\Delta = (1.25t/\pi)\ [1 + \ell n(4\pi W/t)]$

The effective dielectric constant for CPS may be written as

$$\epsilon_{re}^{t} = \epsilon_{re} - \frac{1.4(\epsilon_{re} - 1)t/S}{[K'(k)/K(k)] + 1.4t/S}\ ;\ \epsilon_r \gtrsim 9,\ t/W < 0.1 \tag{7.23}$$

7.3.2 Effect of Tolerances

The sensitivity analysis described earlier for microstrip and slotline can also be applied to coplanar lines to evaluate the effect of tolerances. The maximum change in the values of characteristic impedance and effective dielectric constant may be written as

$$\frac{|(\Delta Z_o)|_{max}}{Z_o} = \left|\frac{\Delta W}{W} S_W^{Z_o}\right| + \left|\frac{\Delta S}{S} S_S^{Z_o}\right| + \left|\frac{\Delta h}{h} S_h^{Z_o}\right| + \left|\frac{\Delta \epsilon_r}{\epsilon_r} S_{\epsilon_r}^{Z_o}\right| + \left|\frac{\Delta t}{t} S_t^{Z_o}\right| \tag{7.24}$$

$$\frac{|(\Delta \epsilon_{re})|_{max}}{\epsilon_{re}} = \left|\frac{\Delta W}{W} S_W^{\epsilon_{re}}\right| + \left|\frac{\Delta S}{S} S_S^{\epsilon_{re}}\right| + \left|\frac{\Delta h}{h} S_h^{\epsilon_{re}}\right| + \left|\frac{\Delta \epsilon_r}{\epsilon_r} S_{\epsilon_r}^{\epsilon_{re}}\right| + \left|\frac{\Delta t}{t} S_t^{\epsilon_{re}}\right| \tag{7.25}$$

The sensitivity of Z_o with respect to a parameter y may be evaluated from the sensitivities of Z_o^a and ϵ_{re} using the relation

$$S_y^{Z_o} = S_y^{Z_o^a} - \tfrac{1}{2} S_y^{\epsilon_{re}} \tag{7.26}$$

where Z_o^a (= $Z_o \sqrt{\epsilon_{re}}$) is the characteristic impedance of a coplanar line with air as dielectric.

Expressions for sensitivities of the characteristics of CPW (Z_{ocp}^a and ϵ_{re}) with respect to various parameters (W, S, h, ϵ_r and t) can be calculated using the closed form expressions for Z_{ocp}^a and ϵ_{re} given by Equations (7.16) - (7.18) and the definition of sensitivity given by Equation (2.104) in Chapter 2. The effect of strip thickness ($t/W \leqslant 0.005$) on CPW characteristics is very small and therefore has not been included here. Various sensitivities may thus be written as

$$S_W^{Z_{ocp}^a} = -S_S^{Z_{ocp}^a} = \frac{60\,P}{Z_{ocp}^a}\,\frac{W}{S}\,k^2 \tag{7.27a}$$

where

$k = S/(S+2W)$

$$P = \begin{cases} \dfrac{k}{(1-\sqrt{1-k^2})\,(1-k^2)^{3/4}} & \text{for } 0.0 \leqslant k \leqslant 0.707 \\[2ex] \dfrac{1}{(1-k)\sqrt{k}}\left(\dfrac{K'}{K}\right)^2 & \text{for } 0.707 \leqslant k \leqslant 1.0 \end{cases} \tag{7.27b}$$

Sensitivities with respect to h and ϵ_r ($S_h^{Z_{ocp}^a}$ and $S_{\epsilon_r}^{Z_{ocp}^a}$) are zero since characteristics of CPW with air as dielectric do not depend on h and ϵ_r. Sensitivities of ϵ_{re} with respect to various parameters are as follows

$$S_W^{\epsilon_{re}} = \frac{\epsilon_r+1}{2\epsilon_{re}}\left[k^3\,\frac{W}{h}\left\{1.465\frac{W}{S} - 0.647 - \epsilon_r\left(0.0013 + 0.0015\frac{W}{S}\right)\right\} - 0.775 \cdot \operatorname{sech}^2\left\{1.785\log\left(\frac{h}{W}\right) + 1.75\right\}\right] \tag{7.28a}$$

$$S_S^{\epsilon_{re}} = \frac{\epsilon_r+1}{2\epsilon_{re}}\,\frac{W}{h}\,\frac{W}{S}\,k^2\left[0.085 - 0.0005\,\epsilon_r - k\left\{2.8 - 0.04\,(1-0.1\,\epsilon_r)\right\}\right] \tag{7.28b}$$

$$S_h^{\epsilon_{re}} = -S_W^{\epsilon_{re}} - S_S^{\epsilon_{re}} \tag{7.28c}$$

$$S_{\epsilon_r}^{\epsilon_{re}} = \frac{\epsilon_r}{2\epsilon_{re}}\left[\tanh\left\{1.785\log\left(\frac{h}{W}\right) + 1.75\right\} + \frac{kW}{h}\left\{0.04 - 0.7k + 0.01 \cdot (1-0.1\,\epsilon_r)\,(0.25+k)\right\} - 0.001\,\frac{\epsilon_r+1}{2}\,\frac{kW}{h}\,(0.25+k)\right] \tag{7.28d}$$

The sensitivities of characteristic impedance and effective dielectric constant of coplanar waveguide with respect to various parameters are plotted in Figures 7.18 and 7.19, respectively. From Figure 7.18 it may be noted that sensitivities of Z_{ocp} with respect to W and h increase when h/W is decreased. A similar observation can be made for sensitivities of ϵ_{re} with respect to h, W and S. Thus the effect of fabrication tolerances is small when thick substrates are used. When h/W = 1.0, ϵ_{re} is very much sensitive to variations in h. For h/W $\geqslant$ 1, the sensitivities of ϵ_{re}, and therefore of Z_{ocp}, with respect to ϵ_r are independent of h/W ratio and also the aspect ratio. The values of these two sensitivities are –0.45 and 0.9, respectively, for ϵ_r = 10.

The sensitivity values thus obtained are used in Equation (7.24) to determine the maximum change in Z_{ocp}. From $(\Delta Z_{ocp})_{max}$ the value of VSWR, when measured along an ideal line connected at the input, is obtained using the relation

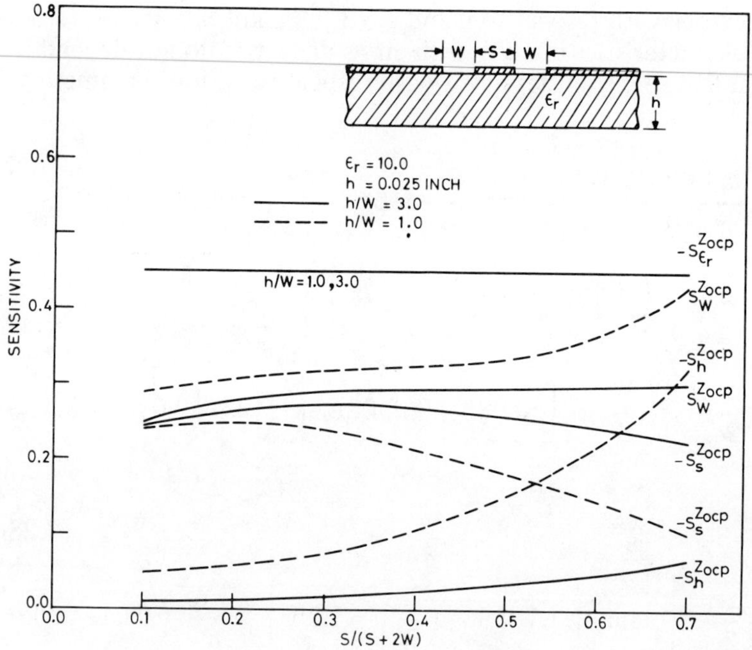

Figure 7.18 Sensitivities of Characteristic Impedance of CPW With Respect to Various Parameters

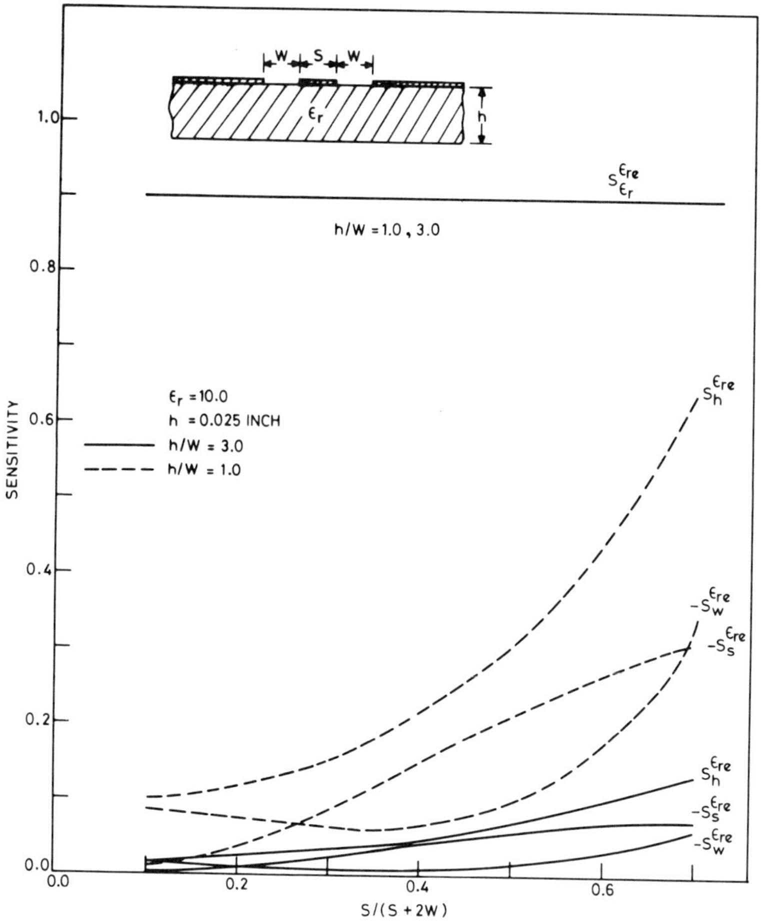

Figure 7.19 Sensitivities of Effective Dielectric Constant of CPW With Respect to Various Parameters

$$\text{VSWR}_{max} = \left[1 - \frac{|\Delta Z_{ocp}|_{max}}{Z_{ocp}}\right]^{-1} \tag{7.29}$$

The VSWR values are plotted in Figure 7.20 for the set of tolerances mentioned therein. Variation of $(\Delta\epsilon_{re})_{max}/\epsilon_{re}$ is also shown in this figure. It may be noted that VSWR values are comparable with the corresponding results for microstrip lines (Figure 2.16) and slotlines (Figure 5.17) while results for $\Delta\epsilon_{re}/\epsilon_{re}$ are slightly worse.

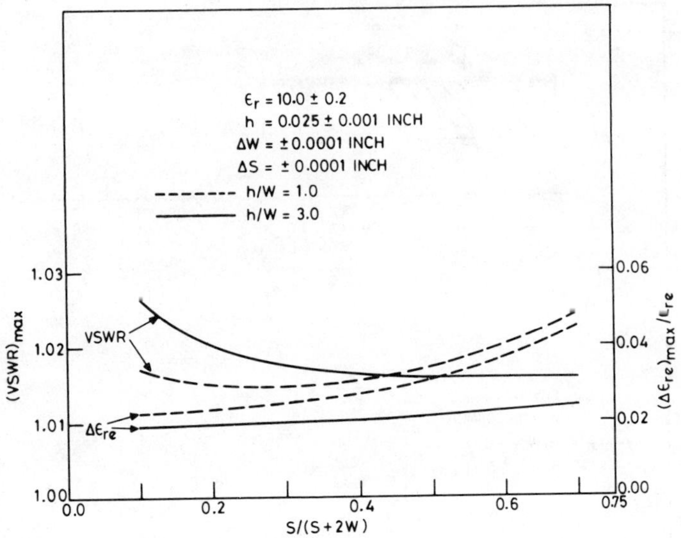

Figure 7.20 Effect of Tolerances on the Change in CPW Characteristics

For coplanar strips, the sensitivities of impedance with air as dielectric (Z^a_{ocs}) with respect to S and W parameters are given as follows:

$$S_W^{Z^a_{ocs}} = -S_S^{Z^a_{ocs}} = -\frac{120k\,(1-k)\,P'}{Z^a_{ocs}} \tag{7.30a}$$

where

$$P' = \left(\frac{K}{K'}\right)^2 P \tag{7.30b}$$

P has been defined earlier in Equation (7.27b).

As for CPW, the sensitivities with respect to h and ϵ_r are zero in this case also. Expressions for sensitivities of ϵ_{re} with respect to various parameters (W, S, h and ϵ_r) are the same as those described for CPW because the expressions for ϵ_{re} are identical in both cases. The sensitivities of coplanar strips impedance with respect to W and S are plotted in Figure 7.21. It may be noted that Z_{ocs} is less sensitive to variation in W as compared to variation in S.

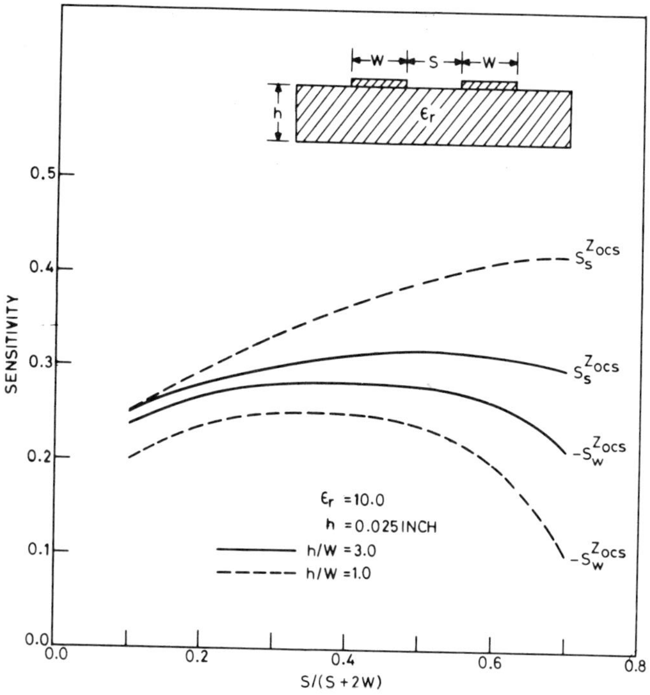

Figure 7.21 Sensitivities of Characteristic Impedance of CPS With Respect to Various Parameters

7.3.3 Losses

Like any other transmission line, coplanar lines also have two types of losses: ohmic and dielectric. When quasi-static approximation is valid, one can use Wheeler's incremental inductance formula for evaluating ohmic losses. This formula has been discussed in Chapter 2. Various recessions (δn) considered in CPW configuration (inset in Figure 7.22) are as follows:

$\delta n = -\delta S$ (recession of either edge of strip conductor)

$\delta n = \ \delta W$ (recession of either edge of strip conductor or edge of ground conductor)

$\delta n = -\delta t$ (recession of top or bottom of conductor)

After taking into account recessions in all the conductor walls, the

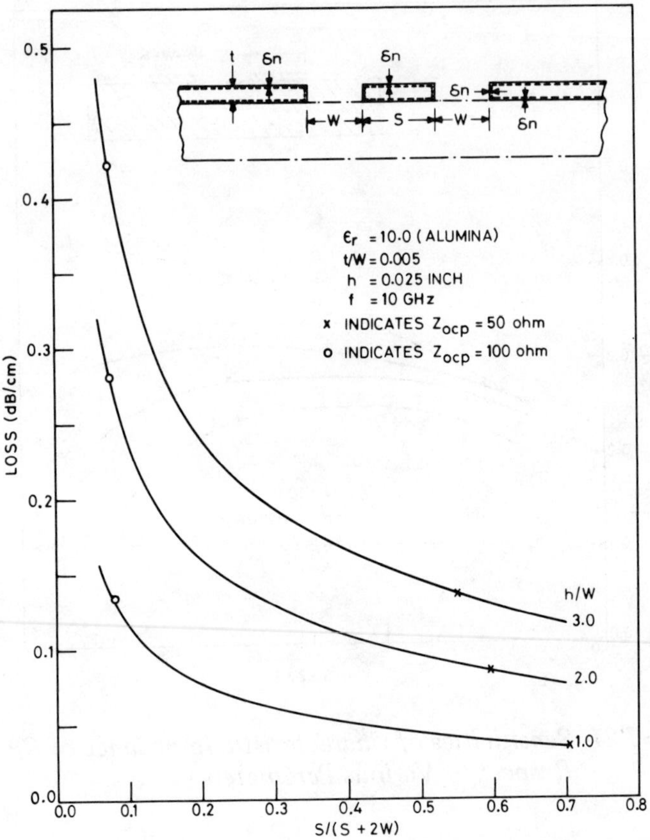

Figure 7.22 Attenuation Coefficient for CPW on Alumina Substrate

expression for the attenuation constant due to ohmic losses may be written as

$$\alpha_c^{cw} = 0.023 \frac{R_s}{Z_{ocp}} \left[\frac{\partial Z_{ocp}^a}{\partial W} - \frac{\partial Z_{ocp}^a}{\partial S} - \frac{\partial Z_{ocp}^a}{\partial t} \right] \text{ dB/unit length} \tag{7.31}$$

where superscript cw denotes coplanar waveguide. Z_{ocp}^a is the characteristic impedance of CPW with air as dielectric and R_s is the surface resistivity of the conductors. After substituting various partial derivatives in Equation (7.31) the final expression for conductor loss may be written as [9]

$$\alpha_c^{cw} = 4.88 \times 10^{-4}\, R_s\, \epsilon_{re}\, Z_{ocp}\, \frac{P'}{\pi W} \cdot \left(1 + \frac{S}{W}\right) \cdot$$

$$\left\{ \frac{\frac{1.25}{\pi}\, \ell n \frac{4\pi S}{t} + 1 + \frac{1.25t}{\pi S}}{\left[2 + \frac{S}{W} - \frac{1.25t}{\pi W}\left(1 + \ell n \frac{4\pi S}{t}\right)\right]^2} \right\} \text{dB/unit length} \qquad (7.32)$$

where P′ is given by Equation (7.30b).

The expression for the attenuation constant due to dielectric loss in CPW is the same as that for microstrip. This has been discussed in Chapter 2, Equation (2.86), and is reproduced below:

$$\alpha_d = 27.3\, \frac{\epsilon_r}{\sqrt{\epsilon_{re}}}\, \frac{\epsilon_{re} - 1}{\epsilon_r - 1}\, \frac{\tan\delta}{\lambda_o} \quad \text{dB/unit length} \qquad (7.33)$$

In the present case, ϵ_{re} is given by Equation (7.18).

The variation of total loss ($\alpha_c^{cw} + \alpha_d$) for coplanar waveguide on alumina substrate of thickness 0.025 inch as a function of aspect ratio is plotted in Figure 7.22. It is observed that loss decreases with decreasing impedance or increasing strip width S.

Losses in coplanar waveguide have also been reported in [12]. This is also a quasi-static analysis with potential distribution computed by an equivalent source method. For large values of W, the agreement between the calculated values for loss (using Equation 7.32) and the corresponding computed values [12] is reasonably good. But for small values of W, results for loss reported by Spielman [12] are higher than the calculated values using Equation (7.32). One of the reasons mentioned for the higher value of computed loss is the discretization of charge density distribution, employed in [12], which could be viewed as a "surface roughness." Equation (7.32), based on the effective width concept, is expected to yield less accurate results for small values of W because the effective increase in width Δ should be a function of gap width W also. Consequently, the error will increase with a decrease in the value of W.

For coplanar strips, the expression for conductor loss becomes:

$$\alpha_c^{cs} = 17.34 \frac{R_s}{Z_{ocs}} \cdot \frac{P'}{\pi S} \cdot \left(1 + \frac{W}{S}\right) \cdot$$

$$\left\{ \frac{\frac{1.25}{\pi} \ln \frac{4\pi W}{t} + 1 + \frac{1.25t}{\pi W}}{\left[1 + 2\frac{W}{S} + \frac{1.25t}{\pi S}\left(1 + \ln \frac{4\pi W}{t}\right)\right]^2} \right\} \text{dB/unit length} \quad (7.34)$$

where P′ is again given by Equation (7.30b).

The expression for dielectric loss is same as given by Equation (7.32). The variation of total loss ($\alpha_c^{cs} + \alpha_d$) for CPS on alumina substrate of thickness 0.025 inch as a function of aspect ratio is shown in Figure 7.23. It may be noted that the loss in the case of CPS is about the same as for CPW for aspect ratios greater than 0.2.

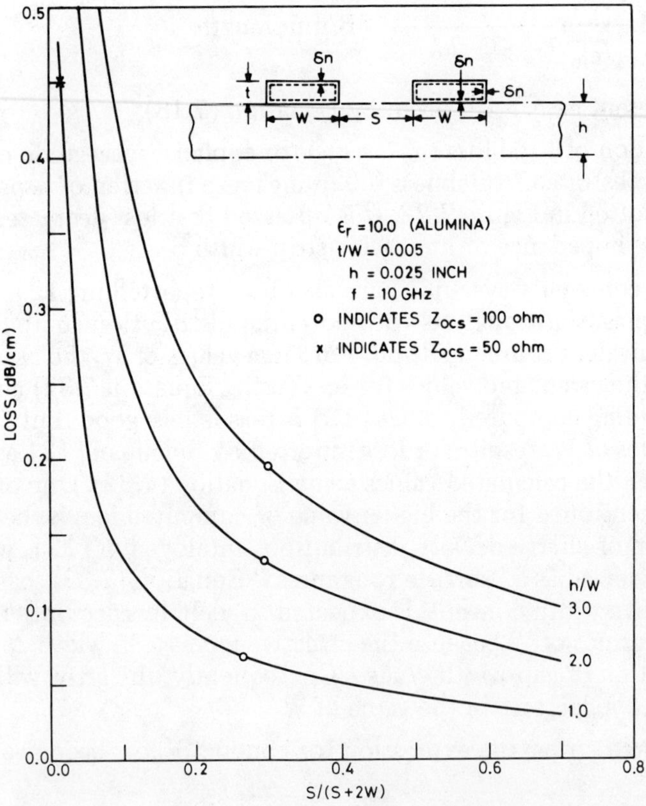

Figure 7.23 Attenuation Coefficient for CPS on Alumina Substrate

7.4 COPLANAR LINE CIRCUITS

Several circuits using CPW have been reported but CPS circuits have not been popular so far. Various circuit applications of CPW can be grouped as follows:

- Circuits with series and shunt reactances in CPW,
- Circuits using slotline-CPW junctions, and
- Circuits using coupled CPWs

7.4.1 Circuits with Series and Shunt Reactances in CPW

The first group of CPW circuits uses the flexibility of the coplanar waveguide configuration to accommodate both the series and the shunt connected components. Various circuit elements that may be realized in CPW configuration [13] are shown in Figures 7.24, 7.25 and 7.26. While calculating line lengths it should be remembered that the propagation velocities are not equal for different impedance sections.

Figure 7.24 represents realization of series connected inductances

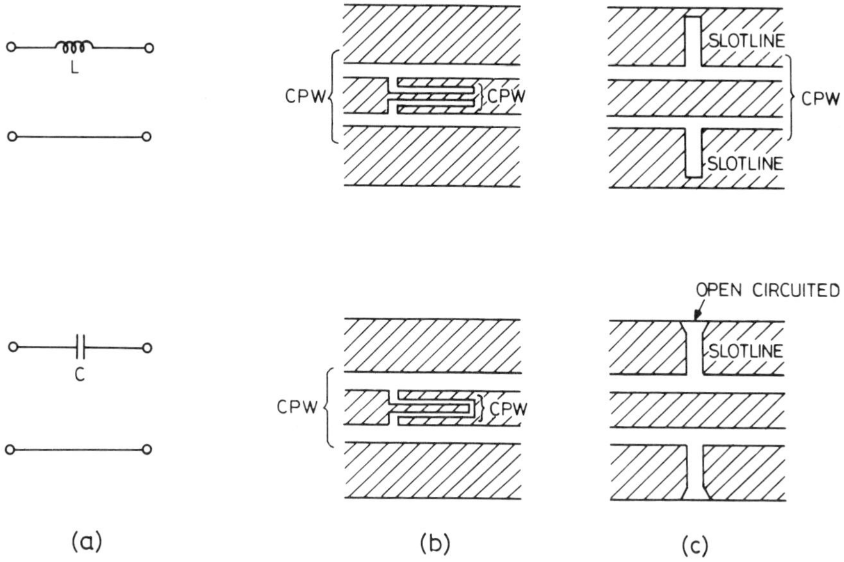

Figure 7.24 Series Circuit Elements in CPW Configuration

(a) Circuit Element

(b) Realization Using CPWs and

(c) Realization Using CPW and Slotline

and capacitances. Circuit representations in Figure 7.24(b) use another coplanar waveguide configuration inside the central strip of the main CPW. The basic idea is borrowed from similar coaxial line circuits [14]. The series inductance is obtained by a CPW section (smaller than $\lambda_{cp}/4$) shorted at the far end, whereas the series capacitance is realized by a CPW section (again smaller than $\lambda_{cp}/4$) open at the far end.

Use of slotline sections, as shown in Figure 7.24(c), is another way of obtaining series connected elements. Short-circuited slotlines are used for inductances and open-circuited slotlines for capacitances.

Figure 7.25 represents a realization of shunt connected reactances

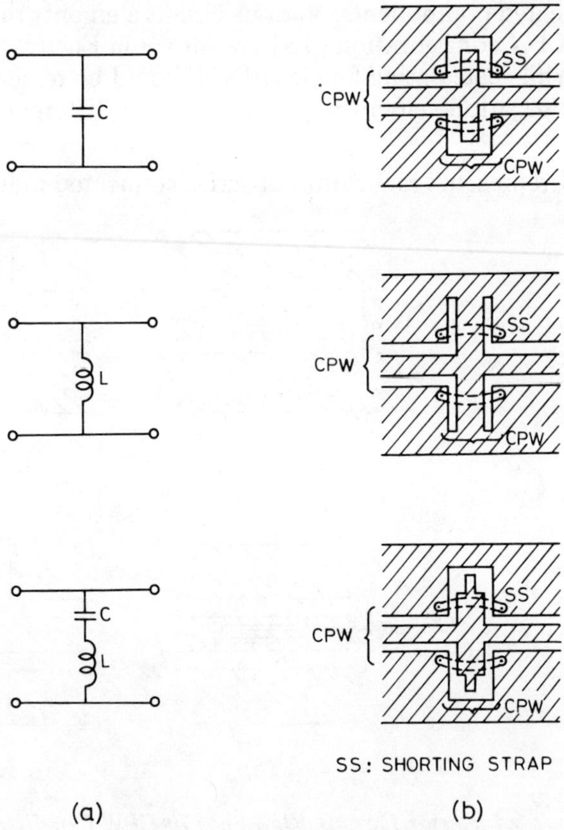

Figure 7.25 Shunt Circuit Elements in CPW Configuration

(a) Circuit Element and

(b) Realization Using CPWs

obtained by adding coplanar waveguide stubs to the main CPW. Open circuited stubs are used for capacitance and short circuited stubs for inductance. Conducting straps are bonded at the junction of the main line and the stubs to ensure that the two ground planes of the CPW stubs are at the same potential. A shunt mounted series-resonant circuit can be realized by using stubs comprising two CPWs of different impedances. An open-circuit high impedance section provides the capacitance, whereas the low impedance section provides inductance. This shunt mounted series-resonant circuit is useful for designing stop-band filters.

It is also possible to realize pi or tee shaped reactance networks by using CPW stubs. Figure 7.26(a) shows a shorted CPW stub without

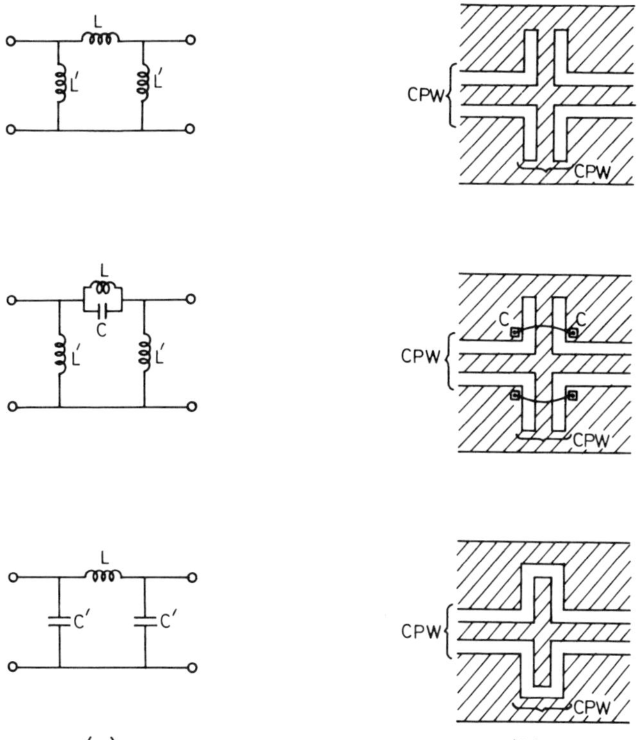

(a) (b)

Figure 7.26 Series and Shunt Circuit Elements in CPW Configuration

(a) Circuit Element and

(b) Realization Using CPWs

any strap to equalize the potentials of the two ground planes of the stub. Thus the stub can support two types of modes: normal CPW mode and the even mode of coupled slotline. The latter mode presents an inductance L that appears in series with the main line. When the straps are added this even mode of coupled slotlines can not exist (that is, the inductance L gets shorted) and the equivalent circuit reduces to that shown in Figure 7.25(b). An external capacitance C can be connected in parallel to the series inductance L by bonding chip capacitors across the stubs as shown in Figure 7.26(b). This provides a useful circuit element for filter circuits. A pi-network having shunt capacitances can be realized by using an open circuited stub without the shorting strap. One could use chip capacitors to provide a capacitance parallel to L in this case also.

A schematic diagram of the Schottky diode detector and the CPW equivalent are shown in Figures 7.27(a) and 7.27(b), respectively.

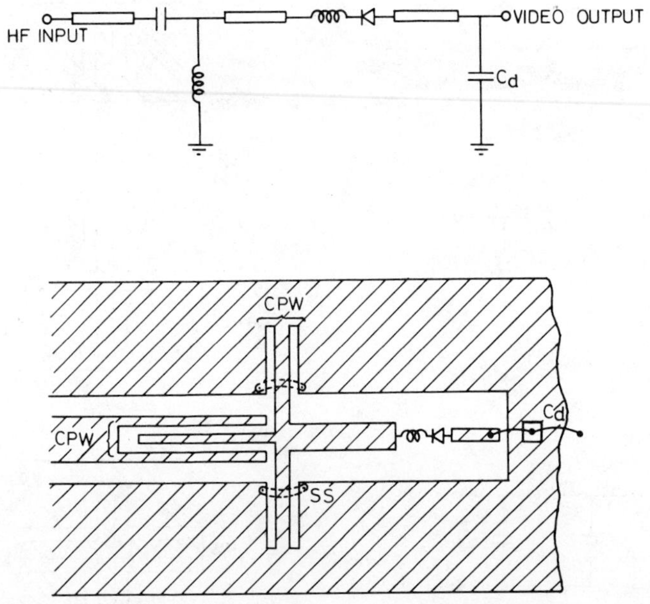

Figure 7.27 Coplanar Waveguide Detector (from [13])

The circuit uses series and shunt reactances realized by using CPW sections as discussed above. This detector circuit has a VSWR less than 2.0 and a tangential sensitivity less than –52 dBm in the 2 to 4.5 GHz band [13].

7.4.2 Circuits Using Slotline-CPW junctions

This group consists of circuits such as balanced mixers and balanced frequency multipliers [15-19]. A CPW can propagate a signal in two modes: an unbalanced signal in the odd mode of coupled slotlines and a balanced signal in the even mode of coupled slotlines. The impedance levels for these two modes (balanced and unbalanced) are different. A slotline to CPW junction shown in Figure 7.28(a) excites

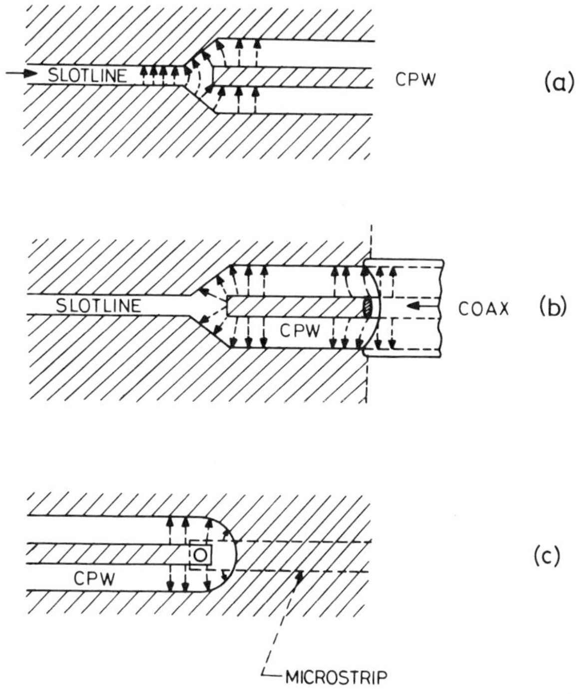

Figure 7.28(a) Excitation of a Balanced Mode in CPW by a Slotline

(b) An Unbalanced Mode in CPW Excited by a Coaxial Line

(c) An Unbalanced Mode in CPW Excited by a Microstrip

a balanced signal in CPW. On the other hand, when a CPW is fed from a coaxial line (Figure 7.28(b)) or through a microstrip (Figure 7.28(c)), an unbalanced signal is launched on CPW. Therefore, a microstrip-CPW-slotline (or a coax-CPW-slotline) combination may be used in circuits where both the balanced and the unbalanced signals are employed. Such circuits are balanced mixers, double balanced mixers, balanced modulators, balanced frequency multipliers, etc.

An arrangement for a double balanced mixer using CPW is shown in Figure 7.29 [16]. This circuit uses a balanced local oscillator input

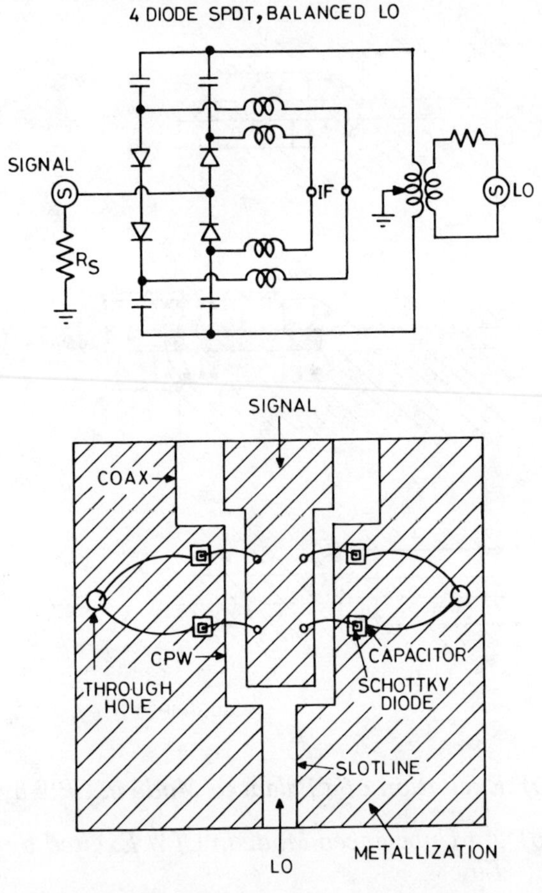

Figure 7.29 A Circuit Arrangement for a Double Balanced Mixer Using CPW (from [16])

and an unbalanced signal input. Local oscillator voltage is applied via the slotline and the signal is fed through the coaxial line. This circuit has been designed for the 1 to 4 GHz frequency range and uses chrome-gold metallization on one side of a 0.080 inch thick sheet of magnesium titanate dielectric ($\epsilon_r = 16$). The sheet is suspended in the center of a metal box. Connection to the slotline is made by a small copper coaxial cable at right angles to the axis while a coaxial connection to the CPW is made directly along the axis. The unbalanced signal from the CPW cannot propagate past the CPW-slot junction. Also, the balanced signal from the slotline can propagate only up to the coaxial connection point where it faces a short circuit. Four beam-lead Schottky diodes are connected across the CPW as shown. The filter capacitors are the silicon dioxide type, which also serve as bonding pads for the tiny beam-lead diodes. The IF connecting wires are brought through holes in the substrate to the filter inductors located below. This circuit has demonstrated a frequency range capability of 6:1 with 6.5 to 7.0 dB conversion loss (with 10 mW incident LO power). Another mixer circuit using a slotline-CPW junction is described by Dickens and Maki [19].

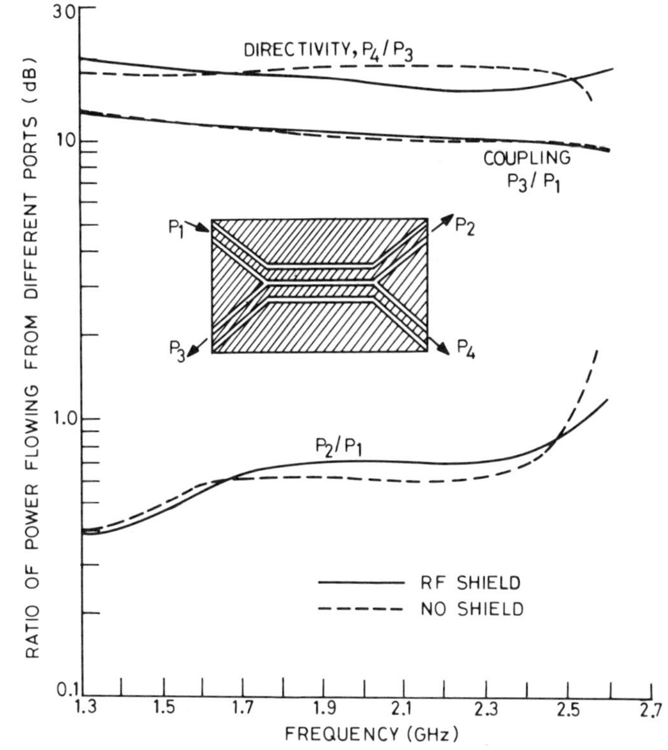

Figure 7.30 Performance of a 10-dB Coplanar Waveguide Directional Coupler as a Function of Frequency (from [20])

7.4.3 Circuits Using Coupled CPWs

Like coupled microstrip lines, coupled coplanar lines can also be used as directional couplers. Analysis of coupled CPWs is given later in Chapter 8. For coupled CPWs, fractions of the field in the air region are about equal for the even and the odd modes. This makes the difference in the even and odd mode velocities smaller than that in the case of microstrip. Experimental results for a directional coupler using coupled CPWs have been reported by Wen [20]. These are shown in Figure 7.30 for a 10 dB directional coupler. The coupling coefficient varies from 11 to 9.6 dB between 1.7 and 2.5 GHz while the directivity is above 17 dB. Over this frequency range the insertion loss is less than 1 dB and VSWR measured at any port is better than 1.1. For this coupler the difference in even and odd mode velocities is about 5 percent (calculated from 17 dB directivity) whereas the corresponding value for a similar microstrip coupler is about 17 percent.

7.5 COMPARISON WITH MICROSTRIP LINES AND SLOTLINES

Four types of planar transmission lines suitable for microwave integrated circuits have been discussed in various chapters so far. These are microstrip line, slotline, coplanar waveguide and coplanar strips. In this section characteristics of these are compared. Various features considered include the range of impedance achievable, losses, effect of tolerances, etc.

7.5.1 Range of Impedance

The range of characteristic impedance that can be practically realized with any particular transmission line is limited by two factors. Technological processes such as photoetching limit the minimum strip width and the spacing between two adjacent strips. For comparison this minimum dimension has been taken as 2 mil (although smaller dimensions are possible with careful processing). The other limitation comes from the possibility of excitation of higher order modes. To avoid the excitation of higher order modes, the substrate thickness and the lateral dimensions should be kept below a quarter wavelength. The impedance limits calculated in this manner are shown in Table 7.2 for four types of lines. In this table the letter "m" in the parentheses indicates that the limit is caused by higher order modes, and the letter "d" indicates that the limit is due to small dimensions.

Table 7.2 Comparison of Z_o limits
(ϵ_r = 10.0, h = 25 mil and frequency = 10 GHz)

Transmission Line	Lower limit for Z_o (ohm)	Upper limit for Z_o (ohm)
Microstrip	20 (m)	110 (d)
Slotline	55 (d)	300 (m)
Coplanar waveguide	25 (m, d)	155 (m, d)
Coplanar strips	45 (m, d)	280 (m, d)

This comparison indicates that microstrip lines are capable of providing low impedance whereas slotlines and coplanar strips may be used for very high impedances.

7.5.2 Losses

Attenuation constant is another important characteristic for these lines. The values of total loss (in dB/cm) at 10 GHz for various lines are compared in Table 7.3. Losses for microstrip, coplanar waveguide and coplanar strip have been calculated from quasi-static considerations. Because of the enhanced non-TEM nature of slotline, this method cannot be used there. Available experimental values for slotline losses [21] are included in the table.

Table 7.3 Comparison of loss for
various lines (ϵ_r = 10.0, h = 25 mil
and frequency = 10 GHz)

Transmission line	Loss (dB/cm)	
	50 ohm	100 ohm
Microstrip	0.04	0.14
Slotline	0.15*	—
Coplanar waveguide (h/W=2)	0.08	0.28
Coplanar strips (h/W=2)	0.83	0.13

*ϵ_r = 16, Z_o = 75 ohm.

For 50 ohm lines, the microstrip has the lowest loss. However, variation of loss with impedance is different for different lines, and for 100 ohm lines coplanar strips have a loss slightly lower than that of the microstrip.

7.5.3 Effect of Tolerances

As discussed earlier, impedance variations caused by tolerances are expressed in terms of the maximum value of VSWR presented to an ideal line connected at the input. The effects of tolerances on the impedance and effective dielectric constant for the four types of lines are compared in Table 7.4. For this comparison, the fabrication accuracy of strip width or gap width has been assumed to be 0.1 mil. The assumed tolerances in h and ϵ_r correspond to a commercially available alumina substrate. Table shows that CPW impedance is less sensitive to variations in parameters as compared to other lines.

Table 7.4 Comparison of effect of tolerances on various lines

($\epsilon_r = 10.0 \pm 0.2$, $h = 25 \pm 1$ mil, $\Delta W = \Delta S = 0.1$ mil and $Z_o = 50$ ohm)

Transmission line	Max. VSWR	Max. $\lvert \Delta\epsilon_{re}/\epsilon_{re} \rvert$
Microstrip ($W/h = 1.0$)	1.038	0.029
Slotline ($h/\lambda_o = 0.04$)	1.036	0.028
Coplanar waveguide ($h/W = 3.0$)	1.016	0.024
Coplanar strips ($h/W = 3.0$)	1.08	0.019

7.5.4 Other Parameters

Several other parameters of the four types of lines are compared qualitatively in Table 7.5. It can be generally seen that CPW and CPS combine some advantageous features of microstrip lines and slotlines.

Their power handling capabilities, radiation losses, Q-factors and dispersion behavior lie in between the corresponding values for microstrip and slotline. Perhaps the best feature of the two coplanar lines is the ease of mounting components in series and shunt configurations, whereas microstrip lines are convenient only for series mounting and slotlines can accommodate only shunt-mounted components.

Table 7.5 Qualitative comparison of various MIC lines

Characteristic	Microstrip	Slotline	Coplanar waveguide	Coplanar strips
Effective dielectric constant ($\epsilon_r = 10$ and h = 0.025 inch)	~6.5	~4.5	~5	~5
Power handling capability	High	Low	Medium	Medium
Radiation loss	Low	High	Medium	Medium
Unloaded Q	High	Low	Medium	Low (lower impedances) High (higher impedances)
Dispersion	Small	Large	Medium	Medium
Mounting of components:				
in shunt configuration	Difficult	Easy	Easy	Easy
in series configuration	Easy	Difficult	Easy	Easy
Technological difficulties	Ceramic holes Edge plating	Double side etching	—	—
Elliptically polarized magnetic field configuration	Not available	Available	Available	Available
Enclosure dimensions	Small	Large	Large	Large

REFERENCES

[1] Wen, C.P., "Coplanar Waveguide: A Surface Strip Transmission Line Suitable for Non-Reciprocal Gyromagnetic Device Application," *IEEE Trans., Vol. MTT-17,* 1969, pp. 1087-1090.

[2] Davis, M.E., *et. al.*, "Finite-Boundary Corrections to the Coplanar Waveguide Analysis," *IEEE Trans., Vol. MTT-21*, 1973, pp. 594-596.

[3] Hatsuda, T., "Computation of Coplanar-Type Strip Line Characteristics by Relaxation Method and its Applications to Microwave Circuits," *IEEE Trans., Vol. MTT-23,* 1975, pp. 795-802.

[4] Knorr, J.B., and K.D. Kuchler, "Analysis of Coupled Slots and Coplanar Strips on Dielectric Substrate," *IEEE Trans., Vol. MTT-23,* 1975, pp. 541-548.

[5] Fujiki, Y., *et. al.*, "Higher-Order Modes in Coplanar-Type Transmission Lines," *Electronics and Comm. in Japan, Vol. 58-B,* 1975, pp. 74-80.

[6] Pregla, R. and S.G. Pintzos, "Determination of the Propagation Constants in Coupled Microslots by a Variational Method," *Proc. V Colloquium Microwave Comm., Budapest, 24-30,* June, 1974, pp. MT-491-500.

[7] Yamashita, E. and K. Atsuki, "Analysis of Microstrip-Like Transmission Lines by Nonuniform Discretization of Integral Equations," *IEEE Trans., Vol. MTT-24,* 1976, pp. 195-200.

[8] Hilberg, W., "From Approximations to Exact Relations for Characteristic Impedances," *IEEE Trans. Vol. MTT-17,* 1969, pp. 259-265.

[9] Bahl, I.J., *et al.,* "Design Considerations for Coplanar Waveguides and Coplanar Strips," *Tech. Rep. 78-MW1,* E.E. Dept., I.I.T., Kanpur, 1978.

[10] Dupuis, P.A.J. and C.K. Campbell, "Characteristic Impedance of Surface-Strip Coplanar Waveguides," *Electron. Lett., Vol. 9,* 1973, pp. 354-355.

[11] Kitazawa, T., *et. al.*, "A Coplanar Waveguide with Thick Metal-Coating," *IEEE Trans., Vol. MTT-24,* 1976, pp. 604-608.

[12] Spielman, B.E., "Computer-Aided Analysis of Dissipation Losses in Isolated and Coupled Transmission Lines for Microwave and Millimeter Wave Integrated Circuit Applications," Naval Research Laboratory, Washington, *NRL Rep. 8009,* 1976.

[13] Houdart, M., "Coupled Lines: Applications to Broadband Microwave Integrated Circuits," *Proc. Sixth European Microwave Conference (Rome), 1976*, pp. 49-53.

[14] Saad, T.S. *et. al.* (Eds.), *Microwave Engineers Handbook, Vol. I*, 1971, Dedham, MA., Artech House, Inc., p. 114.

[15] Hunton, J.K., "A Microwave Integrated Circuit Balanced Mixer with Broad-Bandwidth," *Proc. (IEEE-MTT) Microelectronics Symp., 1969*, pp. A3.1 - A3.2.

[16] Hunton, J.K. and J.S. Takeuchi, "Recent Developments in Microwave Slotline Mixers and Frequency Multipliers," *Digest of Tech. Papers, G-MTT Symp. 1970*, pp. 196-199.

[17] Merkele, J., "A d.c. to 20 GHz Thin Film Signal Sampler for Microwave Instrumentation," *H.P. Jour., Vol. 24*, 1973, pp. 10-13.

[18] Hoss, B. and F. Reisch, "Behind the Design of a Portable Analyser," *Microwaves, Vol. 14*, Jan. 1975, pp. 36-40.

[19] Dickens, L.E. and D.W. Maki, "An Integrated-Circuit Balanced Mixer Image and Sum Enhanced," *IEEE Trans., Vol. MTT-23*, 1975, pp. 276-281.

[20] Wen, C.P., "Coplanar-Waveguide Directional Couplers," *IEEE Trans., Vol. MTT-18*, 1970, pp. 318-322.

[21] Robinson, G.H. and J.L. Allen, "Slotline Applications to Miniature Ferrite Devices," *IEEE Trans., Vol. MTT-17*, 1969, pp. 1097-1101.

Chapter 8
Coupled Lines

8.1 INTRODUCTION

A "coupled line" configuration consists of two transmission lines (such as microstrip lines) placed parallel to each other and in close proximity. In such a case there is a continuous coupling between the electromagnetic fields of two lines. Coupled lines are utilized extensively as basic elements for directional couplers, filters, and a variety of other useful circuits.

Because of the coupling of electromagnetic fields, a pair of coupled lines can support two different modes of propagation. These modes have different characteristic impedances. The velocity of propagation of these two modes is equal when the lines are imbedded in a homogeneous dielectric medium (as, for example, in a triplate stripline structure). This is a desirable property for the design of circuits such as directional couplers. However, for transmission lines such as coupled microstrip lines the dielectric medium is not homogeneous. A part of the field extends into the air above the substrate. This fraction is different for the two modes of coupled lines. Consequently, the effective dielectric constants (and the phase velocities) are not equal for the two modes. This non-synchronous feature deteriorates the performance of circuits using these types of coupled lines.

When the two lines of a coupled line pair are identical we have a symmetrical configuration. This symmetry is very useful for simplifying the analysis and design of such coupled lines. If the two lines do not have the same impedance, the configuration is called asymmetric.

For the lines operating in the TEM mode or when the analysis can be based on quasi-static approximation, properties of coupled lines can be determined from the self and mutual inductances and capaci-

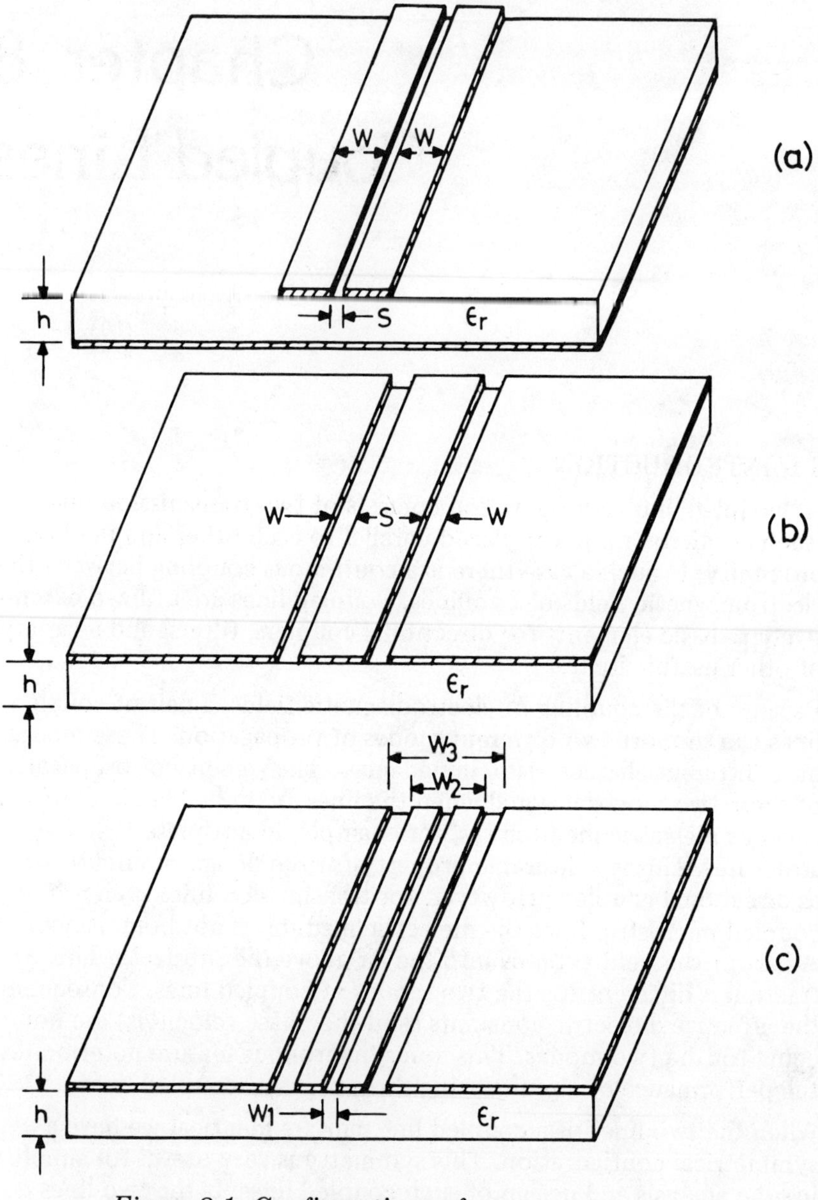

Figure 8.1 Configurations of

(a) Coupled Microstrip Lines
(b) Coupled Slotlines and
(c) Coupled Coplanar Waveguides

tances for the lines. In the case of lines operating in the non-TEM mode (e.g., coupled slotlines), a fullwave analysis is needed for the two modes of propagation.

In this chapter, inhomogeneous parallel coupled lines (i.e., coupled microstrip lines, coupled slotlines, and coupled coplanar waveguides) are discussed. The configuration for these lines is shown in Figure 8.1. Some of the important techniques for analyzing coupled lines are outlined. Coupled mode formulation and even and odd mode methods are described. Both quasi-static and fullwave analyses are used for evaluating the characteristics of symmetric and asymmetric coupled microstrip lines. The effects of non-zero strip thickness, dispersion, enclosure, fabrication tolerances, dielectric overlay and dielectric anisotropy on the characteristics are presented. Methods of measuring the characteristics of coupled microstrip lines are included. The last section of this chapter contains a discussion of coupled slotlines and coupled coplanar waveguides.

8.2 GENERAL ANALYSIS OF COUPLED LINES

8.2.1 Methods of Analysis

Several analytical techniques are available to determine the propagation characteristics of the coupled lines shown in Figure 8.1. The four different methods which are generally employed are: the even and odd mode method [1], the coupled mode formulation [2,3], the graph transformation technique [4] and the congruent transformation technique [5,6].

The even and odd mode method is the most convenient way to describe the behavior of symmetrical coupled lines. In this method wave propagation along a coupled pair of lines is expressed in terms of two modes corresponding to an even or an odd symmetry about a plane which can, therefore, be replaced by a magnetic or electric wall for the purpose of analysis.

In the coupled mode approach, the wave propagation is expressed in terms of the modes of propagation on individual uncoupled lines modified by the coupling because of mutual capacitances and inductances. This approach, therefore, provides an insight into the mechanism of coupling. The method is quite general and is applicable to asymmetric coupled lines also. This approach finds application in all types of coupled systems used in various disciplines.

The other two approaches employ representation of coupled line systems in terms of equivalent networks. The "graph transformation technique" involves the use of a graph equivalent to the general coupled transmission line network for analysis [4]. The use of Richards' transformation [7] allows the coupled line structures to be treated in exactly the same manner as lumped networks.

The equivalent circuit for the coupled lines can also be established using the congruent transformation technique [8]. This is believed to be a powerful method for establishing coupled line properties when there are large number of lines coupled together. Using this technique, a n-conductor coupled transmission lines can be reduced to a set of n decoupled transmission lines connected to two congruent transformers.

Graph transformation and congruent transformation methods are very useful when one deals with a number of lines (more than two) coupled together. Out of the remaining two approaches, the coupled mode technique is more powerful as it can be applied to asymmetric coupled structures also. This approach is discussed in Section 8.2.2 and even and odd mode method is discussed in Section 8.2.3.

8.2.2 Coupled Mode Approach [9-11]

In this approach coupled lines are characterized by the characteristic impedances (or admittances) and phase velocities for two modes. These two modes are obtained by considering the effect of the self and the mutual inductances and capacitances on the modes in individual uncoupled lines.

For coupled mode analysis the voltage on one line is written in terms of the currents on both lines and the self and mutual impedances. Similarly the current is written in terms of voltages and admittances. Elimination of currents or voltages yields the coupled equations. The solution of these coupled equations determines the propagation constants for the two modes.

The coupled mode analysis for coupled lines with unequal impedances, shown in Figure 8.2, is described next.

Analysis

The behavior of two lossless coupled transmission lines is described in general by the following set of differential equations

$$-\frac{dv_1}{dz} = Z_1 i_1 + Z_m i_2 \tag{8.1}$$

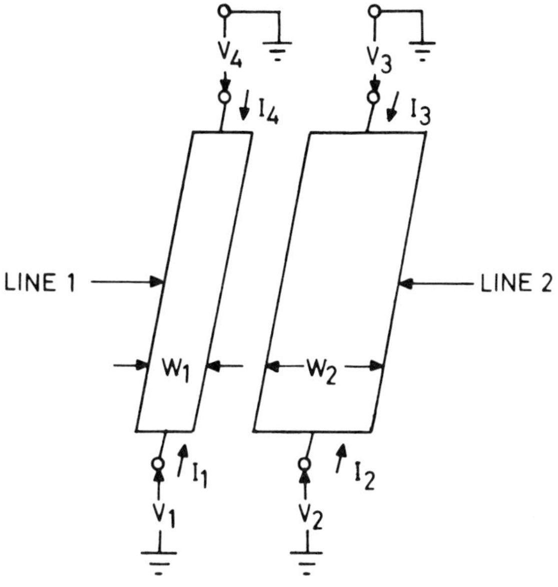

Figure 8.2 A Pair of Coupled Lines With Unequal Impedances

$$-\frac{dv_2}{dz} = Z_m i_1 + Z_2 i_2 \tag{8.2}$$

$$-\frac{di_1}{dz} = Y_1 v_1 + Y_m v_2 \tag{8.3}$$

$$-\frac{di_2}{dz} = Y_m v_1 + Y_2 v_2 \tag{8.4}$$

where Z_j, $Y_j (j=1,2)$ are self-impedances and self-admittances per unit length of lines 1 and 2, and Z_m and Y_m are mutual impedance and admittance per unit length, respectively. Voltages and currents, which are functions of z, are represented by v_k and $i_k (k=1,2)$, respectively. A time variation $e^{j\omega t}$ has been assumed.

Elimination of i_1 and i_2 from Equations (8.1 - 8.4) gives the following set of coupled equations for the voltages v_1 and v_2

$$\frac{d^2 v_1}{dz^2} - a_1 v_1 - b_1 v_2 = 0 \tag{8.5}$$

$$\frac{d^2 v_2}{dz^2} - a_2 v_2 - b_2 v_1 = 0 \tag{8.6}$$

where

$$a_1 = Y_1 Z_1 + Y_m Z_m$$

$$b_1 = Z_1 Y_m + Y_2 Z_m$$

$$a_2 = Y_2 Z_2 + Y_m Z_m$$

$$b_2 = Z_2 Y_m + Y_1 Z_m \tag{8.7}$$

The coefficients a_1, a_2, b_1 and b_2 are constants.
Assuming a variation of the type $v(z) = v_o\, e^{-\gamma z}$ for the voltages v_1 and v_2, the coupled Equations (8.5) and (8.6) reduce to the following eigenvalue equation

$$[\gamma^4 - \gamma^2 (a_1 + a_2) + a_1 a_2 - b_1 b_2]\, v_o = 0 \tag{8.8}$$

Solution of Equation (8.8) leads to the following four roots for γ:

$$\gamma_{1,2} = \pm\, \gamma_c \text{ and } \gamma_{3,4} = \pm\, \gamma_\pi \tag{8.9}$$

where

$$\gamma_{c,\pi}^2 = \frac{a_1 + a_2}{2} \pm \frac{1}{2} [(a_1 - a_2)^2 + 4\, b_1 b_2]^{1/2} \tag{8.10}$$

The subscripts "c" and "π" refer to the c and π modes for asymmetric coupled lines. The propagation constants for these modes, γ_c and γ_π, correspond to in-phase and anti-phase waves which reduce to even and odd mode waves for symmetrical lines. The roots with plus and minus signs in Equation (8.9) represent waves travelling in the +z and -z directions, respectively.
The ratio of voltages v_2 and v_1 on the two lines for the c and π modes is obtained from Equations (8.5), (8.6) and (8.10), and is given below

$$\frac{v_2}{v_1} = \frac{\gamma^2 - a_1}{b_1} = \frac{b_2}{\gamma^2 - a_2} \tag{8.11}$$

If the corresponding ratios for the c and π modes are represented by R_c and R_π, then

$$R_c\left(=\frac{v_2}{v_1} \text{ for } \gamma = \pm\gamma_c\right) = \frac{1}{2b_1}\left[(a_2-a_1) + \left\{(a_2-a_1)^2 + 4\,b_1 b_2\right\}^{1/2}\right] \tag{8.12}$$

and

$$R_\pi\left(=\frac{v_2}{v_1} \text{ for } \gamma = \pm\gamma_\pi\right) = \frac{1}{2b_1}\left[(a_2-a_1) - \left\{(a_2-a_1)^2 + 4\,b_1 b_2\right\}^{1/2}\right] \tag{8.13}$$

It may be observed from Equations (8.12) and (8.13) that R_c is positive real and R_π is negative real thus representing in-phase and anti-phase waves.

In terms of the four waves $\pm\gamma_c$ and $\pm\gamma_\pi$ the general solution for the voltages on the two lines may be written as

$$v_1 = A_1 e^{-\gamma_c z} + A_2 e^{\gamma_c z} + A_3 e^{-\gamma_\pi z} + A_4 e^{\gamma_\pi z} \tag{8.14}$$

$$v_2 = R_c\,(A_1 e^{-\gamma_c z} + A_2 e^{\gamma_c z}) + R_\pi\,(A_3 e^{-\gamma_\pi z} + A_4 e^{\gamma_\pi z}) \tag{8.15}$$

The currents i_1 and i_2 are obtained by substituting the corresponding voltage v_1 and v_2 from Equations (8.14) and (8.15) in Equations (8.1) and (8.2), and may be written as

$$i_1 = Y_{c1}(A_1 e^{-\gamma_c z} - A_2 e^{\gamma_c z}) + Y_{\pi 1}(A_3 e^{-\gamma_\pi z} - A_4 e^{\gamma_\pi z}) \tag{8.16}$$

$$i_2 = Y_{c2} R_c\,(A_1 e^{-\gamma_c z} - A_2 e^{\gamma_c z}) + Y_{\pi 2} R_\pi\,(A_3 e^{-\gamma_\pi z} - A_4 e^{\gamma_\pi z}) \tag{8.17}$$

where Y_{c1}, Y_{c2}, $Y_{\pi 1}$ and $Y_{\pi 2}$ are the characteristic admittances of lines 1 and 2 for the two modes. These are given by

$$Y_{c1} = \gamma_c\,\frac{Z_2 - Z_m R_c}{Z_1 Z_2 - Z_m{}^2} = \frac{1}{Z_{c1}} \tag{8.18}$$

$$Y_{c2} = \frac{\gamma_c}{R_c}\,\frac{Z_1 R_c - Z_m}{Z_1 Z_2 - Z_m^2} = \frac{1}{Z_{c2}} \tag{8.19}$$

Similar relations hold for the π mode. Substitution of the values of R_c and R_π in Equations (8.18) and (8.19) gives

$$\frac{Y_{c1}}{Y_{c2}} = -R_c R_\pi = \frac{Y_{\pi 1}}{Y_{\pi 2}} \tag{8.20}$$

The above analysis has been carried out in terms of the two independent modes of propagation termed 'c' and 'π' modes with propagation constants γ_c and γ_π. The voltages v_1 and v_2 on the two lines are related through $v_2/v_1 = R_c$ and R_π. The corresponding ratios for the currents are given by $i_2/i_1 = -1/R_\pi$ and $-1/R_c$, respectively. For symmetric lines, "c" and "π" modes reduce to even and odd modes.

Symmetric Lines

For the case of symmetric lines, $a_2 = a_1$ and $b_2 = b_1$. Therefore, Equations (8.12) and (8.13) give for v_2/v_1

$$v_2/v_1 = R_c = +1; \text{ for c mode}$$

$$v_2/v_1 = R_\pi = -1; \text{ for } \pi \text{ mode} \tag{8.21}$$

Also, Equations (8.16) and (8.17) yield

$$i_2/i_1 = +1 \quad \text{for c mode}$$

$$i_2/i_1 = -1 \quad \text{for } \pi \text{ mode} \tag{8.22}$$

Evaluation of Characteristics for c and π Modes

As discussed above, asymmetric coupled lines can be represented in terms of two modes called c and π modes. The phase constants and the characteristic impedances of these modes are related to the line constants in the following manner [10];

$$\gamma_{c,\pi} = j\beta_{c,\pi} = j\frac{\omega}{\sqrt{2}}\left[L_1C_1 + L_2C_2 - 2L_mC_m \pm \sqrt{(L_2C_2 - L_1C_1)^2 + 4(L_mC_1 - L_2C_m)(L_mC_2 - L_1C_m)}\right]^{1/2} \tag{8.23}$$

$$Z_{c1} = \frac{\omega}{\beta_c}(L_1 - L_m/R_\pi) \tag{8.24}$$

$$Z_{\pi 1} = \frac{\omega}{\beta_\pi} (L_1 - L_m/R_c) \tag{8.25}$$

and

$$R_{c,\pi} = \frac{L_2C_2 - L_1C_1 \pm \sqrt{(L_2C_2 - L_1C_1)^2 + 4(L_mC_2 - L_1C_m)(L_mC_1 - L_2C_m)}}{2(L_mC_2 - L_1C_m)} \tag{8.26}$$

Self capacitances C_1 and C_2, self inductances L_1 and L_2 as well as mutual capacitance C_m and mutual inductance L_m can be determined from quasi-static analysis.

8.2.3 Even and Odd Mode Approach

Thus far the analysis of coupled lines has been very general. Now we will restrict our attention to the case of symmetric coupled lines, i.e. lines of equal characteristic impedances.

It has been pointed out earlier that the c and π modes reduce to the even and odd modes, respectively, for symmetric coupled lines. The propagation constants for these modes are given by

$$\gamma_{e,o} = \gamma_{c,\pi} = [(Y_o \pm Y_m)(Z_o \pm Z_m)]^{1/2} \tag{8.27}$$

where

$$Y_o = Y_1 \text{ or } Y_2\,, \quad Z_o = Z_1 \text{ or } Z_2$$

In terms of line constants the characteristics of even and odd modes can be obtained from Equations (8.23) - (8.25) by substituting $L_1 = L_2 = L_o$ and $C_1 = C_2 = C_o$. The expressions are given below

$$\beta_{e,o} = \omega[L_oC_o - L_mC_m \pm (L_mC_o - L_oC_m)]^{1/2} \tag{8.28}$$

$$Z_{oe} = \frac{\omega}{\beta_e}(L_o + L_m)\,, \quad Y_{oe} = 1/Z_{oe} \tag{8.29}$$

$$Z_{oo} = \frac{\omega}{\beta_o}(L_o - L_m)\,, \quad Y_{oo} = 1/Z_{oo} \tag{8.30}$$

where $\beta_{e,o}$ are the phase constants of lossless coupled lines given by $\gamma_{e,o} = j\beta_{e,o}$. The lines are characterised by inductance per unit length

L_o and capacitance per unit length C_o. The mutual inductance is L_m and mutual capacitance is C_m.

Alternatively, the propagation constants may be written in terms of the phase constant of the lines and the coefficients of inductive and capacitive couplings k_L and k_c. If we define [12]

$$k_L = L_m/L_o \tag{8.31}$$

$$k_c = C_m/C_o \tag{8.32}$$

and

$$\beta_o = \omega\sqrt{L_o C_o} \tag{8.33}$$

we can write Equation (8.28) as

$$\beta_{e,o} = \beta_{eff}\sqrt{1 \pm \delta} \tag{8.34}$$

where effective propagation constant is given by

$$\beta_{eff} = \beta_o(1 - k_L k_c)^{1/2} \tag{8.35}$$

and

$$\delta = \frac{k_L - k_c}{1 - k_L k_c} \tag{8.36}$$

In Equation (8.34), positive and negative signs correspond to the even and odd mode, respectively.

For coupled lines propagating TEM modes, coupled mode parameters are normally expressed in terms of even and odd mode capacitances C_e^a, C_o^a for the dielectric ($\epsilon_r = 1$) structure, and those with dielectric substrate $C_e(\epsilon_r)$, $C_o(\epsilon_r)$. These are related to self and mutual inductances and capacitances through the following equations

$$L_o = \frac{\mu_o \epsilon_o}{2}\left\{\frac{1}{C_o^a} + \frac{1}{C_e^a}\right\} \tag{8.37}$$

$$L_m = \frac{\mu_o \epsilon_o}{2}\left\{\frac{1}{C_e^a} - \frac{1}{C_o^a}\right\} \tag{8.38}$$

$$C_o = \frac{1}{2}\,[C_o(\epsilon_r) + C_e(\epsilon_r)] \tag{8.39}$$

and

$$C_m = \frac{1}{2}\,[C_o(\epsilon_r) - C_e(\epsilon_r)] \tag{8.40}$$

The coupling coefficients k_L and k_c are defined by

$$k_L = \frac{L_m}{L_o} = \frac{C_o^a - C_e^a}{C_o^a + C_e^a} \tag{8.41}$$

and

$$k_c = \frac{C_m}{C_o} = \frac{C_o(\epsilon_r) - C_e(\epsilon_r)}{C_o(\epsilon_r) + C_e(\epsilon_r)} \tag{8.42}$$

The effective propagation constant, β_{eff} can be expressed as

$$\beta_{eff} = \frac{\omega}{c}\,\sqrt{\epsilon_{re}}\;\sqrt{\frac{1 - k_L k_c}{1 - k_L{}^2}} \tag{8.43}$$

where

$$\epsilon_{re} = \frac{C_o(\epsilon_r) + C_e(\epsilon_r)}{C_o^a + C_e^a} \tag{8.44}$$

and impedances can be written as

$$Z_{oe} = \frac{\omega}{\beta_e}\,\frac{\mu_o \epsilon_o}{C_e^a} \tag{8.45}$$

$$Z_{oo} = \frac{\omega}{\beta_o}\,\frac{\mu_o \epsilon_o}{C_o^a} \tag{8.46}$$

with

$$\beta_{e,o} = \omega\sqrt{\mu_o \epsilon_o}\;\sqrt{\frac{C_{e,o}(\epsilon_r)}{C_{e,o}^a}} \tag{8.47}$$

The methods of evaluation of even and odd mode capacitances will be described in Section 8.3 and closed form expressions will be presented in Section 8.5.

8.3 CHARACTERISTICS OF COUPLED MICROSTRIP LINES

The methods of analysis discussed in the previous section are quite general. They may be applied to coupled lines in a homogeneous medium such as coupled striplines, or coupled lines in an inhomogeneous medium such as coupled microstrip lines. Whereas coupled striplines are non-dispersive in nature, coupled microstrip lines exhibit dispersive characteristics at higher frequencies. Quite often, coupled microstrip lines are used at frequencies where quasi-static analysis holds good and dispersion effects are negligible. Nevertheless, full wave analysis helps in determining the frequency range of validity of quasi-static analysis. Both the quasi-static analysis as well as fullwave analysis for coupled microstrip lines with equal impedances is described in this section. The geometry of coupled microstrip lines is shown in Figure 8.3(a), and the field distributions for even and odd modes are given in Figure 8.3(b).

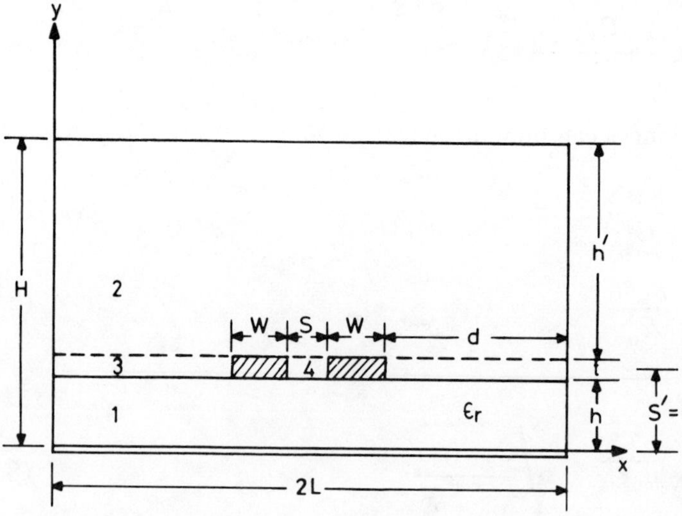

Figure 8.3(a) Symmetric Coupled Microstrip Lines in an Enclosure

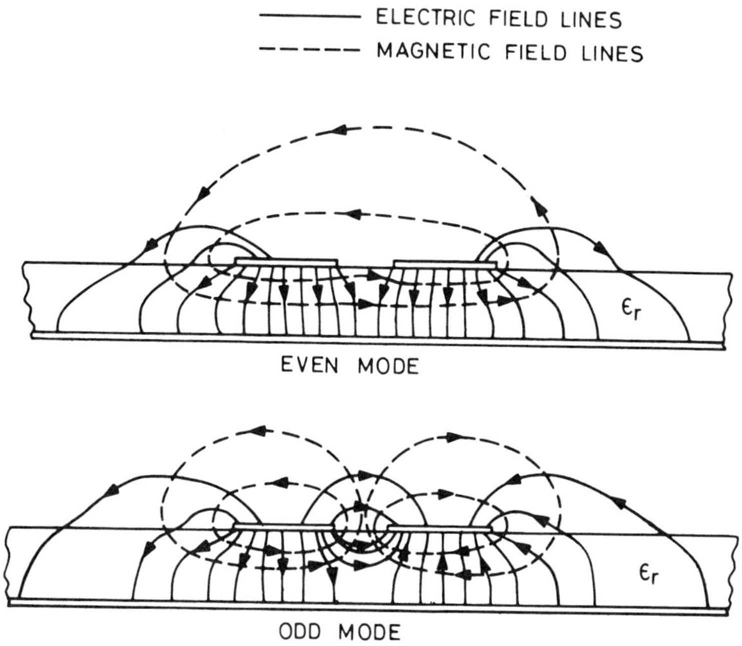

Figure 8.3(b) Even and Odd Mode Field Configurations in Coupled Microstrip Lines

8.3.1 Quasi-Static Analysis

Almost all the methods described in Chapter 1 for the quasi-static analysis of microstrip have also been employed for calculation of even and odd mode capacitances of coupled microstrip lines. The conformal transformation method does not yield a simple closed form solution in this case [13]. Green's function technique has been described by Bryant and Weiss [14-15]. The variational method in the space domain has been used by Krage and Haddad [12], and Bergandt and Pregla [16] to determine the upper bound on capacitances for the coupled line configuration enclosed in a box. The variational method in FTD has been described in reference [17].

Variational Method in Space Domain [12, 16]

In this method scalar potential functions, which are the solution of Laplace's equation, are expanded in a Fourier series. The Fourier coefficients are determined from the continuity conditions of potential functions and the stationary property of the stored electric energy with respect to Fourier coefficients. Once the potential functions for even and odd modes are known, these can be used to determine the capacitances for these modes.

For the purpose of analysis, the coupled microstrip configuration can be divided into four separate regions as shown in Figure 8.3(a).

Potentials are assumed to be $\phi = V_1$ and $\phi = V_2$ on the left and right strips, respectively. The outer conducting walls are at $\phi = 0$ potential. The field configuration in each of the four regions is obtained from a solution of Laplace's equation

$$\nabla^2 \phi_i = 0 \quad i = 1, 2, 3, 4 \tag{8.48}$$

The potentials ϕ_i satisfying Laplace's equation may be written in terms of Fourier expansions as given below

$$\phi_1 = \sum_{m=1}^{\infty} A_m \sinh\left(\frac{m\pi y}{H}\right) \sin\left(\frac{m\pi x}{2L}\right) \tag{8.49}$$

$$\phi_2 = \sum_{m=1}^{\infty} B_m \sinh \frac{m\pi(H-y)}{H} \sin\left(\frac{m\pi x}{2L}\right) \tag{8.50}$$

$$\phi_3 = \sum_{m=1}^{\infty} \left\{ \left[C_m \sinh \frac{m\pi(Y-S')}{d} + D_m \cosh \frac{m\pi(Y-S')}{d} \right] \cdot \sin \frac{m\pi x}{d} + V_1 \frac{x}{d} \right\} \tag{8.51}$$

$$\phi_4 = \sum_{m=1}^{\infty} \left\{ \left[E_m \sinh \frac{m\pi(Y-S')}{S} + F_m \cosh \frac{m\pi(Y-S')}{S} \right] \cdot \sin \frac{m\pi(x-d-W)}{S} + V_1 + (V_2-V_1)(x-d-W)/S \right\} \tag{8.52}$$

where $S' = h + t/2$, $d = (2L - 2W - S)/2$. For the even mode $V_1 = V_2$, and $V_1 = -V_2$ for the odd mode.

The Fourier coefficients $A_m, B_m \ldots F_m$ are determined from the continuity of potentials at the boundaries and the stationary property of the stored electric energy with respect to Fourier coefficients. The stored energy in region i is given by

$$W_i = \frac{\epsilon_i}{2} \iint [(E_{xi})^2 + (E_{yi})^2]\, dx\, dy \tag{8.53}$$

where

$$E_{xi} = -\frac{\partial \phi_i}{\partial x}$$

$$E_{yi} = -\frac{\partial \phi_i}{\partial y}$$

The total capacitance of the structure may then be obtained from

$$C = \frac{2}{V^2}(W_1 + W_2 + W_3 + W_4) \tag{8.54}$$

where $V(=|V_1|=|V_2|)$ is the potential of a strip. The value of C is twice the even or odd mode capacitance of a single strip to ground.

Evaluation of Fourier Coefficients

The stored energy W_i can be evaluated in terms of the coefficients A_m, B_m, C_m, D_m, E_m and F_m. The continuity of potential at $y = h$ and $y = h + t$ helps in eliminating A_m and B_m. Therefore, W_i can be written in terms of C_m, D_m, E_m and F_m.

The stationary property of the energy W_i with respect to Fourier coefficients C_m, D_m, E_m, F_m gives

$$\frac{\partial W_i}{\partial C_m} = 0, \quad \frac{\partial W_i}{\partial D_m} = 0, \quad \frac{\partial W_i}{\partial E_m} = 0, \quad \frac{\partial W_i}{\partial F_m} = 0 \tag{8.55}$$

for $m = 1, 2, 3 \ldots\ldots, \infty$; $i = 1, 2, 3, 4$

Equation (8.55) generates four sets of equations. Each set will contain an infinite number of simultaneous, linear, inhomogeneous equations. These equations can be solved with a computer to determine the Fourier coefficients.

For an exact computation the series in Equations (8.49 - 8.52) should be infinite. However, in practice only a finite number of terms M are used. Detailed convergence considerations indicate that [16] convergence using a finite number of terms is faster for larger values of ϵ_r, large W/H and small S/H. Moreover, convergence is faster for even mode capacitance compared to odd mode capacitance. It has also been observed that M = 23 gives a resonable compromise between accuracy and computation time [16].

Variational Method in FTD [17]

This method is similar to the variational method in FTD described for a single microstrip in Chapter 1.

In this method capacitance is calculated from a variational expression in terms of charge distribution. Evaluation is carried out in the Fourier transform domain, and the capacitance may be written as

$$\frac{\epsilon_o}{C} = \frac{1}{\pi} \int_0^\infty G(\alpha)\, \tilde{\rho}^2(\alpha)\, d\alpha \tag{8.56}$$

For coupled lines Equation (8.56) becomes

$$\frac{\epsilon_o}{C_e} = \frac{1}{\pi} \int_0^\infty G(\alpha)\, \tilde{\rho}_e^2(\alpha)\, d\alpha \tag{8.57}$$

and

$$\frac{\epsilon_o}{C_o} = \frac{1}{\pi} \int_0^\infty G(\alpha)\, \tilde{\rho}_o^2(\alpha)\, d\alpha \tag{8.58}$$

where

$$G(\alpha) = \frac{1}{\alpha[\epsilon_r \coth(\alpha h) + \coth(\alpha h')]} \tag{8.59}$$

$\tilde{\rho}_e$ and $\tilde{\rho}_o$ are the Fourier transforms of charge density functions for the even and odd mode, respectively.

Discussion of Results

Figure 8.4 shows the variation of even and odd mode impedance with strip width W/h and gap spacing S/h for $\epsilon_r = 9.6$[18]. It has been assumed that the strip thickness t is zero and the enclosure recedes to infinity. The effect of gap spacing and strip width on effective dielectric constants ϵ_{re}^e and ϵ_{re}^o is shown in Figure 8.5. It may be observed from these figures that, impedances decrease and effective dielectric constants increase with an increase in strip width. For a given value of S/h and W/h, the even mode impedance and effective dielectric constant are higher than odd mode values. Even and odd mode characteristics show opposite variations with an increase in S/h such that, for S/h tending to infinity, the even and the odd mode

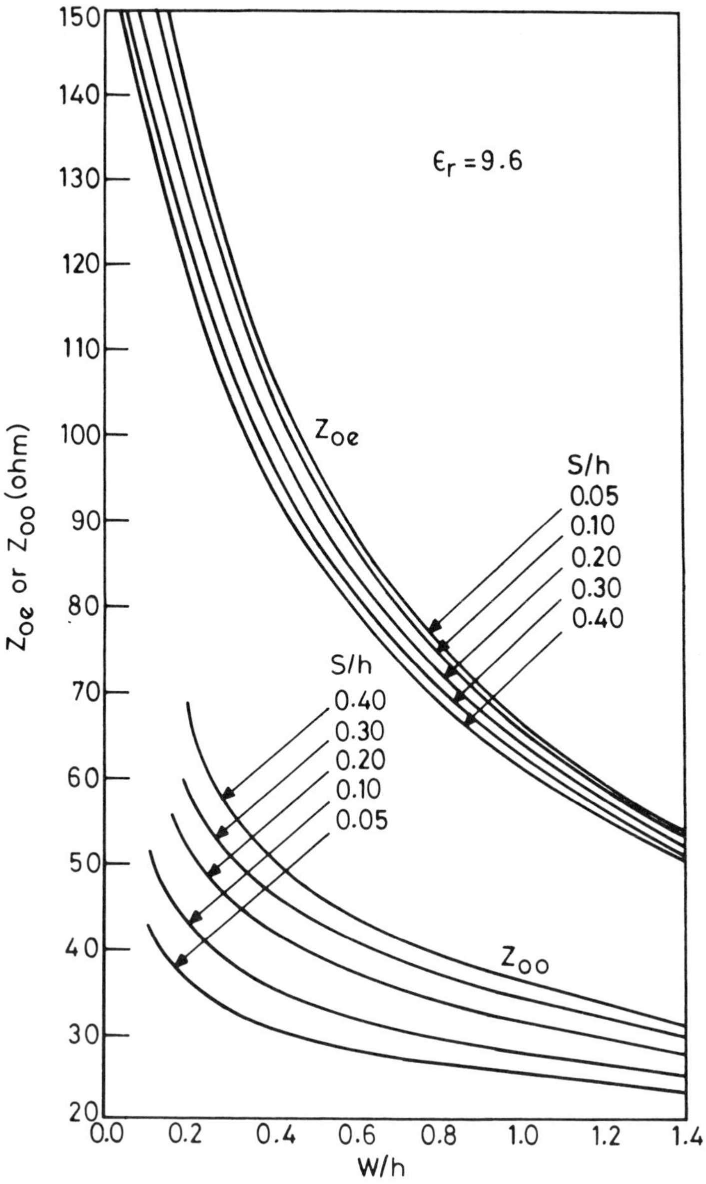

Figure 8.4(a) Even and Odd Mode Characteristic Impedances for Coupled Microstrip Lines (ϵ_r = 9.6, S/h = 0.05 to 0.4, W/h = 0.1 to 1.4) (from [18])

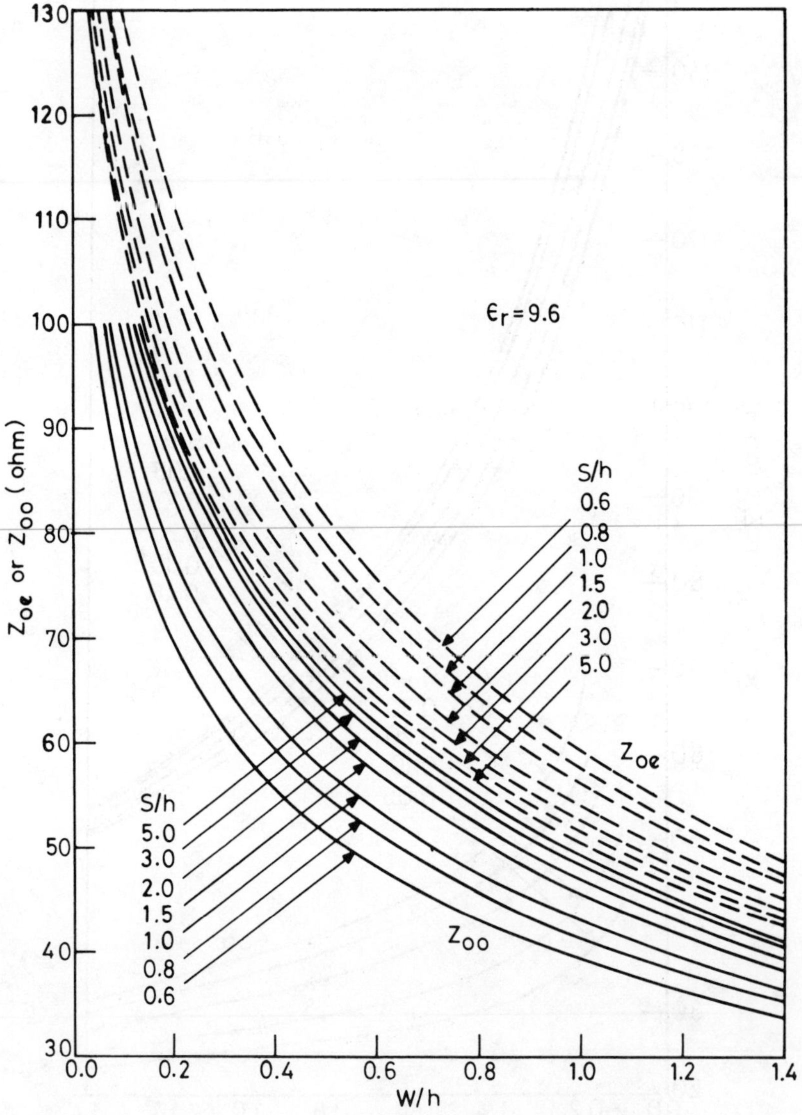

Figure 8.4(b) Even and Odd Mode Characteristic Impedances for Coupled Microstrip Lines (ϵ_r = 9.6, S/h = 0.6 to 5.0, W/h = 0.04 to 1.4) (from [18])

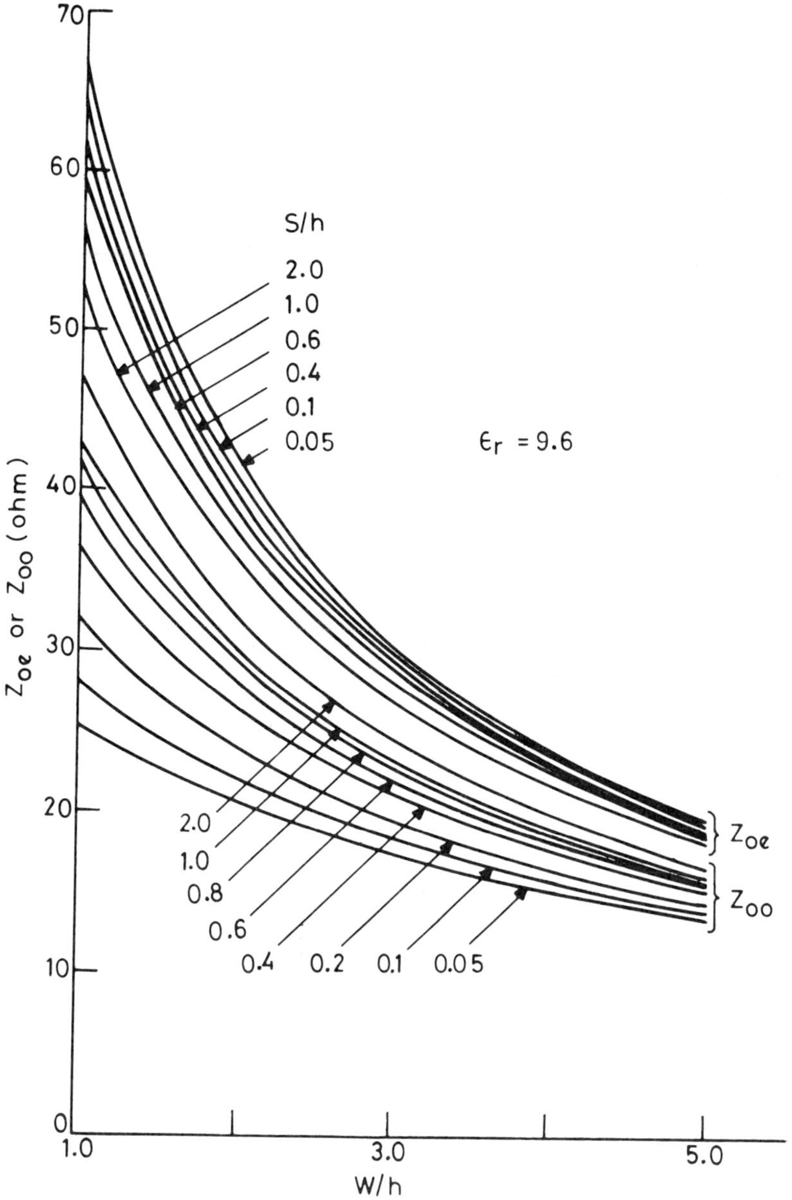

Figure 8.4(c) Even and Odd Mode Characteristic Impedances for Coupled Microstrip Lines (ϵ_r = 9.6, S/h = 0.05 to 2.0, W/h = 1.0 to 5.0) (from [18])

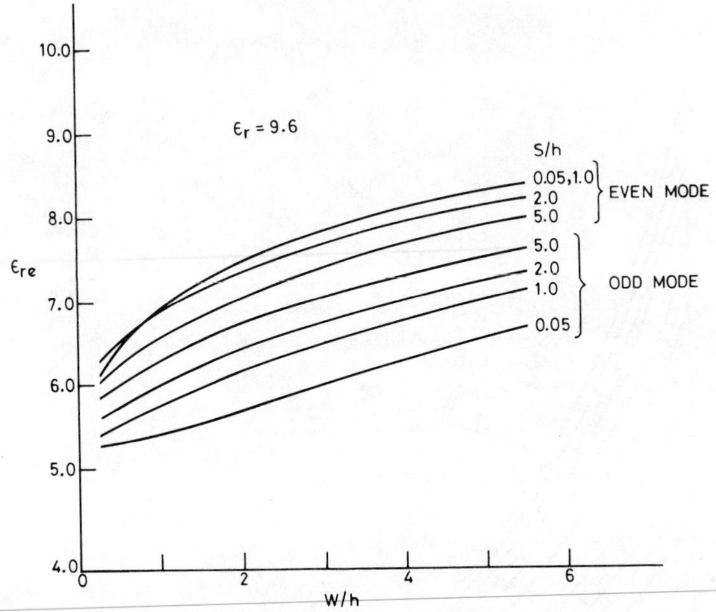

Figure 8.5 Even and Odd Mode Effective Dielectric Constants for Coupled Microstrip Lines (ϵ_r = 9.6, S/h = 0.05 to 5.0, W/h = 0.2 to 5.5) (from [18])

characteristics approach each other and are equal to single microstrip values.

For the special case of H = 2h and L = ∞ the characteristics of coupled microstrip lines can be obtained in a simple closed form expression by using the method of conformal transformation. In this case coupled microstrip lines behave like coupled striplines with the effective dielectric constant given by $(\epsilon_r + 1)/2$. The even and odd mode impedances are obtained [19] as

$$Z_{oo} = \frac{30\pi}{\sqrt{(\epsilon_r+1)/2}} \frac{K(k_o')}{K(k_o)} \tag{8.60}$$

$$Z_{oe} = \frac{30\pi}{\sqrt{(\epsilon_r+1)/2}} \frac{K(k_e')}{K(k_e)} \tag{8.61}$$

where $K(k_e)$ and $K(k_e')$ are the elliptic function and its complement with

$$k_e = \tanh\left(\frac{\pi}{4}\frac{W}{h}\right)\tanh\left[\frac{\pi}{4}\left(\frac{W+S}{h}\right)\right], \quad k_e'^2 = 1-k_e^2 \tag{8.62}$$

$$k_o = \tanh\left(\frac{\pi}{4}\frac{W}{h}\right)\coth\left[\frac{\pi}{4}\left(\frac{W+S}{h}\right)\right], \quad k_o'^2 = 1-k_o^2 \tag{8.63}$$

8.3.2 Fullwave Analysis

It was pointed out in Chapter 2 that quasi-static analysis for microstrip holds for wavelengths greater than the transverse dimensions of the line. At higher frequencies the line shows a dispersive nature, and a fullwave analysis is needed. The analytical techniques used for fullwave analysis of single microstrip and slotline can be applied to the coupled line configuration also. Krage and Haddad [20] have used the same field matching technique for both single microstrip and coupled microstrip configurations. The spectral domain technique has been used in references [21,22,45] for the fullwave analysis of single and coupled microstrip lines, single and coupled slot lines, and coplanar lines. Its application to various configurations differs only in the choice of basis functions for expressing current density (for microstrip) and electric field (for slotline). The rate of convergence of the resultant series depends upon the choice of basis functions.

In this section Galerkin's method in FTD is employed to analyze both symmetric and asymmetric coupled microstrip lines.

Symmetric Coupled Microstrip Lines [23]

For applying Galerkin's method in FTD, it is assumed that the current distribution on each strip is the same as that given for a single strip in free space. The Fourier transformation of the current distribution is taken to be

$$\tilde{I}_z(\alpha) = \begin{cases} J_o(\alpha W/2)\cos\alpha\left(\dfrac{W+S}{2}\right) & \text{for the even mode} \\[2ex] J_o(\alpha W/2)\sin\alpha\left(\dfrac{W+S}{2}\right) & \text{for the odd mode} \end{cases} \tag{8.64}$$

$$\tilde{I}_x(\alpha) = \begin{cases} 0.5 & \text{for the even mode} \\ \\ j0.5 & \text{for the odd mode} \end{cases} \tag{8.65}$$

Other details of this method are similar to those discussed for a single microstrip in Chapter 2.

The characteristic impedances for even and odd modes defined on power-current basis agree well with experimental results and may be obtained from the following relation

$$Z_o = 2 \frac{\iint P_z \, dx \, dy}{\iint (I_z^2 + I_x^2) \, dx \, dy} \tag{8.66}$$

where P_z is the z-component of the Poynting vector, and the integral is evaluated over the cross-section of a coupled microstrip configuration.

The numerical results obtained in reference [23] are shown in Figures (8.6) and (8.7) for $\epsilon_r = 9.7$, W/h = 1 and S/h = 0.2, 0.5, 1. Comparison

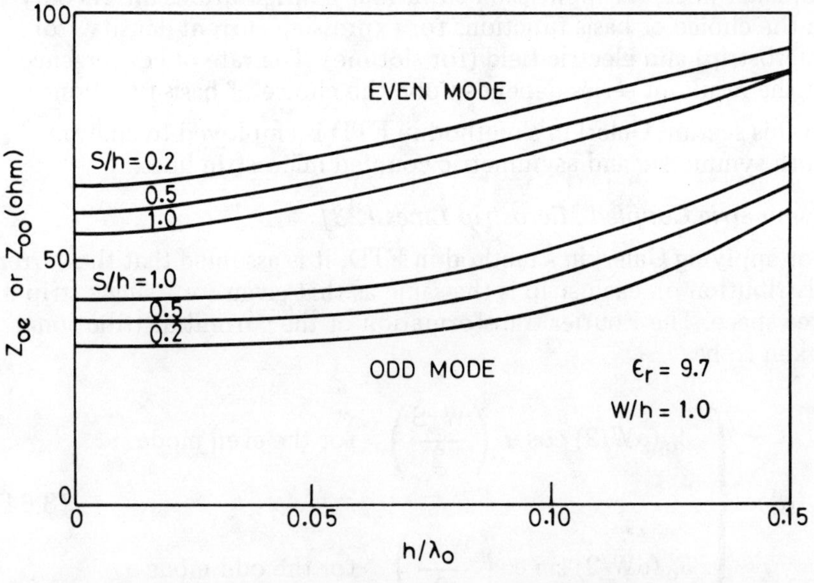

Figure 8.6 Effect of Dispersion on Even and Odd Mode Impedances of Coupled Microstrip Lines (from [23])

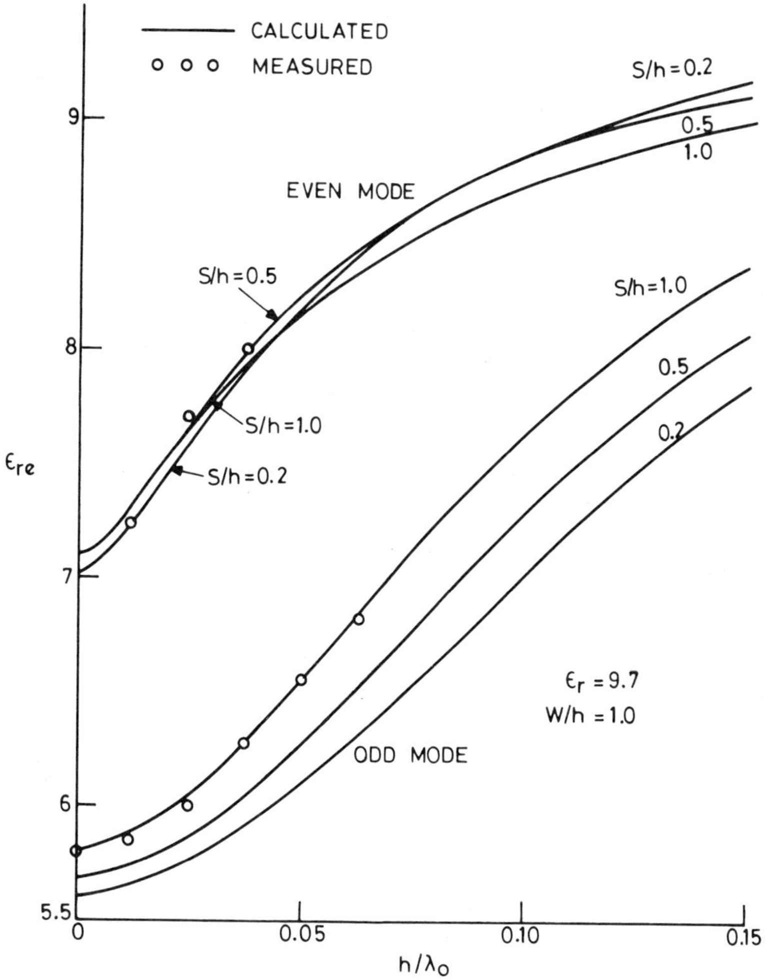

Figure 8.7 Effect of Dispersion on Even and Odd Mode Effective Dielectric Constants of Coupled Microstrip Lines (from [23])

with the results of Davies and Corr [24] shows good agreement for ϵ_{re} even for a very simple current distribution.

Asymmetric Coupled Microstrip Lines [25]

Galerkin's method in FTD has been applied to evaluate the characteristics of asymmetric coupled microstrip lines also. The basis functions chosen for expanding the current density components are such that the transverse component can be obtained from the integration of the logitudinal component. For the coordinate system shown in Figure 8.8 the basis functions for strip "1" of

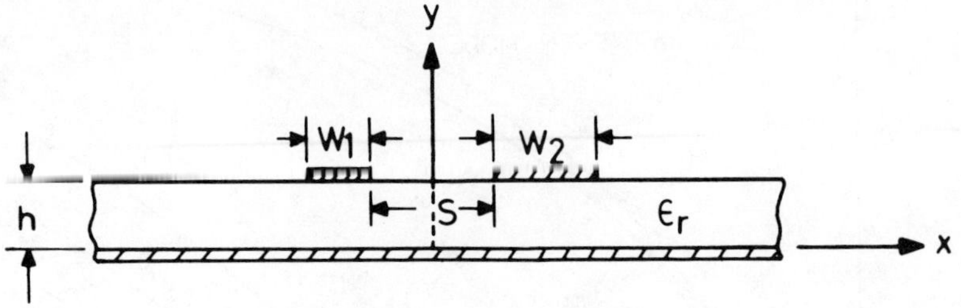

Figure 8.8 Coupled Microstrip Lines With Unequal Impedances (Asymmetric Lines)

width W_1 and strip "2" of width W_2 are given below

$$I_{zn}^{(1)}(x) = \frac{\cos\left[\frac{n\pi}{W_1}(x+S/2)\right] - (-1)^{n/2} A_n J_o(n\pi/2)}{\left[1 - \left(\frac{x+S/2}{W_1/2} - 1\right)^2\right]^{1/2}} \qquad n=0, 1 \ldots \infty \tag{8.67}$$

$$I_{zn}^{(2)}(x) = \frac{\cos\left[\frac{n\pi}{W_2}(x-S/2)\right] - (-1)^{n/2} A_n J_o(n\pi/2)}{\left[1 - \left(\frac{x-S/2}{W_2/2} - 1\right)^2\right]^{1/2}} \qquad n=0, 1 \ldots \infty \tag{8.68}$$

$$I_{xn}^{(1)}(x) = \int_{-S/2}^{x} I_{zn}^{(1)}(x')\, dx' \tag{8.69}$$

$$I_{xn}^{(2)}(x) = \int_{S/2}^{x} I_{zn}^{(2)}(x')\, dx' \tag{8.70}$$

where $A_n = [1 + (-1)^n]/2$, $A_o = 0$; and J_o is the Bessel function of zero order and first kind. It is seen that by employing these basis functions an accuracy of 0.5 percent for tightly coupled lines can be achieved by using a 2×2 matrix [25].

The characteristic impedance for the two strips is defined on a voltage-current basis. This is given below

$$Z_o^{(1)} = \frac{V^{(1)}}{I^{(1)}} = \frac{\int_0^h E_y\left(-\frac{W_1+S}{2}, y\right) dy}{\int_{-S/2}^{-(W_1+S)/2} I_z(x')\, dx'} \tag{8.71}$$

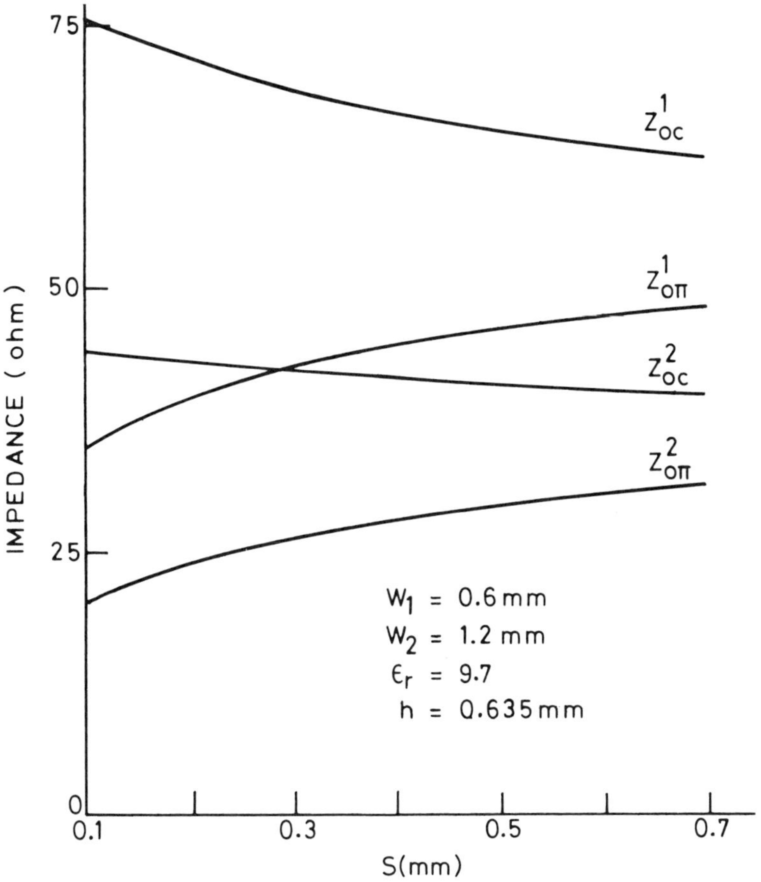

Figure 8.9 Variation of Characteristic Impedances of an Asymmetric Coupled Microstrip Lines With Gap Spacing S (from [25])

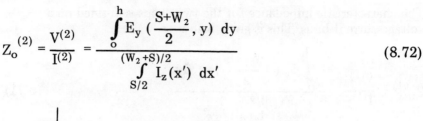

$$Z_o^{(2)} = \frac{V^{(2)}}{I^{(2)}} = \frac{\int_0^h E_y\left(\frac{S+W_2}{2}, y\right) dy}{\int_{S/2}^{(W_2+S)/2} I_z(x')\, dx'} \tag{8.72}$$

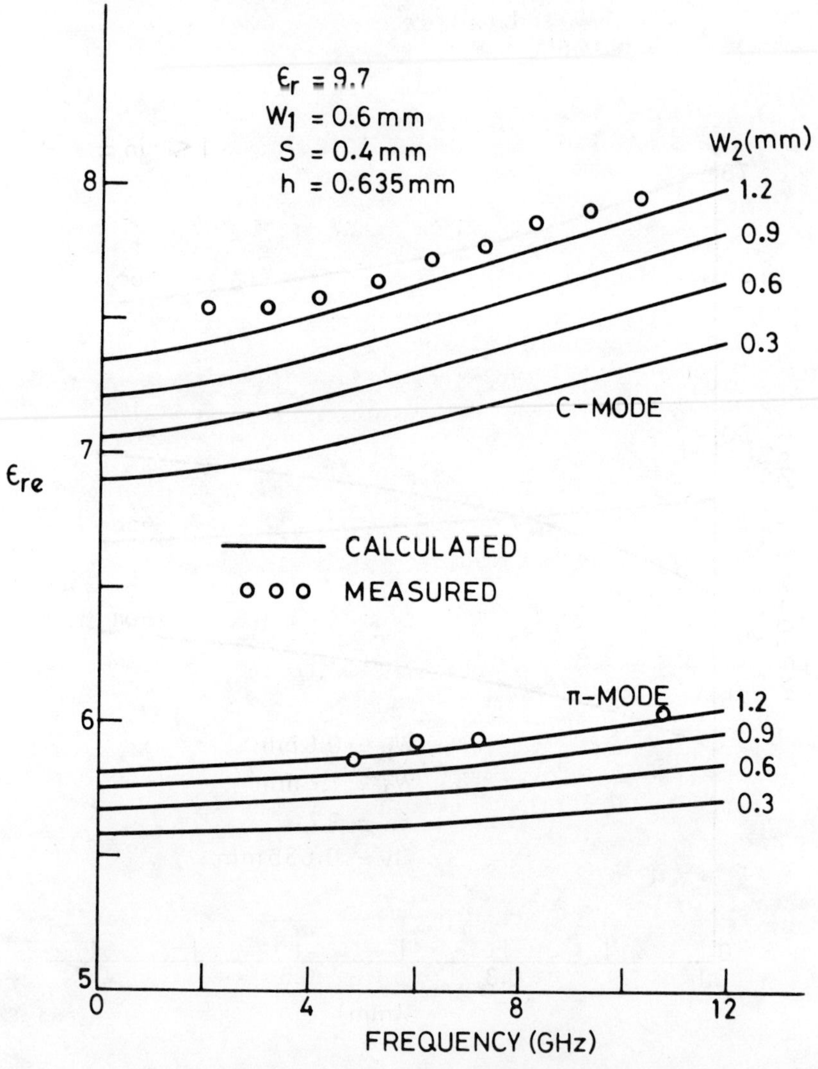

Figure 8.10 Effect of Dispersion on the Effective Dielectric Constants of Asymmetric Coupled Microstrip Lines (from [25])

The analysis of asymmetric coupled lines is described in terms of c and π modes defined in Section 8.2.

Figure 8.9 shows the characteristic impedances for the case of asymmetric coupled microstrip lines [25]. Note that the two lines have different impedances for the c and π modes. The narrow line has a higher impedance than the wider line. Moreover, for larger spacing the c and π mode impedances for the two lines approach their respective single line impedances. The effect of dispersion on the effective dielectric constant for the two modes is shown in Figure 8.10. It may be observed from this figure that effective dielectric constants for the c and π modes increase with the increase in strip width of line 2. Also, the measured values show a good agreement with calculated results.

Fullwave analysis is useful for calculating very accurately the effect of dispersion on the even and odd mode phase velocities and characteristic impedances. However, sufficient accuracy compatible with fabrication tolerances and measurement errors can also be achieved in the limited range of parameters by using suitable dispersion models. These models have the advantage of saving computational time. Dispersion models for coupled microstrip lines are described in the following subsection.

8.3.3 Dispersion Models

It has been observed [26] that the LSE-mode model for the dispersion in a single microstrip line can be used for coupled microstrip lines also. For its application to coupled microstrip lines, Z_{om} in Equations (1.55) and (1.57) should represent even and odd mode impedances of the total parallel-coupled configuration rather than that of a single line of the coupled pair. Relations (1.55) to (1.57) are rewritten below

$$\epsilon_{re}(f) = \epsilon_r - \frac{\epsilon_r - \epsilon_{re}(0)}{1+G(f/f_p)^2} \tag{8.73}$$

where

$$f_p = \frac{Z_{om}}{2\mu_o h} \tag{8.74}$$

$$G \approx 0.6 + 0.009\, Z_{om} \tag{8.75}$$

For the even mode, total mode impedance is half that of a single line of the coupled pair since the two strips are at the same potential and the total current is twice that of a single strip. Therefore, the effect of dispersion on ϵ_{re} for the even mode can be computed by substituting $Z_{oe}/2$ for Z_{om} in Equations (8.74) and (8.75). In the case of the odd mode, the two strips are at opposite potentials, and the voltage between the strips is twice that of a single strip to ground. Thus Z_{om} should be replaced by $2\,Z_{oo}$ for the odd mode. Consequently, Equations (8.74) and (8.75) for constants f_p and G may be written for the two modes as follows:

$$f_p = \begin{cases} \dfrac{Z_{oe}}{4\mu_o h} & \text{even mode} \\ \\ \dfrac{Z_{oo}}{\mu_o h} & \text{odd mode} \end{cases} \tag{8.76}$$

$$G = \begin{cases} 0.6 + 0.0045\,Z_{oe} & \text{even mode} \\ \\ 0.6 + 0.018\,Z_{oo} & \text{odd mode} \end{cases} \tag{8.77}$$

The odd mode dielectric constant is less dispersive compared to the even mode dielectric constant. For example, the increase in the effective dielectric constant is about 2 percent for the odd mode and about 6 percent for the even mode at a frequency of 10 GHz for 50 ohm coupled microstrip lines on a 25-mil alumina substrate. Dispersion at other frequencies can be obtained from Figure 8.11.

Dispersion in coupled microstrip lines has also been described using the coupling between a TEM line and a homogeneous TE line for each of the even and odd modes [27]. This is an extension of the method described earlier (Section 1.3) for dispersion in a single microstrip. In this model also, the effective dielectric constant for the two modes can be obtained from Equation (1.63) by replacing Z_{om} by $Z_{oe}/2$ for the even mode, and $2Z_{oo}$ for the odd mode. No such model has been reported for variation in coupled line impedances with frequency. Numerical results shown in Figure 8.6 indicate that impedances increase with frequency [23]. The rate of increase for the odd mode is very small for frequencies up to 10 GHz for microstrip lines on alumina substrate.

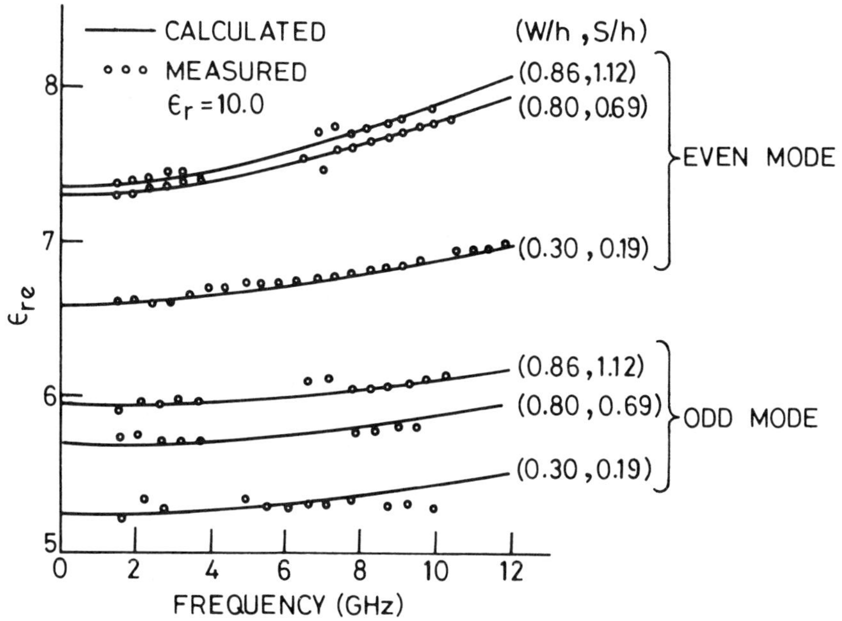

Figure 8.11 Measured and Calculated Dispersion in ϵ_{re} for Symmetric Coupled Microstrip Lines (from [26])

8.4 MEASUREMENTS ON COUPLED MICROSTRIP LINES

Symmetrical coupled microstrip lines are characterized by even and odd mode impedances and even and odd mode propagation constants. Knowledge of these characteristics is essential for designing directional couplers and edge-coupled resonators. Under ordinary conditions, both of the modes are excited and it is difficult to determine the odd and even mode parameters from the measured data. One way to measure these characteristics is to selectively excite one mode and measure its characteristics. The selective excitation of modes and measurements become easier with the use of a Microwave Network Analyzer. Measurements of impedance and phase constants are described in the following subsections.

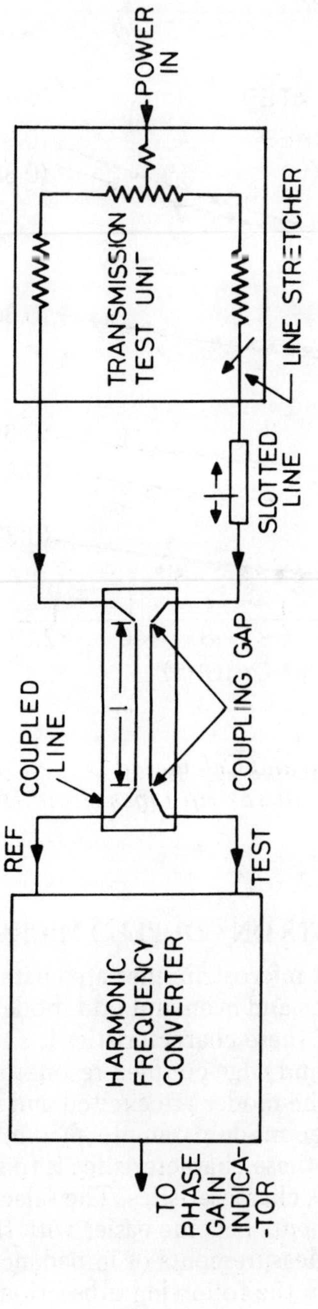

Figure 8.12 Test Set Up for Measuring Even and Odd Mode Impedances of Coupled Lines

8.4.1 Impedance Measurements

The setup for measuring even and odd mode impedances is illustrated in Figure 8.12 [28]. As shown, the signal from the source is divided equally into two transmission lines. The path length of one of these lines is adjustable so that the relative phase of the waves propagating in them can be controlled for selectively exciting the even or odd mode. The amplitude ratio of the waves is unity. The relative phase and amplitude can be measured using a harmonic frequency converter and a phase-gain indicator (two subunits of the network analyser system).

The coupled microstrip section is now introduced between the transmission test unit and harmonic frequency converter. The mode of excitation can be selected by controlling the phase. The phase indicator should read 0° for even mode excitation, 180° for odd mode excitation.

Characteristic impedance can be determined from the VSWR measurement. For measuring VSWR, a slotted line should be inserted in one arm between the transmission test unit and the coupled lines. A compensating air line length should be inserted in the other arm. The measurements should preferably be carried out at a frequency where the coupling length is approximately $\lambda_m/4$, because at this wavelength the effect of the even or odd mode impedance on VSWR is at a maximum. At the same time, the effect of any discontinuity capacitance is minimum.

Even and odd mode impedances can be obtained from the following relations

$$Z_{oe} = Z_o\sqrt{VSWR_e}\,, \quad Z_{oo} = Z_o/\sqrt{VSWR_o} \tag{8.78}$$

since Z_{oe} is greater than Z_o and Z_{oo} is less than Z_o. $VSWR_e$ and $VSWR_o$ are the VSWR values for even and odd mode excitations, respectively.

8.4.2 Phase Constant Measurements

The phase constants for the two modes can be determined by measuring the resonance frequencies corresponding to these modes. Loading effects on the resonator due to the transmission test unit and the harmonic frequency converter can be minimized by introducing coupling gaps between them and the coupled lines, as shown in Figure 8.13. The coupled pair will act as a lightly loaded single resonator and will exhibit two resonant frequencies. The odd mode

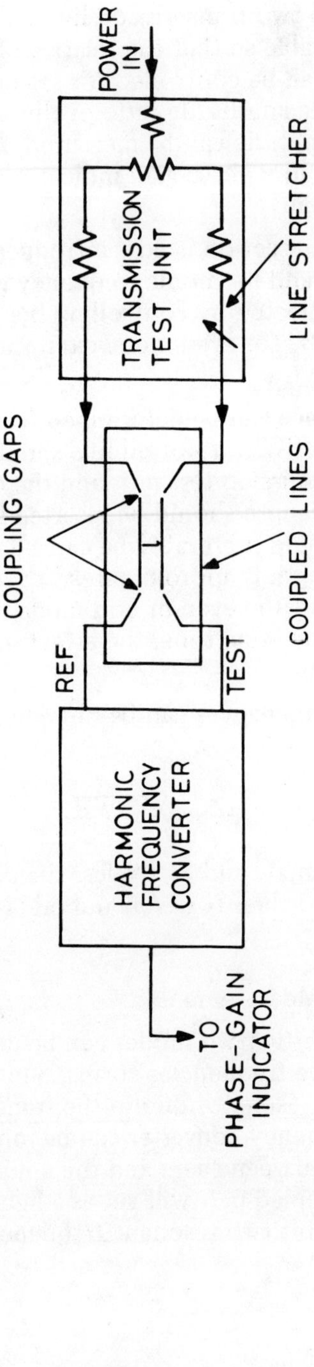

Figure 8.13 Set-Up for Measuring Phase Velocities in Coupled Lines

resonance frequency will be higher than the even mode resonance frequency. While calculating guide wavelength from resonance frequency the effect of gap capacitance should be taken into account. The guide wavelength for a half wave coupled section is given by

$$\lambda = 2(\ell + 2\Delta\ell_g) \tag{8.79}$$

where ℓ is the length of resonant line and $\Delta\ell_g$ is the equivalent line length associated with the gap capacitance C_g, given approximately by

$$\Delta\ell_g = f\lambda_m C_g Z_o \tag{8.80}$$

and f is the resonance frequency for the half-wave resonator.

Even and odd mode resonances may also be obtained by proper terminations at the two ends of a coupled line section [29]. If a coupled line section is $(2n+1)\lambda/4$ long and the two ends are connected in parallel, an even mode resonator is obtained when one end is open and the other is grounded. This situation is shown in Figure 8.14(a).

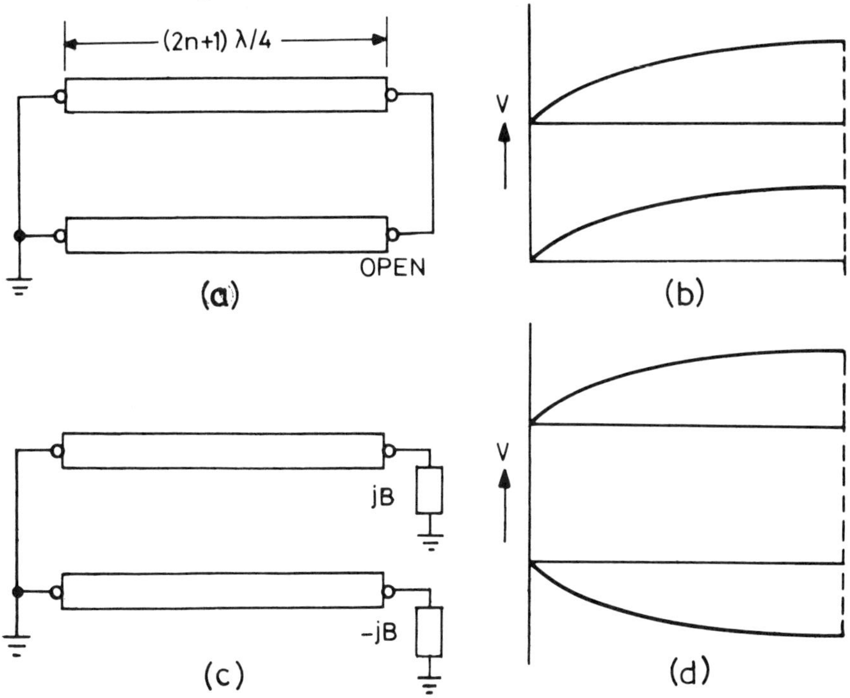

Figure 8.14 Voltage Distribution for Even and Odd Mode Excitations

Voltage distribution on two lines (for n = 0 case) is shown in Figure 8.14(b). Since the two lines are connected in parallel at both the ends, the voltages on these two lines are in phase everywhere. This structure behaves as an even mode resonator for any excitation, and the network analyser setup is not needed for exciting the even mode. A similar arrangement for an odd mode resonator is shown in Figure 8.14(c). At one end of the coupled section, the two lines are connected in parallel and shorted to ground. This end becomes a voltage node. At the other end the two lines are loaded by two susceptances of opposite sign, and thus the antiphase nature of the voltage waveform on two lines is ensured.

Even and odd mode parameters can now be evaluated by measuring resonance frequency, Q-factor, and input VSWR for two types of resonators [29].

8.5 DESIGN CONSIDERATIONS FOR COUPLED MICROSTRIP LINES

Coupled microstrip structures are characterized by the characteristic impedances (or admittances) and phase velocities for the two modes. The analysis of coupled microstrip lines for these characteristics can be carried out by using one of the methods outlined in Sections 8.2 and 8.3. Although, the analysis can be carried out to determine the characteristics for a given set of coupled line parameters, it does not provide simple design equations for the direct synthesis of coupled line circuits. For purposes of synthesis, one prepares either a table or a graph for a number of sets of coupled line parameters and uses these tables etc. to obtain the desired information. This procedure is time consuming and may also involve some sacrifice in accuracy. However, to avoid these disadvantages, one can write synthesis design equations instead. These equations may be derived from the results of analysis. In order to save computation time the analysis results may also be written in the form of closed form equations.

Closed form approximate expressions can be used to initiate the analysis or synthesis procedure. These can also be used as final results whenever the demand on specifications of the circuit is not very tight. Closed form approximate expressions for the capacitances of symmetric coupled microstrip lines are derived in the following subsection.

8.5.1 Design Equations [30]

Design equations for coupled microstrip lines should relate even and odd mode impedances and effective dielectric constants to coupled line geometry; i.e., strip width W, spacing S between the strips, dielectric thickness h and dielectric constant ϵ_r. One may write design equations for these characteristics directly in terms of the parameters of coupled lines. Alternatively, static capacitances for the coupled line geometry may be used as an intermediate step. It is seen that the latter approach yields simpler design equations. Therefore, even and odd mode characteristics will be described in terms of static capacitances.

Even Mode Capacitance

As shown in Figure 8.15(a) even mode capacitance C_e can be divided

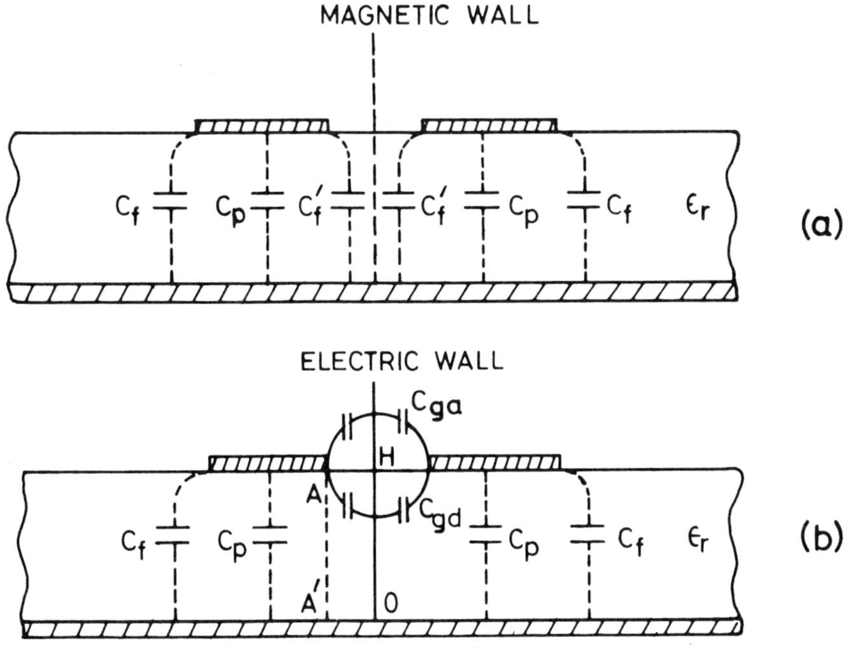

Figure 8.15 Analysis of Coupled Microstrip Lines in Terms of Capacitances (a) Even Mode Capacitances and (b) Odd Mode Capacitances

into three capacitances; i.e., $C_{even} = C_p + C_f + C_f'$. C_p denotes parallel plate capacitance between the strip and the ground plane. C_f is a fringe capacitance which can be evaluated from the capacitance of single microstrip geometry and the value of C_p. The term C_f' accounts for the modification of fringe capacitance C_f of a single line due to the presence of another line. Expressions for C_p, C_f and C_f' are given below

$$C_p = \epsilon_o \epsilon_r W/h \tag{8.81}$$

$$2C_f = \sqrt{\epsilon_{re}}/cZ_{om} - \epsilon_o \epsilon_r W/h \tag{8.82}$$

$$C_f' = \frac{C_f}{1 + A(h/s)\tanh(10S/h)} \sqrt{\frac{\epsilon_r}{\epsilon_{re}}} \tag{8.83}$$

where $A = \exp[-0.1 \exp(2.33 - 2.53 W/h)]$

Odd Mode Capacitance

Odd mode capacitance C_o can be decomposed into four constituents: C_f, C_p, C_{gd} and C_{ga} as shown in Figure 8.15(b); i.e.,

$$C_o = C_f + C_p + C_{gd} + C_{ga} \tag{8.84}$$

Expressions for C_f and C_p are the same as those given earlier in the case of C_e. Capacitance C_{ga} describes the gap capacitance in air. Its value can be obtained from the capacitance of a slotline of width W with air as dielectric. Owyang and Wu [31] give the following equation for C_{ga}:

$$C_{ga} = \epsilon_o \frac{K(k')}{K(k)}, \quad k = \frac{S/h}{S/h + 2W/h} \tag{8.85}$$

where K(k) and K(k′) denote the elliptic function and its complement. Use of simplified expressions for K(k′)/K(k) yields the following value for C_{ga}:

$$C_{ga} = \frac{\epsilon_o}{\pi} \ln \left\{ 2 \frac{1 + \sqrt{k'}}{1 - \sqrt{k'}} \right\} \quad \text{for } 0 \leq k^2 \leq 0.5 \tag{8.86}$$

$$C_{ga} = \pi\epsilon_o / \ln \left\{ 2 \frac{1 + \sqrt{k}}{1 - \sqrt{k}} \right\} \quad \text{for } 0.5 \leq k^2 \leq 1 \tag{8.87}$$

where

$$k'^2 = 1 - k^2$$

The last term C_{gd} represents the capacitance value due to the electric flux in the region formed by planes AA′, A′O, OH and the air-dielectric interface. Its value is evaluated as follows

$$C_{gd} = \frac{\epsilon_o \epsilon_r}{\pi} \ln \coth\left(\frac{\pi S}{4h}\right) + 0.65\, C_f \left\{ \frac{0.02}{S/h} \sqrt{\epsilon_r} + \left(1 - \frac{1}{\epsilon_r^2}\right) \right\} \tag{8.88}$$

The first term in Equation (8.88) is obtained from coupled stripline geometry. The second term represents its modification for coupled microstrip.

Characteristic Impedances

Characteristic impedances Z_{oe} and Z_{oo} can be obtained from Equations (8.45 - 8.47) and may be written as follows

$$Z_{oe} = [c\sqrt{C_e^a C_e}\,]^{-1} \tag{8.89}$$

$$Z_{oo} = [c\sqrt{C_o^a C_o}\,]^{-1} \tag{8.90}$$

where C_e^a and C_o^a are even and odd mode capacitances for the coupled microstrip configuration with air as dielectric.

The value of impedances obtained by using the above design equations have an error less than 3 percent for the parameters lying in the range $\epsilon_r \geqslant 1$, $0.2 \leqslant W/h \leqslant 2$ and $0.05 \leqslant S/h \leqslant 2$.

Effective Dielectric Constants

Effective dielectric constants ϵ_{re}^e and ϵ_{re}^o for even and odd modes, respectively, can be obtained from C_e and C_o by the relations given below

$$\epsilon_{re}^e = C_e/C_e^a \tag{8.91}$$

and

$$\epsilon_{re}^o = C_o/C_o^a \tag{8.92}$$

Design equations for the analysis and synthesis of coupled microstrip lines have been reported by Akhtarzad *et. al.* [32], also. But their results indicate an error of the order of 10 percent. Nomograms for the design of coupled lines have been reported in [33-34]. A scaling procedure is also available [35-36] for determining even and odd mode impedances which requires for its usage the accurate design values for any other dielectric.

The capacitance expressions discussed above are valid for coupled microstrip lines with zero strip thickness. In actual practice, the metal strips have finite thickness, and the coupled lines are enclosed in a metallic box for purposes of handling etc. In addition, the effect of fabrication tolerances and the finite amount of losses should also be considered while designing a coupled line circuit. These effects are considered next.

Effect of Strip Thickness

When the strip conductors are of finite thickness t, C_e can be evaluated using Equation (8.81) for C_p and modifying C_f, Equation (8.82), to include the effect of strip thickness. In this case C_f becomes [30]

$$C_f(t) = 0.5 \left\{ \frac{\sqrt{\epsilon_{re}(t)}}{cZ_{om}(t)} - \epsilon_o \epsilon_r \frac{W}{h} \right\} \tag{8.93}$$

where $\epsilon_{re}(t)$ and $Z_{om}(t)$ are the characteristics of microstrip with finite thickness t and are given by Equations (1.124-1.127). The increase in the value of C_o due to finite thickness t is given by $C_f(t)$, Equation (8.93), and another term representing gap capacitance evaluated from

$$C_{gt} = 2\epsilon_o t/S \tag{8.94}$$

Due to the increase in even and odd mode capacitances with finite strip thickness, the even and odd mode impedances are expected to decrease. The amount of decrease in impedance can be evaluated. It is seen that the percentage of increase in C_o^a or C_e^a with thickness is more than that in C_o or C_e. Therefore, effective dielectric constants $\epsilon_{re}^e(t)$ and $\epsilon_{re}^o(t)$, should decrease with thickness. The percentage of decrease in $\epsilon_{re}^o(t)$ is found to be more than that in $\epsilon_{re}^e(t)$ because of an additional gap capacitance C_{gt} with air as dielectric. These observations are verified by exact numerical results available in [16]. The percentage of increase in C_o is found to be twice that of C_e.

Effect of Enclosure

When coupled microstrip lines are enclosed in a metallic box the electric field lines in air terminate prematurely at the walls of the box. This will give rise to an increase in the mode capacitances resulting in a decrease in the mode impedances and effective dielectric constants. The percentage of decrease in odd mode values with the size of the enclosure should be less than that for the even mode because C_o is greater than C_e without the enclosure. Figures 8.16(a) and (b), obtained from exact numerical evaluation, show this trend [15].

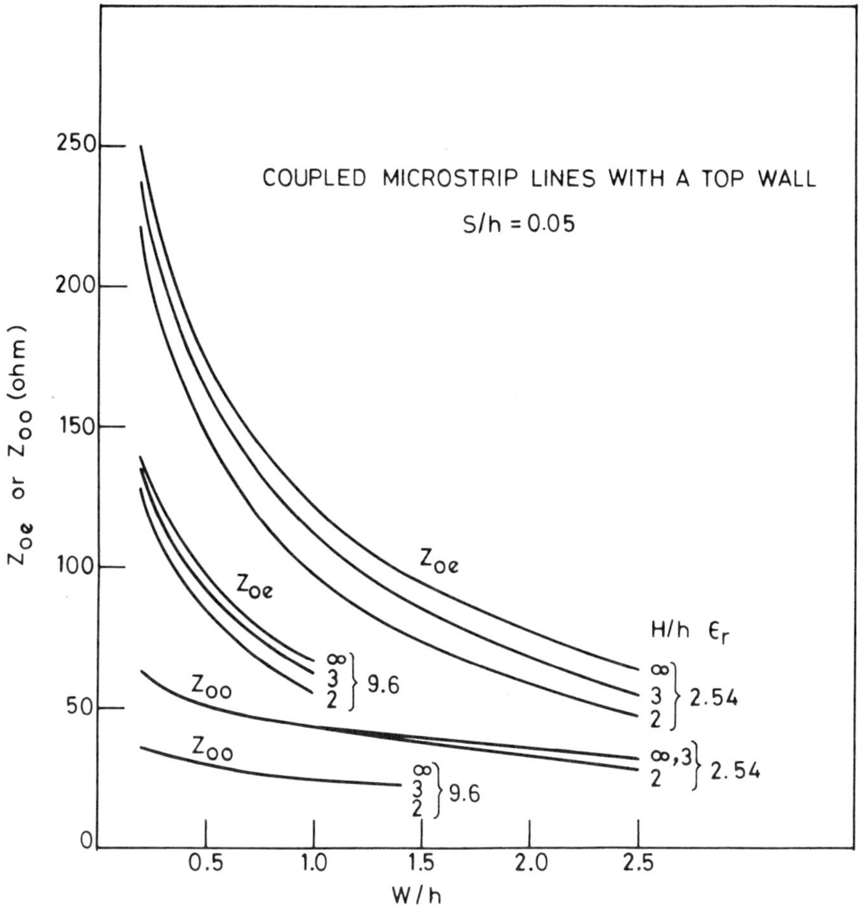

Figure 8.16(a) Variation of Characteristic Impedances of Coupled Microstrip Lines With Shield-Height Ratio H/h

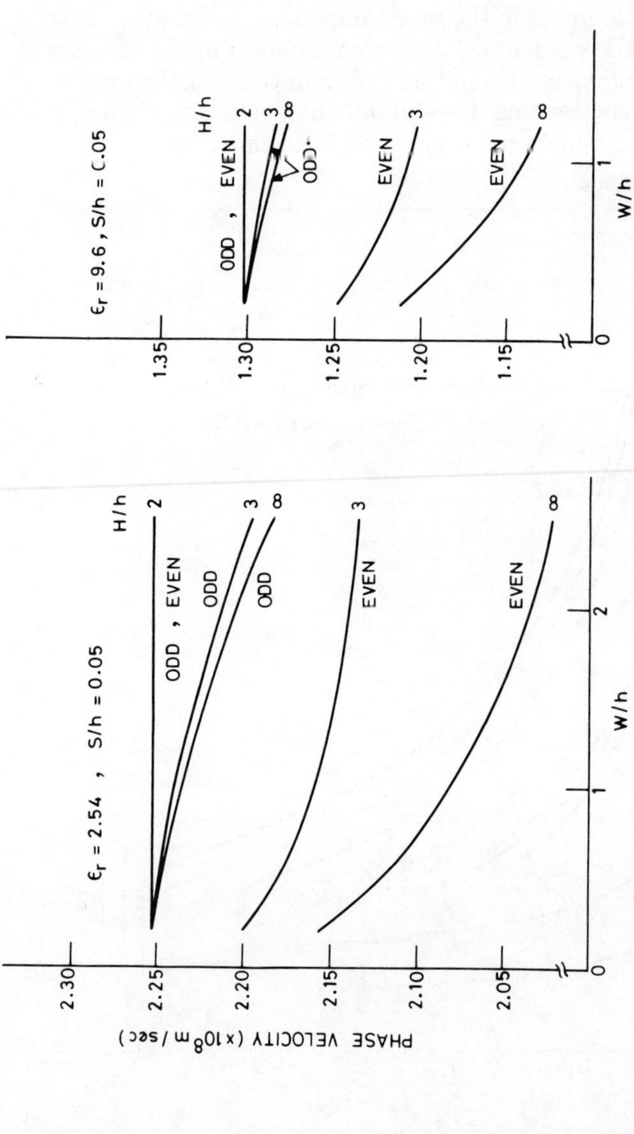

Figure 8.16(b) Variation of Phase Velocities in Coupled Microstrip Lines With Shield-Height Ratio H/h

8.5.2 Losses [37]

Coupled microstrip line also has two types of losses: ohmic and dielectric. The even and odd mode attenuation constants due to ohmic losses in coupled microstrip lines can be determined using Wheeler's incremental inductance formula. Its application to the coupled line configuration (Figure 8.17) gives for the odd mode

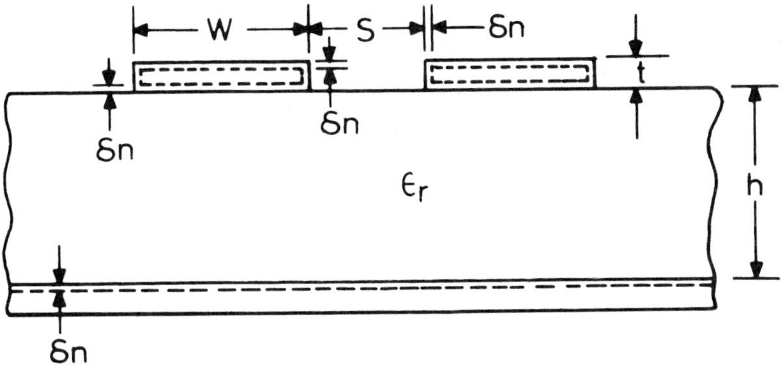

Figure 8.17 Coupled Microstrip Lines Configuration for the Calculation of Ohmic Losses

attenuation constant (due to strips only)

$$\alpha_{co} = \frac{8.686\, R_s}{240\pi\, Z_{oo}} \frac{\delta(\sqrt{\epsilon_{re}^{o}}\, Z_{oo})}{\delta n} \text{ (dB/unit length)} \tag{8.95}$$

where

$$\frac{\delta(\sqrt{\epsilon_{re}^{o}}\, Z_{oo})}{\delta n} = \frac{2}{h}\left\{\left(1 - \frac{S}{2h}\right)\frac{\partial(\sqrt{\epsilon_{re}^{o}}\, Z_{oo})}{\partial(S/h)} - \left(1 + \frac{t}{2h}\right)\frac{\partial(\sqrt{\epsilon_{re}^{o}}\, Z_{oo})}{\partial(t/h)} - \left(1 + \frac{W}{2h}\right)\frac{\partial(\sqrt{\epsilon_{re}^{o}}\, Z_{oo})}{\partial(W/h)}\right\} \tag{8.96}$$

Similarly, the even mode attenuation constant is given by

$$\alpha_{ce} = \frac{8.686\, R_s}{240\pi\, Z_{oe}} \frac{\delta(\sqrt{\epsilon_{re}^{e}}\, Z_{oe})}{\delta n} \text{ (dB/unit length)} \tag{8.97}$$

where

$$\frac{\delta(\sqrt{\epsilon_{re}^{e}}\,Z_{oe})}{\delta n}=\frac{2}{h}\left\{\left(1-\frac{S}{2h}\right)\frac{\partial(\sqrt{\epsilon_{re}^{e}}\,Z_{oe})}{\partial(S/h)}-\left(1+\frac{t}{2h}\right)\frac{\partial(\sqrt{\epsilon_{re}^{e}}\,Z_{oe})}{\partial(t/h)}\right.$$

$$\left.-\left(1+\frac{W}{2h}\right)\frac{\partial(\sqrt{\epsilon_{re}^{e}}\,Z_{oe})}{\partial(W/h)}\right\} \qquad (8.98)$$

In the above relations R_s is the sheet resistivity of metallization. It is observed that the odd mode attenuation constant is always higher than the even mode value. Also, it is more sensitive to changes in the spacing S between the lines than is α_{ce}. This is borne out by some of the representative values given in Table 8.1.

Table 8.1/Even and Odd Mode Attenuation Constants Due to Ohmic Losses in Coupled Microstrip Lines

$\epsilon_r = 9.5$, W/h = 0.87, t/h = 0.0047, f = 8 GHz

S/h	Even mode dB/cm	Odd mode dB/cm
0.212	0.028	0.088
0.162	0.028	0.101

The attenuation due to dielectric loss α_d is given by [37]

$$\alpha_{do} = 27.3\,\frac{\epsilon_r}{\sqrt{\epsilon_{re}^{o}}}\,\frac{\epsilon_{re}^{o}-1}{\epsilon_r-1}\,\frac{\tan\delta}{\lambda_o} \quad \text{(dB/unit length)} \qquad (8.99)$$

$$\alpha_{de} = 27.3\,\frac{\epsilon_r}{\sqrt{\epsilon_{re}^{e}}}\,\frac{\epsilon_{re}^{e}-1}{\epsilon_r-1}\,\frac{\tan\delta}{\lambda_o} \quad \text{(dB/unit length)} \qquad (8.100)$$

where $\tan\delta$ is the loss tangent of the dielectric substrate.

The total attenuation constants α_o and α_e for odd and even modes are given by

$$\alpha_o = \alpha_{co} + \alpha_{do} \qquad (8.101)$$

and

$$\alpha_e = \alpha_{ce} + \alpha_{de} \tag{8.102}$$

The resultant even and odd mode impedances of lossy coupled lines are complex and may be obtained from the following relations

$$Z_{oo}(\text{Lossy}) = Z_{oo} \left\{ 1 - j\frac{\alpha_{co}}{\beta_o} + j\frac{\alpha_{do}}{\beta_o} \right\} \tag{8.103}$$

$$Z_{oe}(\text{Lossy}) = Z_{oe} \left\{ 1 - j\frac{\alpha_{ce}}{\beta_e} + j\frac{\alpha_{de}}{\beta_e} \right\} \tag{8.104}$$

The relations for impedances are useful for studying the effect of line losses on circuit performance, e.g., directivity of a directional coupler.

8.5.3 Effect of Fabrication Tolerances [38]

The sensitivity analysis described earlier for other lines can also be applied to coupled transmission lines to account for the effect of tolerances. Since coupled lines are characterized by even and odd mode impedances and phase velocities, the effect of tolerances on coupled lines can be represented in terms of the effect on these characteristics.

The maximum change in the value of impedances may be written as

$$\left|\frac{\Delta Z_{ox}}{Z_o}\right|_{max} = \left|\frac{\Delta W}{W} S_W^{Z_{ox}}\right| + \left|\frac{\Delta S}{S} S_S^{Z_{ox}}\right| + \left|\frac{\Delta h}{h} S_h^{Z_{ox}}\right| + \left|\frac{\Delta \epsilon_r}{\epsilon_r} S_{\epsilon_r}^{Z_{ox}}\right| \tag{8.105}$$

where x designates the mode, even or odd. Similarly the maximum change in the effective dielectric constants is given by

$$\left|\frac{\Delta \epsilon_{re}^x}{\epsilon_{re}}\right|_{max} = \left|\frac{\Delta W}{W} S_W^{\epsilon_{re}^x}\right| + \left|\frac{\Delta S}{S} S_S^{\epsilon_{re}^x}\right| + \left|\frac{\Delta h}{h} S_h^{\epsilon_{re}^x}\right| + \left|\frac{\Delta \epsilon_r}{\epsilon_r} S_{\epsilon_r}^{\epsilon_{re}^x}\right| \tag{8.106}$$

The above relations can be utilized to determine the change in coupled line characteristics like VSWR performance and change in coupling constant. Alternatively, for a given set of values of ΔZ_{ox} and $\Delta \epsilon_{re}^x$ the trade-off between tolerances can be determined i.e. tolerance in one parameter may be increased or decreased at the cost of tolerances in other parameters.

The effect of tolerances on VSWR performance and coupling constant are described below

VSWR Performance of Coupled Microstrip Lines

The VSWR performance of coupled microstrip lines may be obtained from

$$\text{VSWR} = \left[1 - \frac{|\Delta Z_o|_{max}}{Z_o}\right]^{-1} \tag{8.107}$$

where the change in coupler impedance Z_o $(=\sqrt{Z_{oe} \cdot Z_{oo}})$ represented by $|\Delta Z_o|_{max}$ is obtained from

$$\frac{|\Delta Z_o|_{max}}{Z_o} = \left|\frac{\Delta Z_{oo}}{Z_{oo}} S_{Z_{oo}}^{Z_o}\right| + \left|\frac{\Delta Z_{oe}}{Z_{oe}} S_{Z_{oe}}^{Z_o}\right| \tag{8.108}$$

Since $Z_o = \sqrt{Z_{oe} Z_{oo}}$,

$$S_{Z_{oe}}^{Z_o} = S_{Z_{oo}}^{Z_o} = 0.5 \tag{8.109}$$

and Equation (8.108) becomes

$$\frac{|\Delta Z_o|_{max}}{Z_o} = 0.5 \left[\left|\frac{\Delta Z_{oo}}{Z_{oo}}\right| + \left|\frac{\Delta Z_{oe}}{Z_{oe}}\right|\right] \tag{8.110}$$

where

$$\left|\frac{\Delta Z_{oe}}{Z_{oe}}\right| = \left|\frac{\Delta W}{W} S_W^{Z_{oe}}\right| + \left|\frac{\Delta S}{S} S_S^{Z_{oe}}\right| + \left|\frac{\Delta \epsilon_r}{\epsilon_r} S_{\epsilon_r}^{Z_{oe}}\right| + \left|\frac{\Delta h}{h} S_h^{Z_{oe}}\right| \tag{8.111}$$

and a similar relation for ΔZ_{oo}.

Change in the Coupling Constant C

The coupling constant C is defined by

$$C = \frac{Z_{oe} - Z_{oo}}{Z_{oe} + Z_{oo}} \tag{8.112}$$

Since the coupling constant is a function of W, h, S and ϵ_r, one can write

$$\frac{|\Delta C|_{max}}{C} = \left|\frac{\Delta W}{W} S_W^C\right| + \left|\frac{\Delta h}{h} S_h^C\right| + \left|\frac{\Delta S}{S} S_S^C\right| + \left|\frac{\Delta \epsilon_r}{\epsilon_r} S_{\epsilon_r}^C\right| \tag{8.113}$$

Using Equations (8.110) and (8.113) the effect of tolerances on the coupled microstrip characteristics can be estimated. It is shown in Figure 8.18 for VSWR performance [38]. Figure 8.19 presents the

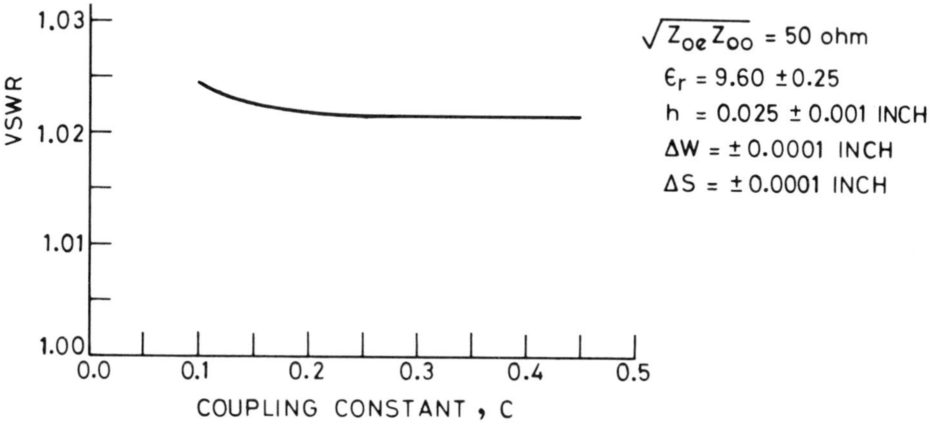

Figure 8.18 VSWR Caused by Tolerances in W, h, S and ϵ_r

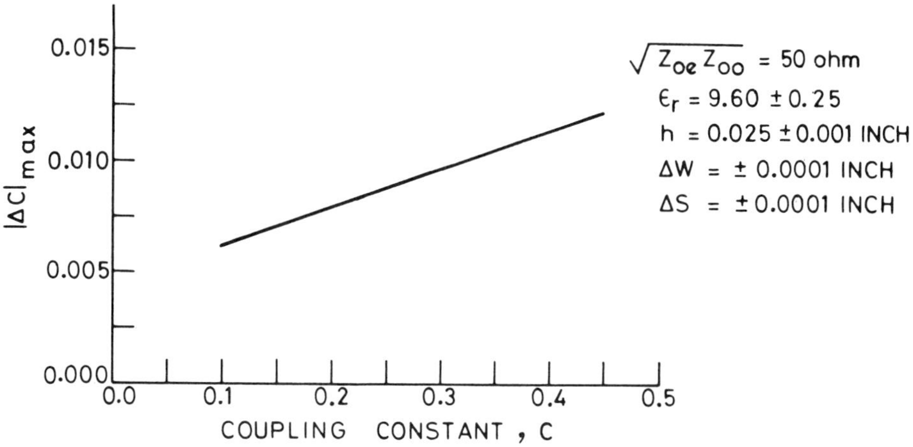

Figure 8.19 Change in Coupling Caused by Tolerances in W, h, S and ϵ_r

change in the coupling constant for $\epsilon_r = 9.6$ [38]. It may be observed from these figures that the effect of tolerances increases with the increase in the coupling constant. Further analysis shows that the dielectric thickness h and the gap width S are the most critical parameters affecting the coupling constant [38]. Also, VSWR is mainly controlled by variations in h and ϵ_r.

8.5.4 Coupled Microstrip Lines With Dielectric Overlays

The analysis of coupled microstrip lines reported in Section 8.3 shows that the effective dielectric constants for even and odd modes of coupled microstrip lines are not equal. The even mode effective dielectric constant is higher than its odd mode counterpart value. This is because of the relatively higher density of the electric field lines in air for the odd mode. On alumina substrate the difference is normally less than 12 percent. Although different even and odd mode phase velocities produce only a small perturbation on the coupler impedance $Z_o = \sqrt{Z_{oo} \cdot Z_{oe}}$ and midband voltage coupling coefficient C (Equation 8.112) in most practical cases, the change in directively of the coupler is significant. From infinite directivity for an ideal coupler, the directivity of a microstrip 10-dB coupler on alumina substrate with $v_{odd}/v_{even} = 1.125$ decreases to about 12.5 dB. The deterioration in directivity is higher for loose coupling [39].

If a dielectric slab (having dielectric constant close to that of the substrate) is placed over the gap and a portion of the lines (Figure 8.20), the odd mode effective dielectric constant will increase more

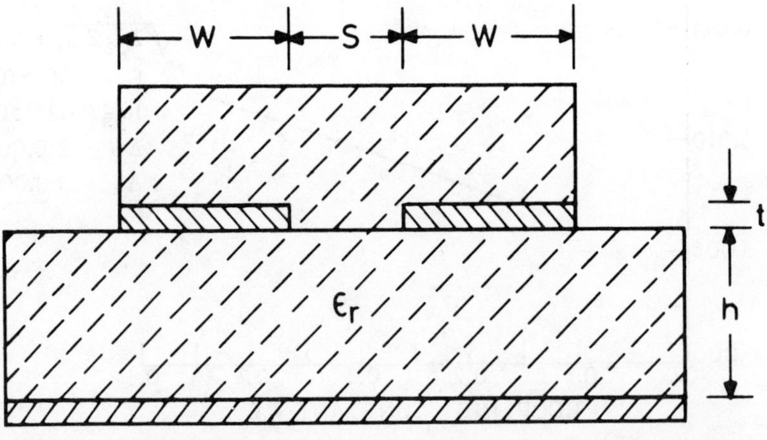

Figure 8.20 Coupled Microstrip Lines Configuration With Dielectric Overlay

than that of the even mode. The increase in ϵ_{re}^{o} will be higher for thick overlay slabs of higher dielectric constants. With the right amount of overlay thickness and dielectric constant, the effective dielectric constants for the two modes can be made equal. The use of a dielectric overlay not only improves the velocity ratio, but it also tightens the midband coupling compared to coupled microstrip lines without dielectric overlays. One would also expect a decrease in coupler impedance Z_o because of the increased effective dielectric constants for the two modes.

The change in the amount of coupling and impedance due to the overlay can be determined analytically if the equalized value of phase velocity is known. For coupled lines without overlay we know that the coupler impedance Z_o is given by

$$Z_o = \sqrt{Z_{oo}\, Z_{oe}} \tag{8.114}$$

with

$$Z_{oo} = Z_{oo}^{a}/\sqrt{\epsilon_{re}^{o}} \tag{8.115}$$

and

$$Z_{oe} = Z_{oe}^{a}/\sqrt{\epsilon_{re}^{e}} \tag{8.116}$$

Now, with the dielectric overlay in place, let the effective dielectric constant for both modes be ϵ_{re}^{c} (where c stands for coupled lines). Then, the new values of impedances are given by

$$Z'_{oo} = Z_{oo}^{a}/\sqrt{\epsilon_{re}^{c}} = Z_{oo}\sqrt{\epsilon_{re}^{o}/\epsilon_{re}^{c}} \tag{8.117}$$

$$Z'_{oe} = Z_{oe}^{a}/\sqrt{\epsilon_{re}^{c}} = Z_{oe}\sqrt{\epsilon_{re}^{e}/\epsilon_{re}^{c}} \tag{8.118}$$

Therefore,

$$Z'_o = \sqrt{Z'_{oo}\, Z'_{oe}} = Z_o\sqrt{\epsilon_{re}^{o}\, \epsilon_{re}^{e}/(\epsilon_{re}^{c})^2} \tag{8.119}$$

The change in coupling can be estimated as follows:

The voltage coupling coefficient with overlay is

$$C' = \frac{Z'_{oe} - Z'_{oo}}{Z'_{oe} + Z'_{oo}} \tag{8.120}$$

or

$$C' = \frac{Z_{oe} - Z_{oo}\,g}{Z_{oe} + Z_{oo}\,g} \tag{8.121}$$

where $g = \sqrt{\epsilon_{re}^{o}/\epsilon_{re}^{e}}$

Substituting the value of Z_{oe}/Z_{oo} from Equation (8.112) gives

$$C' = \frac{(1+C) - (1-C)\,g}{(1+C) + (1-C)\,g} \tag{8.122}$$

It shows that the new coupling C' depends only on the ratio of ϵ_{re}^{e} and ϵ_{re}^{o} and the coupling of the uncompensated coupler. It does not depend on the final value of ϵ_{re}^{c} nor on Z_o'.

The final value of ϵ_{re}^{c}, at which even and odd mode phase velocities are equal, has been determined empirically by Buntschuh [39]. The relation for ϵ_{re}^{c} is given below

$$\epsilon_{re}^{c} = \epsilon_{re}^{e} + \frac{\epsilon_r - \epsilon_{re}^{e}}{1.8}\,(1-e^{-S/h}) \tag{8.123}$$

where ϵ_{re}^{e} is the even mode effective dielectric constant for the uncompensated coupled lines. The dielectric constant and the dimensions of the overlay should be determined empirically.

Wolters *et. al.* [40] have shown that by using a modified overlay, Figure 8.21, one can obtain better equalization of even and odd mode

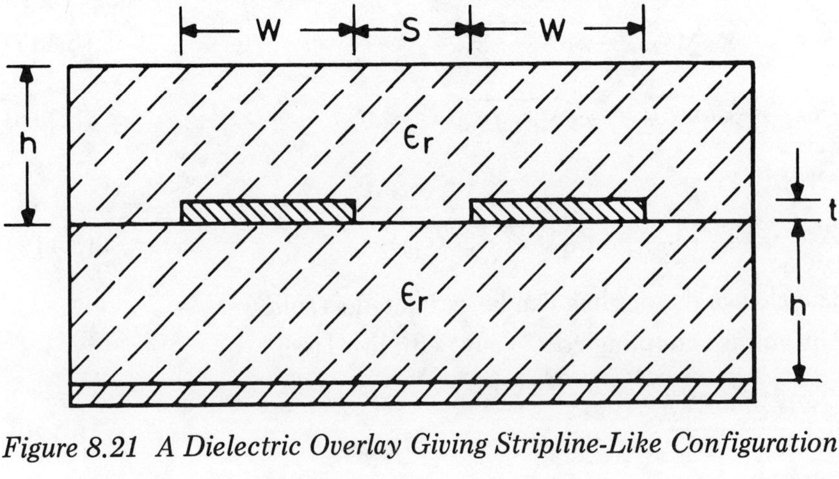

Figure 8.21 A Dielectric Overlay Giving Stripline-Like Configuration

phase velocities. In this case, the overlay thickness and dielectric constant are taken to be the same as that of the substrate. The difference between even and odd mode phase velocities has been found to be less than 1 percent. Such good agreement is due to the fact that the configuration resembles a stripline coupler.

8.5.5 Effect of Dielectric Anisotropy

It has been assumed in the analysis presented in Section 8.3 and in the design equations given in this section that the dielectric substrate is isotropic. However, substrates such as sapphire and Epsilam-10 are anisotropic. This anisotropy can be used to advantage in the design of coupled microstrip lines as shown by Szentkuti [41]. The transformation from anisotropic to the isotropic case can be carried out in the same manner as has been done for single microstrip (discussed in Section 2.4.4). The relative difference between the odd and even mode phase velocities has been plotted in Figure 8.22 for four types

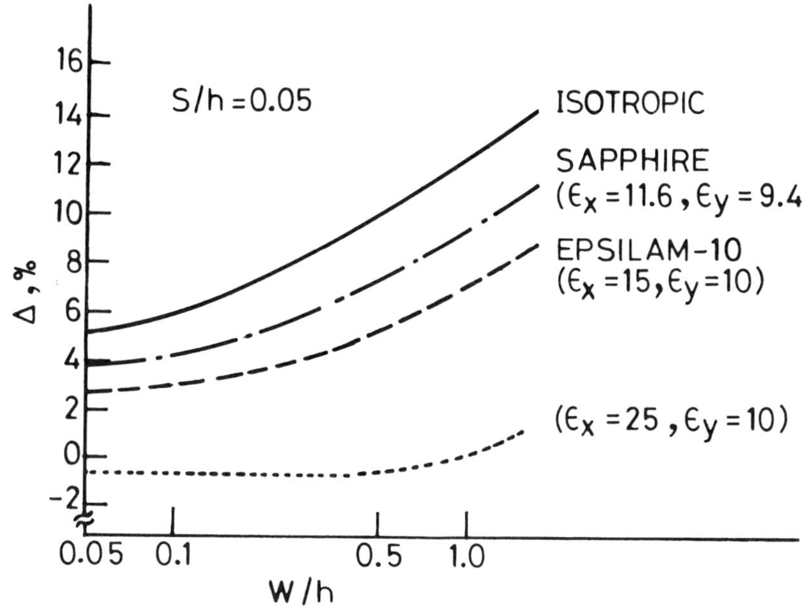

Figure 8.22 Relative Difference Between Odd and Even Mode Phase Velocities for anisotropic substrates (from [41])

of substrates. It may be observed from here that the difference in phase velocities decreases with the increase in ratio $\epsilon_r^x/\epsilon_r^y$, where ϵ_r^x and ϵ_r^y are the x and y components, respectively, of the dielectric constant vector.

8.6 COUPLED SLOTLINES AND COPLANAR WAVEGUIDES

8.6.1 Characteristics of Coupled Slotlines

Coupled slotlines are obtained by separating the two slots by a strip as illustrated in Figure 8.1(b). The width S of the strip controls the coupling coefficient. The electric field configuration for even and odd modes are shown in Figure 8.23. It may be noted that the plane of

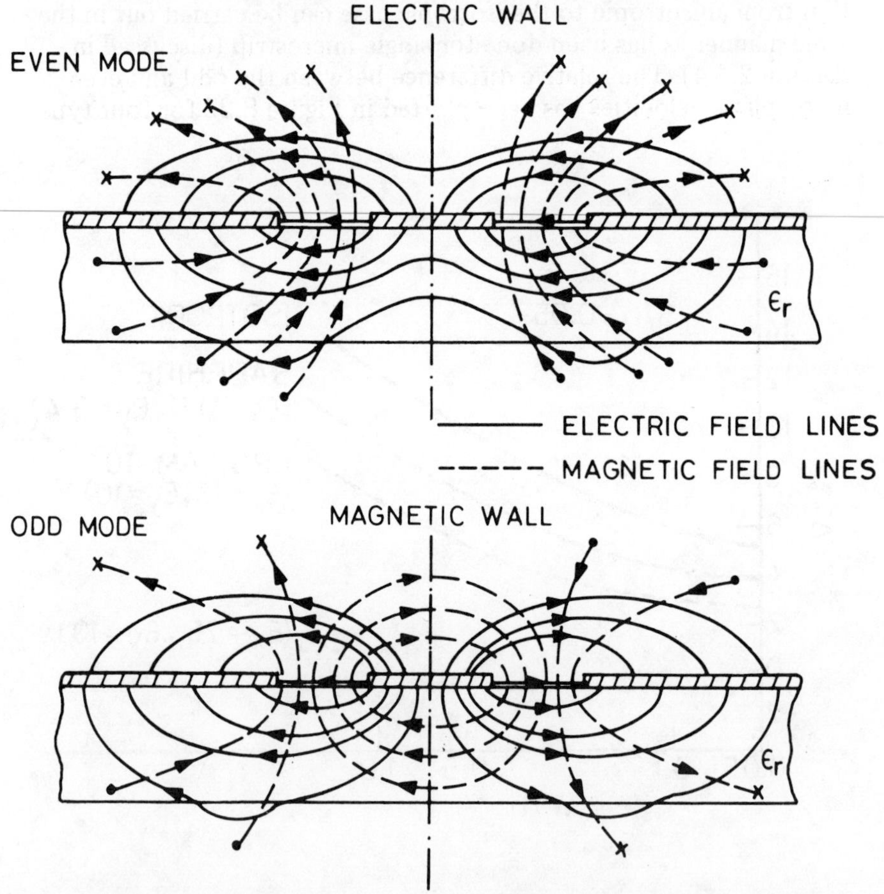

Figure 8.23 Even and Odd Mode Field Configurations in Coupled Slotlines

symmetry for the odd mode of coupled slotlines corresponds to a magnetic wall and not an electric wall as in case of coupled microstrip. This distinction arises because of the fact that for both of these lines the odd mode is characterized by the odd symmetry of the dominant component of the electric field of uncoupled lines. In case of microstrip, the dominant component is parallel to the plane of symmetry, while in case of slotline it is perpendicular to the plane of symmetry. Similarly, the even mode of coupled slotlines is characterized by an electric wall at the plane of symmetry.

Coupled slotlines can be analyzed by using Galerkin's method in the Fourier transform domain. The analysis differs from the analysis of single slotline only in the choice of basis functions. The following expressions for fields, obtained by quasi-static analysis when $h \rightarrow \infty$, may be used as the basis function [42]:

$$E_{xo} = \left[\left\{ 1 - \left(\frac{x-x_o}{W/2} \right)^2 \right\}^{-1/2} - \left\{ 1 - \left(\frac{x+x_o}{W/2} \right)^2 \right\}^{-1/2} \right] \quad \text{for } S/2 \leqslant |x| \leqslant W+S/2 \tag{8.124}$$

$$E_{xe} = \left[\left\{ 1 - \left(\frac{x-x_o}{W/2} \right)^2 \right\}^{-1/2} + \left\{ 1 - \left(\frac{x+x_o}{W/2} \right)^2 \right\}^{-1/2} \right] \quad \text{for } S/2 \leqslant |x| \leqslant W+S/2 \tag{8.125}$$

$$E_{xo} = E_{xe} = 0 \qquad \text{elsewhere} \tag{8.126}$$

$$E_{zo} = j \left[\frac{x-x_o}{W/2} \left\{ 1 - \left(\frac{x-x_o}{W/2} \right)^2 \right\}^{1/2} - \frac{x+x_o}{W/2} \left\{ 1 - \left(\frac{x+x_o}{W/2} \right)^2 \right\}^{1/2} \right]$$

$$\text{for } S/2 \leqslant |x| \leqslant W+S/2 \tag{8.127}$$

$$E_{ze} = j \left[\frac{x-x_o}{W/2} \left\{ 1 - \left(\frac{x-x_o}{W/2} \right)^2 \right\}^{1/2} + \frac{x+x_o}{W/2} \left\{ 1 - \left(\frac{x+x_o}{W/2} \right)^2 \right\}^{1/2} \right]$$

$$\text{for } S/2 \leqslant |x| \leqslant W+S/2 \tag{8.128}$$

$$E_{zo} = E_{ze} = 0 \qquad \text{elsewhere} \tag{8.129}$$

where $x_o = (W+S)/2$

The characteristic impedances for even and odd modes in coupled slots may be defined on the voltage-power basis as given below

$$Z_o = \frac{V_o^2}{(P_z)_{avg}} \tag{8.130}$$

where V_o is the slot voltage given by

$$V_o = \int_{\text{one slot}} E_x \, dx \tag{8.131}$$

$(P_z)_{avg}$ is the time-averaged power flow obtained from

$$(P_z)_{avg} = \tfrac{1}{2} \, \mathrm{Re} \iint E_x H_y^* \, dx \, dy \tag{8.132}$$

The characteristics of coupled slotlines are shown in Figure 8.24 for

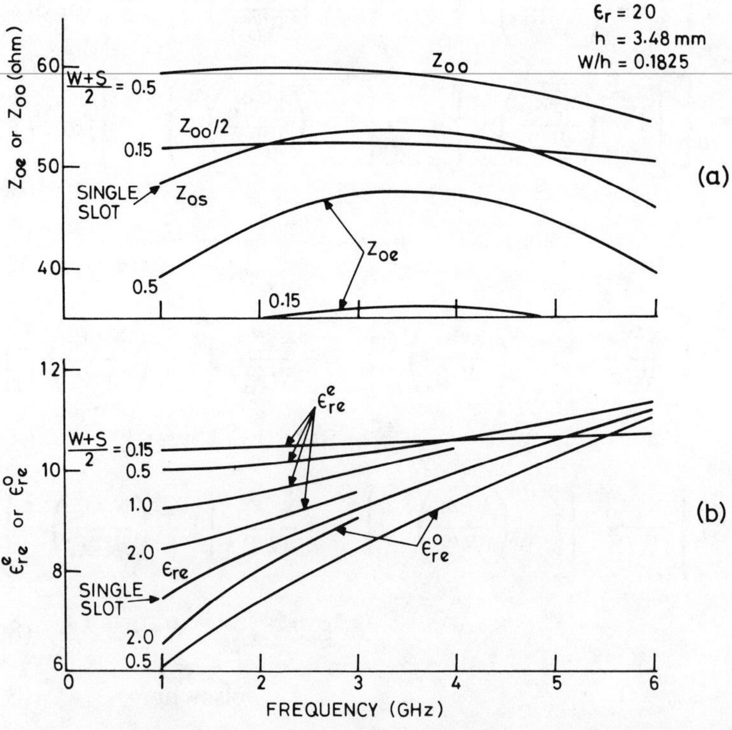

Figure 8.24 Characteristics of Coupled Slotlines, (a) Characteristic Impedance and (b) Effective Dielectric Constant (from [42])

$\epsilon_r = 20$ and $W/h = 0.1825$. It may be observed from this figure that as the frequency increases, the effective dielectric constant increases which means the waves become more closely bound to the slots. This results in smaller interaction between the two waves.

The even and odd mode characteristics for small S/h values can be explained in a simple way. For the even mode, the metal strip between the slots has little effect on the propagating wave, and the wave propagates as if it were in a slot of width (2W+S). Therefore, even mode impedance will be about half the impedance of a single slot of width (2W+S). In the case of the odd mode, the impedance will be about twice the impedance of a single slot. It may also be observed that for the odd mode the effective dielectric constant for small S/h (= 0.12) is very close to the zero order approximation $\epsilon_{re} = 0.5\,(\epsilon_r + 1)$. In fact, before the analysis for coupled slotlines was reported, the coupled slotline configuration (odd mode) was treated as a coplanar waveguide [43]. This configuration was analyzed in terms of a quasi-TEM approximation with the zero order value of the effective dielectric constant given by $\epsilon_{re} = 0.5\,(\epsilon_r + 1)$. Coplanar waveguide has been discussed in Chapter 7, and the characteristics of coupled coplanar waveguides are presented in the following subsection.

8.6.2 Characteristics of Coupled Coplanar Waveguides

The configuration of a coupled coplanar waveguide (CPW) is shown in Figure 8.1(c). It may be noted that this configuration consists of two coplanar strips with a ground plane on either side. One ground plane from each of the CPWs has been deleted to obtain the required coupling. Coupled CPWs have been analyzed by Hatsuda [44] using the relaxation technique.

The even and odd mode field configurations in coupled CPWs are shown in Figure 8.25. The characteristics are plotted in Figure 8.26 for $\epsilon_r = 9.35$, h = 0.61 mm, H = 4.30 mm, $(W_3 - W_2)/2H = 0.143$, L = 10.7 mm and for three different values of coupling width W_1/H [44]. It may be observed from this figure that even mode characteristics are relatively less sensitive to coupling width W_1. Also, even mode phase velocity is independent of W_1 for small values of strip width, $(W_2 - W_1)/2$.

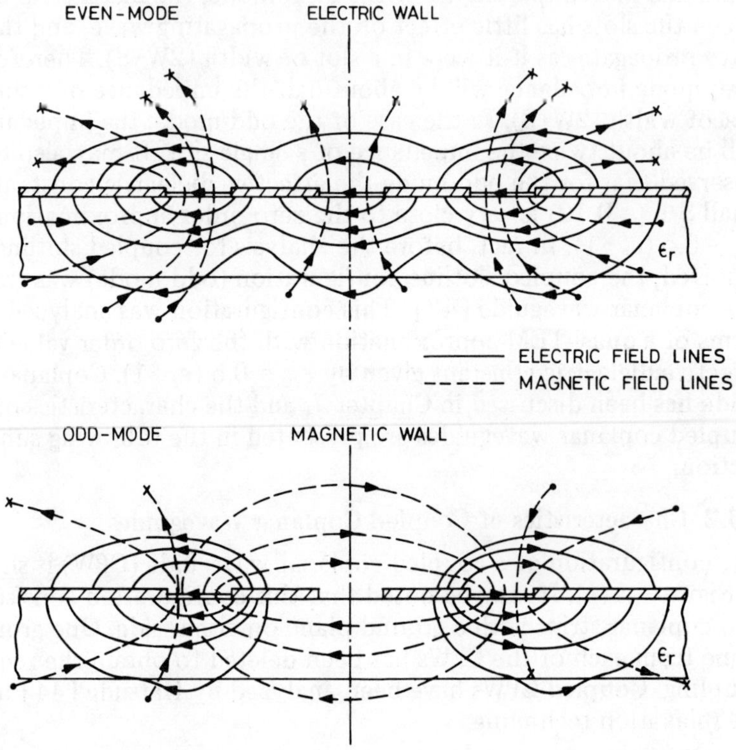

Figure 8.25 Even and Odd Mode Field Configurations in Coupled Coplanar Waveguides

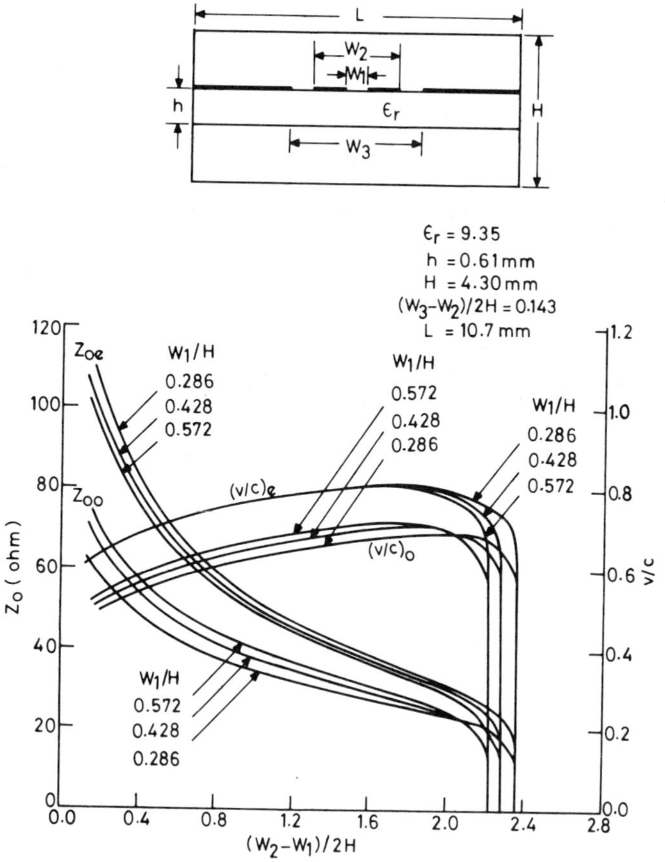

Figure 8.26 Characteristics of Coupled Coplanar Waveguides (from [44])

REFERENCES

[1] Ozaki, H. and J. Ishii, "Synthesis of a Class of Stripline Filters," *IRE Trans. Vol. CT-5,* 1958, pp. 104-109.

[2] Louisell, W.H., *Coupled Mode and Parametric Electronics,* New York: John Wiley, 1960.

[3] Isaacs, J.C. and N.A. Strakhov, "Crosstalk in Uniformly Coupled Lossy Transmission Lines," *Bell System Technical Journal, Vol. 52,* 1973, pp. 101-115.

[4] Sato, R. and E.G. Cristal, "Simplified Analysis of Coupled Transmission-line Network," *IEEE Trans., Vol. MTT-18,* 1970, pp. 122-131.

[5] Hazony, D., *Elements of Network Synthesis,* New York: Reinhold, 1963, Ch. 13.

[6] Chang, F.Y., "Transient Analysis of Lossless Coupled Transmission Lines in a Non-Homogeneous Dielectric Medium," *IEEE Trans., Vol. MTT-18,* 1970, pp. 616-626.

[7] Richards, P.I., "Resistor Transmission Line Circuits," *Proc. IRE, Vol. 36,* 1948, pp. 217-220.

[8] Chao, C.L., "On the Analysis of Inhomogeneous Asymmetrical Coupled Transmission Lines," *18th Mid-West Symposium on Circuits and Systems (Montreal), 1975,* pp. 568-572.

[9] Tripathi, V.K., "Asymmetric Coupled Transmission Lines in an Inhomogeneous Medium," *IEEE Trans., Vol. MTT-23,* 1975, pp. 734-739.

[10] Tripathi, V.K., "Properties and Applications of Asymmetric Coupled Line Structures in an Inhomogeneous Medium," *Proc. 5th European Microwave Conf., Hamburg, 1975,* pp. 278-282.

[11] Costamagna, E. and U. Maltese, "Linee Accoppiate Asimmetriche in Dielettrico non Omogeneo, *Alta Frequenza, Vol. 40,* 1971, pp. 737-741 (in Italian).

[12] Krage, M.K. and G.I. Haddad, "Characteristics of Coupled Microstrip Transmission Lines - I: Coupled-Mode Formulation of Inhomogeneous Lines, II: Evaluation of Coupled-Line Parameters," *IEEE Trans., Vol. MTT-18,* 1970, pp. 217-228.

[13] Pregla, R., "Calculation of the Distributed Capacitances and Phase Velocities in Coupled Microstrip Lines by Conformal Mapping Techniques," *AEU, Vol. 26,* 1972, pp. 470-474.

[14] Bryant, T.G. and J.A. Weiss, "Parameters of Microstrip Transmission Lines and of Coupled Pairs of Microstrip Lines," *IEEE Trans., Vol. MTT-16*, 1968, pp. 1021-1027.

[15] Young, L. and H. Sobol, (Eds.), *Advances in Microwaves, Vol. 8*, New York: Academic Press, 1974, pp. 295-320.

[16] Bergandt, H.G. and R. Pregla, "Calculation of Even-and Odd-Mode Capacitance Parameters for Coupled Microstrips," *AEU, Vol. 26*, 1972, pp. 153-158.

[17] Kowalski, G. and R. Pregla, "Calculation of the Distributed Capacitances of Coupled Microstrips Using a Variational Integral," *AEU, Vol. 27*, 1973, pp. 51-52.

[18] Gunston, M.A.R., *Microwave Transmission Line Impedance Data*, London: Van Nostrand Reinhold, 1972, Ch. 6.

[19] Gladwell, G.M.L. and S. Coen, "A Chebyshev Approximation Method for Microstrip Problems," *IEEE Trans., Vol. MTT-23*, 1975, pp. 865-870.

[20] Krage, M.K. and G.I. Haddad, "Frequency Dependent Characteristics of Microstrip Transmission Lines," *IEEE Trans., Vol. MTT-20*, 1972, pp. 678-688.

[21] Knorr, J.B., *et. al.*, "Hybrid Mode Analysis of Planar Lines," *Proc. 8th Asilomar Conference, 1974.*

[22] Knorr, J.B. and K.D. Kuchler, "Analysis of Coupled Slots and Coplanar Strips on Dielectric Substrate," *IEEE Trans., Vol. MTT-23*, 1975, pp. 541-548.

[23] Kowalski, G. and R. Pregla, "Dispersion Characteristics of Single and Coupled Microstrips," *AEU, Vol. 26*, 1972, pp. 276-280.

[24] Davies, J.B. and D.G. Corr, "Computer Analysis of the Fundamental and Higher Order Modes in Single and Coupled Microstrip," *Electron. Lett., Vol. 6*, 1970, pp. 806-808. See Also errata, *Vol. 7*, 1971, p. 284.

[25] Jansen, R.H., "Fast Accurate Hybrid Mode Computation of Nonsymmetrical Coupled Microstrip Characteristics," *Proc., 7th European Microwave Conf., Copenhagen, 1977*, pp. 135-139.

[26] Getsinger, W.J., "Dispersion of Parallel-Coupled Microstrip," *IEEE Trans., Vol. MTT-21*, 1973, pp. 144-145.

[27] Carlin, H.J. and P.P. Civalleri, "A Coupled-Line Model for

Dispersion in Parallel-Coupled Microstrips," *IEEE Trans., Vol. MTT-23*, 1975, pp. 444-446.

[28] Napoli, L.S. and J.J. Hughes, "Characteristics of Coupled Microstrip Lines," *RCA Review, Vol. 31*, 1970, pp. 479-498.

[29] Rizzoli, V., "Resonance Measurement of Even and Odd Mode Propagation Constants in Coupled Microstrips," *Proc. Int. Microwave Symposium, 1975.*

[30] Garg, R. and I.J. Bahl, "Characteristics of Coupled Microstrip Lines," *IEEE Trans., Vol. MTT-28*, 1980, p. 272.

[31] Owyang, G.H. and T.T. Wu, "The Approximate Parameters of Slotlines and their Complement," *IRE Trans., Vol. AP-6*, 1958, pp. 49-55.

[32] Akhtarzad, S., *et. al.*, "The Design of Coupled Microstrip Lines," *IEEE Trans., Vol. MTT-23*, 1975, pp. 486-492.

[33] Shamanna, K.N., *et. al.*, "Parallel-Coupled Microstrip Line Is Easy to Determine with Nomograms," *Electronic Design, Vol. 11*, May 24 (1976), pp. 78-81.

[34] Avdeyev, E.V. and V.I. Potapova, "Nomograms for Coupled Open Microstrip Lines," *Telecomm. and Radio Eng., Pt. 2, Vol. 28*, 1973, pp. 89-93.

[35] Shamasundara, S.D. and N. Singh, "Design of Coupled Microstrip Lines," *IEEE Trans., Vol. MTT-25*, 1977, pp. 232-233.

[36] Shamasundara, S.D., *et. al.*, "Apply Standard Curves to Strange Substrates," *Microwaves, Vol. 16*, Sept. 1977, pp. 116-117.

[37] Rama Rao, B., "Effect of Loss and Frequency Dispersion on the Performance of Microstrip Directional Couplers and Coupled Line Filters," *IEEE Trans., Vol. MTT-22*, 1974, pp. 747-750.

[38] Shamasundara, S.D. and K.C. Gupta, "Sensitivity Analysis of Coupled Microstrip Directional Couplers," *IEEE Trans., Vol. MTT-26, Oct. 1978*, pp. 788-794.

[39] Buntschuh, C., "High Directivity Microstrip Couplers Using Dielectric Overlays," *IEEE 1975 G-MTT Symposium Digest.*

[40] Wolters, K.C., *et. al.*, "Analysis and Experimental Evaluation of Distributed Overlay Structures in Microwave Integrated Circuits," *IEEE 1968 G-MTT Symposium Digest.*

[41] Szentkuti, B.T., "Simple Analysis of Anisotropic Microstrip Lines by a Transform Method," *Electron. Lett., Vol. 12*, 1976, pp. 672-673.

[42] Pregla, R. and S.G. Pintzos, "Determination of the Propagation Constants in Coupled Microslots by a Variational Method," *Proc. V. Colloq. Microwave Commun., Budapest, 1974,* pp. MT491-500.

[43] Wen, C.P., "Coplanar Waveguide: A Surface Strip Transmission Line Suitable for Nonreciprocal Gyromagnetic Device Applications," *IEEE Trans., Vol. MTT-17,* Dec. 1969, pp. 1087-1090.

[44] Hatsuda, T., "Computation of Coplanar-type Strip-line Characteristics by Relaxation Method and its Application to Microwave Circuits," *IEEE Trans., Vol. MTT-23,* 1975, pp. 795-802.

[45] Jansen, R.H., "High-speed Computation of Single and Coupled Microstrip Parameters Including Dispersion, High-order Modes, Loss and Finite Strip Thickness," *IEEE Trans., Vol. MTT-26,* 1978, pp. 75-82.

LIST OF SYMBOLS

The following list contains those symbols and acronyms that have been used quite frequently in the text. Because of the large number of quantities to be represented and the undesirability of using alphabets other than English and Greek, it has been necessary to use some symbols to represent different quantities at different places. In every instance the symbol has been defined where introduced to avoid misinterpretation of its meaning.

A	Magnetic vector potential
APHC	Average power handling capability
B_t	Total susceptance
C	Capacitance Capacitance per unit length Coupling constant
C_a	Capacitance with substrate dielectric replaced by air
C_b, C_e, C_{even}, C_g, C_m, C_{oc}, C_{odd}, C_p, C_s, C_T, C_+	Various discontinuity capacitances
C_e, C_o	Even and Odd mode capacitance per unit length
C_e^a, C_o^a	C_e and C_o with substrate dielectric replaced by air
C_o	Self capacitance per unit length (coupled lines) Odd mode capacitance per unit length
CPS	Coplanar strips
CPW	Coplanar waveguide
c	Velocity of electromagnetic waves in free space
c, π	Modes of propagation in coupled lines
Det	Determinant
E	Electric field
E_x, E_y, E_z E_ρ, E_ϕ, E_t	Components of E
EH_{mn}, HE_{mn}	Hybrid modes
FTD	Fourier transform domain

$\tilde{f}(\alpha)$	Tilde (~) indicates Fourier transform
$G(x,y;x_o,y_o)$	Green's function
H	Magnetic field, height of enclosure
$H_x, H_y, H_z, H_\rho, H_\phi, H_r, H_t$	Components of magnetic field H
HE_{mn}, EH_{mn}	Hybrid modes
$H_n^{(1)}(x), H_n^{(2)}(x)$	Hankel functions of first and second kind respectively
h	Height of the substrate
I, I_o, I_x, I_z	Electric currents
J, J_x, J_y	Electric current densities
$J_n(x)$	Bessel's function of first kind
$K(m), K'(m)$	Complete elliptic function and its complement
k	Wave number Aspect ratio
k_0, k_1, k_2	Wave numbers in various media
k_L, k_c	Inductive and capacitive coupling coefficients
L, L_{w_1}, L_{w_2}	Inductance per unit length
L_i	Incremental inductance
L_b, L_s, L_1, L_2, L_3	Various discontinuity inductances
L_m	Mutual inductance
LSE	Longitudinal section electric
LSM	Longitudinal section magnetic
ℓ	Length of transmission line section
ℓn	Natural logarithm (to the base e)
log	Common logarithm (to the base 10)
MIC	Microwave integrated circuit
n	Transformer turns ratio
PPHC	Peak power handling capability

Q	Charge Quality factor
Q_c, Q_d, Q_r, Q_T, Q_o	Various quality factors
q	Filling fraction Charge density
R_s	Surface resistivity
R_c, R_π	Ratio of voltages on the two lines (of a coupled line section) for c and π modes
S	Strip width for CPW Separation between strips for CPS and coupled microstrip lines Separation between slots for coupled slot lines
S_{mn}	Scattering parameters
S_y^x	Sensitivity of x with respect to y
T, T_{max}, T_{amb}	Temperatures
TDR	Time domain reflectometer/reflectometry
TE	Transverse electric
TEM	Transverse electromagnetic
TM	Transverse magnetic
$\tan \delta$	Loss tangent
$(\tan \delta)_e$	Effective $\tan \delta$
V, V_o	Voltages
VSWR	Voltage standing wave ratio
v_{cp}	Phase velocity in a coplanar waveguide
v_g	Group velocity
v_p	Phase velocity
W	Strip width for microstrip and CPS Slot width for slotline and CPW
W_e	Effective width
$W_e(f)$	Frequency dependent W_e
Y, Y_o	Admittance (self admittance) per unit length

Y_m	Mutual admittance
Y_{oe}, Y_{oo}	Admittances for even and odd modes
Z, Z_o	Impedance (self impedance) per unit length
Z_o^a	Characteristic impedance with substrate replaced by air
Z_{c1}	Z_o for coaxial line
Z_m	Mutual impedance
Z_{ocp}	Z_o for CPW
Z_{ocs}	Z_o for CPS
Z_{oe}, Z_{oo}	Z_o for even and odd modes
Z_{om}	Z_o for microstrip
Z_{os}	Z_o for slotline
Z_s	Surface impedance
α	Attenuation constant
α_c	α because of conductor loss
α_d	α because of dielectric loss
α_e, α_o, α_{ce}, α_{co}, α_{de}, α_{do}	Attenuation constants for even and odd modes
β	Phase constant
β_e, β_o	β for even and odd modes
β_c, β_π	β for c and π-modes
γ	Propagation constant
γ_c, γ_π	γ for c and π modes
Δx, ΔT	Small change in x, temperature
$\Delta \ell_{oc}$, $\Delta \ell_g$, $\Delta \ell_o$	Incremental line lengths because of discontinuities
δ	Skin depth
$\delta(x-x_o)$	Dirac's delta function
ϵ	Permittivity
ϵ_o	ϵ for free space

ϵ_r	Relative permittivity
ϵ_{re}	Effective dielectric constant
$\epsilon_{re}(f)$	Frequency dependent ϵ_{re}
ϵ', ϵ''	Real and imaginary parts of ϵ
ϵ_x, ϵ_y	x and y components of ϵ_r
$\epsilon_{re}^e, \epsilon_{re}^o$	ϵ_{re} for even and odd modes
η	Free space impedance (= 120π ohms)
θ	Angular co-ordinate Electrical length
λ	Wavelength
λ_o	Free space λ
$\lambda_m, \lambda_s,$ $\lambda_{cp}, \lambda_{cs}$	λ for microstrip, slotline, coplanar waveguide and coplanar strips
μ	Permeability
μ_o	Free space μ
μ_r	Relative μ
π	A constant (3.1416) A mode in coupled lines
ρ	Charge density
σ	Conductivity Surface charge density
σ_e	Effective conductivity
ϕ	Electrostatic potential
$\phi_e, \phi_o, \phi_{si}$	Potential distributions used in discontinuity analysis
ψ^e, ψ^h	Scalar potentials used for expressing E and H
Ω	Ohm
ω	Angular frequency (= $2\pi f$)
$\sim$	Tilde indicates Fourier transform
$\wedge$	Circumflex indicates unit vectors

Index

A

B

C

D

E

F

G

H

I

L

M

R

S

T

V

W